Wind-Tunnel Testing

Birth of a warplane: Wind-tunnel model of the Boeing B-29.

Wind-Tunnel Testing

ALAN POPE, M.S.
Associate Professor of Aerodynamics
Daniel Guggenheim School of Aeronautics
Georgia Institute of Technology

New York · JOHN WILEY & SONS, Inc.
CHAPMAN & HALL, Limited
London
1947

PREFACE

The science of wind-tunnel testing has grown in the past two decades from secondary—almost academic—importance to a vital position in aircraft development. During this time numerous papers on the development of the various components of the tunnel have appeared, as well as papers on corrections to be applied to wind-tunnel data; but surprisingly no integrated work embracing design, procedures, and corrections has been published. The need for such a work has been felt acutely by the author in his contacts with tunnel engineers of many companies fostering wind-tunnel research at the Georgia Institute of Technology and in his contacts with students in the wind-tunnel laboratory classes. This textbook is the author's effort to fill the gap.

Another group feeling the lack of an integrated wind-tunnel textbook is composed of engineers—not necessarily aeronautical engineers—who, caught in the expansion of aeronautical engineering teaching facilities, find themselves saddled with the responsibility of designing a small tunnel. The author has had the pleasure of assisting in some of these projects and has felt acutely the lack of a direct reference book for wind-tunnel work.

For these three groups: students, tunnel engineers, and those engaged in low-cost wind-tunnel design, this book has been written.

CONTENTS

ABBREVIATIONS

ABBREVIATION	COMPLETE MEANING
ACA	Australian Council for Aeronautics, CSIR
ARC	Air Research Committee (British)
ARI, TIU	Air Research Institute, Tokyo Imperial University (Japanese)
AVA	Aerodynamische Versuchsanstalt (Göttingen Institute for Aerodynamics), Göttingen
CAI	Central Aerohydrodynamic Institute, Moscow
CSIR	Council for Scientific and Industrial Research, Australia
CNRC	Canadian National Research Council, Ottawa
DVL	Deutsche Versuchsanstalt für Luftfahrtforschung (German Institute for Aeronautical Research), Berlin and Göttingen
ETH	Eidgenossische Technische Hochschule (Swiss Institute of Technology)
GALCIT	Guggenheim Aeronautical Laboratory of the California Institute of Technology
IAeS	Institute of Aeronautical Sciences (United States)
JAS	*Journal of the Aeronautical Sciences* (United States)
JRAS	*Journal of the Royal Aeronautical Society* (British)
LFA	Luftfahrtforschungsanstalt Hermann Göring (Hermann Göring Institute for Aeronautics), Braunschweig
MIT	Massachusetts Institute of Technology
NACA	National Advisory Committee for Aeronautics (United States)
NPL	National Physical Laboratory, Teddington (British)
ONERA	Office National d'Etudes et de Recherches Aeronautiques (National Bureau of Aeronautical Research)
PRS	*Proceedings of the Royal Society of London* (British)
R & M	Reports and Memoranda (of the Air Research Committee)
RAE	Royal Aeronautical Establishment, Farnborough, England.
SAE	Society of Automotive Engineers (United States)
TM	Technical Memorandum of the NACA.
TN	Technical Note of the NACA.
TR	Technical Report of the NACA.

CHAPTER I

THE WIND TUNNEL

The development of a new aircraft requires a vast amount of research, design, and construction, the cost of which frequently runs into hundreds of thousands of dollars and many months of time. Any process that can reduce this expenditure of time and money is, of course, vigorously pursued. Here, then, is the justification for the wind tunnel, wherein small models are tested to save the design, construction, and completion of full-scale experiments. Many thousands of dollars and many man-hours are saved annually in this manner. Lives too are saved, for designs that could prove dangerous later are sometimes abandoned after wind-tunnel tests.

The various nations of the world support the whole field of aeronautical research, of which wind-tunnel testing is a major item, according to their abilities and desires. Usually each nation sets up a separate organization that augments the activities of the armed services, and further work is farmed out to the engineering universities. In America this central agency is the National Advisory Committee for Aeronautics (NACA) whose offices are in Washington, D. C., and laboratories at Langley Field, Virginia; Cleveland, Ohio; and Moffett Field, California. In England a similar organization is called the National Physical Laboratory (NPL); in Germany, the Deutsche Versuchsanstalt für Luftfahrt (DVL); in Italy, the Guidonia Laboratories; in Japan, the Tokyo Imperial University (TIU). Additional agencies are listed on p. xi.

The cost of a large modern wind tunnel is quite high. The chief engineer of a prominent aircraft company recently declared, "A tunnel of the type necessary for our needs would cost $800,000, and for $800,000 my company can buy a lot of testing." One California concern built its 300-mph tunnel for $200,000, considered a very low figure.

Some of the efforts to beat this cost have been ingenious and some humorous. The Japanese used the abandoned Nammuya

1

railway tunnel, rushing the model along on a sort of glorified go-cart. The Russians built a return-type tunnel having two independent working sections, one behind the other. One wonders which group carried top priority. Several open-circuit tunnels function only when the wind is in the right direction and when it is not raining. The suggestion has been made that the high velocities of mountain-top winds be utilized for testing. Tunnels using water as a fluid have been built, and other tunnels that would use gases more dense than air have been proposed.

The following paragraphs discuss the nomenclature and types of wind tunnels, and examples of each are given. It is regrettable that some of the new and more advanced tunnels are at present on the restricted list.

1:1. Nomenclature. A conventional single-return wind tunnel with the component parts marked with their common names is outlined in Fig. 1:1. Other terms are frequently encountered since full agreement in terminology has not yet been reached.

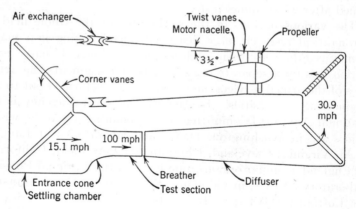

FIG. 1:1. A conventional single-return wind tunnel.

The tunnel itself is often called a "wind channel." The contracting cone may be called an "entrance cone" or a "nozzle." The wind-tunnel propeller may also be referred to as a "fan." The testing section may be called the "working section," "throat," "channel," or "jet." Sometimes the word "jet" means "open jet" (no solid boundaries). The uncertainty of the nomenclature is rarely confusing, however, for the sense of the context usually removes any doubts as to the meaning intended.

1:2. Types of Wind Tunnels. There are two basic types of wind tunnels. The first, called an open-circuit (or "Eiffel" or "NPL") * tunnel, has no guided return of the air (see Fig. 1:2). After the air leaves the diffuser, it circulates by devious paths back to the intake. If the tunnel draws its air directly from the atmosphere, entirely fresh air is used.

The second type, called a closed-circuit or "Prandtl," "Göttingen," or "return-flow" tunnel, has, as the names imply, a continuous path for the air (see Fig. 1:1).

Except for the induction-type high-speed tunnel and a few special-purpose low-speed tunnels, such as the NACA Free-Flight tunnel, the open-circuit arrangement is rarely employed.

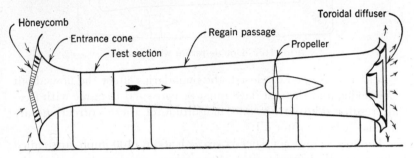

FIG. 1:2. Open-circuit wind tunnel.

The closed circuit may be one of three types: single (Fig. 1:1); double (Fig. 1:3); or annular (Fig. 1:4) return. Of these, only the first is in general acceptance at present. In the double and annular return arrangements, the particular air that scrapes along the walls of the return passage forms the center of the jet and hence passes directly over the model. Unless the contraction ratio is large, this air is extremely turbulent and tends to make the interpretation of the test data difficult. A further disadvantage of the double-return tunnel is that a variation in velocity distribution may be caused by yawing a large model. In the single-return tunnel, the general mixing and stabilizing effect of the propeller tends to reestablish any flow variation due to the model, but in the double-return type the flow deflected to one side can remain there, impairing the roll and yaw data.

Further identification of wind tunnels may be made through

* Strictly speaking, the Eiffel-type tunnel has an open jet, while the NPL type has a closed jet. Both are open-circuit tunnels.

the cross-sectional form of the test section. It may be square, rectangular, rectangular with tempered corners, octagonal, circular, or elliptic. The test section may be completely walled in (closed jet) or consist simply of an open space with the air streaming from the entrance cone to the exit cone. Whether the

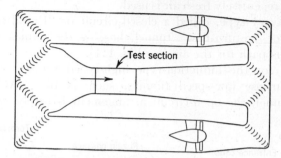

FIG. 1:3. Double-return wind tunnel.

test section is open or closed, the boundaries affect the flow about the model, and the test data must be corrected to agree with free-air results. The nature and magnitude of these corrections are discussed in Chapter VI.

Tunnels whose jet speeds exceed about 400 mph are called "high-speed" tunnels, and those whose jet speeds exceed the velocity of sound are called "supersonic." Both these types require refined calculations both in design and in operation. It

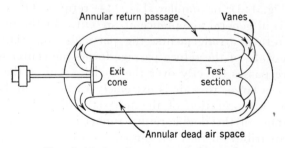

FIG. 1:4. Annular return wind tunnel.

will be noted that the supersonic tunnels are usually quite small, having jet areas anywhere from 10 sq in. to 4 sq ft.

A few specialized tunnels exist wherein the models fly freely and moving-picture cameras record their movements for later consideration. These include the NACA Spinning tunnels and the NACA Free-Flight tunnel.

1:3. Single-Return Tunnel. Several of the schools in this country have wind tunnels generally similar to the design outlined in Fig. 1:1. This group includes the University of Detroit, the University of Michigan, the Georgia School of Technology, and the California Institute of Technology. The test section is about 9 ft in diameter, and about 300 hp is employed. This size makes a good low-speed (about 125 mph) set-up, economical to build and operate, and fully capable of the majority of tests required. Some of the tunnels can be operated with either open or closed jet.

Typical equipment for this type of tunnel includes a three-point suspension system for the models and a turntable for panel tests.

1:4. Single-Return Pressure Tunnel. The Wright Brothers Wind tunnel at the Massachusetts Institute of Technology is a step above the lower-power tunnel mentioned in Sect. 1:3. Using 2000 hp, the tunnel is capable of 250 mph with the test section at standard pressure, 396 mph with it at 0.23 atmosphere, or 145 mph at 3.5 atmospheres. The low pressure yields the highest Mach number, and the high pressure yields the highest Reynolds number.[*] It takes about two hours to obtain either of the non-standard pressures.

The Wright Brothers tunnel is one of the few with an elliptic jet, having one of that form 10 ft by 7.5 ft. The major portion of the tunnel is of metal, while the test section is wood. Cooling for the 2000 hp is obtained by running water over the metal shell. (See also Ref. 1:1.)

1:5. High-Speed Pressure Tunnel. An example of the high-power, high-speed tunnel is found in the Southern California Co-op tunnel in Pasadena, California. Here 12,000 hp are used in a single-return-type tunnel, with facilities available for pressure changes from 0.25 to 4.0 atmospheres. The working section is rectangular, 8.5 ft by 12 ft with tempered corners which reduce the test section area to about 95 sq ft. The expected maximum performance may be summed up as follows:

1. At 0.25 atmosphere, $V_{max.} = 700$ mph and $q = (\rho/2)V^2$ $= 315$ lb/ft².

2. At atmospheric pressure, $V_{max.} = 475$ mph and $q = 575$ lb/ft².

3. At 4 atmospheres, $V_{max.} = 300$ mph and $q = 930$ lb/ft².

[*] See p. 266 and footnote, p. 31.

Similar capacity tunnels are at Boeing in Seattle; Cornell Aeronautical Laboratory at Buffalo, N. Y.; Wright Field, Ohio; and the NACA, both at Langley Field and Moffett Field.

1:6. Variable-Density Tunnel. The Variable-Density tunnel of the NACA (Ref. 1:2) was the pioneer high-pressure tunnel, being capable of 20 atmospheres. For structural reasons it had an unusual annular return passage, with the 5-ft diameter working section at the tunnel center. This arrangement or, in fact, any pressure arrangement must be relieved before the operators may enter and make adjustments. Further, an inaccessible balance must be provided as the complications involved in taking forces out through air seals are almost prohibitive.

The advantage of the pressure tunnel lies in the possibility of attaining high Reynolds numbers without either very large models or very high speeds. For example, the full-scale Reynolds number of a quarter-scale model of a 200-mph airplane would require 800 mph under normal pressure conditions. This is far beyond the compressibility burble and is unreasonable from a power standpoint. With a pressure of 8 atmospheres, the full-scale Reynolds number is attained with only 100 mph.

Though the Variable-Density tunnel is no longer used for testing because of its extremely high turbulence, it did provide early clues to the effect of the Reynolds number on airfoil characteristics. The VDT now serves as a pressure reservoir for the small, high-speed induction tunnel.

The British Compressed-Air Tunnel" is a second tunnel similar in size and capacity to the American "VDT."

1:7. Full-Scale Tunnel. The Full-Scale tunnel at Langley Field (Ref. 1:3) is capable of testing actual airplanes of moderate size under near-flight conditions. Housed in a large building whose walls form part of the double-return passages, this remarkable tunnel attains wind velocities up to 118 mph with an open jet 60 ft wide and 30 ft high.

The Full-Scale tunnel serves several purposes impossible to attain in any tunnel accommodating models only:

1. Full-scale prototypes may be "cleaned up."

2. Alterations to actual airplanes may be made without regard to weight or airworthiness.

3. Flying scale models of very large planes may be tested.

4. Actual engine installations may be run under near-flight conditions.

5. A correlation between flight and small model tests may be obtained.

In addition to the well-known tunnel at Langley Field, two other full-scale tunnels are in existence: the large wind tunnel at Chalais-Meudon, France, whose jet is 26 ft by 52 ft; and the Full-Scale tunnel at Moffett Field, California, whose jet is 40 ft by 80 ft.

1:8. Smoke Tunnel.   A different approach to the problem of studying air flow is made possible by a smoke tunnel (Ref. 1:4).

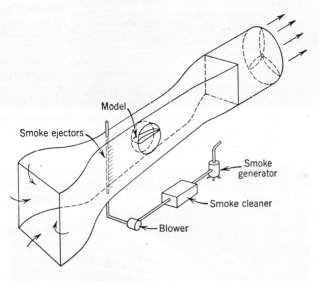

FIG. 1:5. Smoke tunnel.

In this type of apparatus, nozzles just ahead of the model emit cleaned smoke in streamer form.   This smoke follows the air flow and makes the flow patterns visible.   Smoke tunnels are usually low-velocity tunnels (about 40 mph) and have test sections of the two-dimensional type.   Examples of smoke pictures are shown in Figs. 1:6 and 1:7.

1:9. Free-Flight Tunnels.   The NACA has several free-flight tunnels in which no balance is utilized.   In these tunnels, models dynamically as well as dimensionally similar to their full-scale counterparts fly under the influence of gravitational, aerodynamic, and inertia forces, and motion pictures are made of their flight.

In the NACA Free-Flight tunnel the model is kept in a steady-state glide, balanced between gravitational forces and the slightly inclined airstream. The model controls are remotely movable. Various glide paths can be simulated by changing the tilt of the tunnel and its airspeed. Two operators are thus required, one

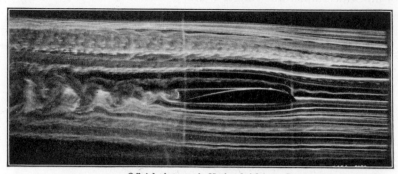

Official photograph, National Advisory Committee for Aeronautics

FIG. 1:6. Smoke picture, low α.

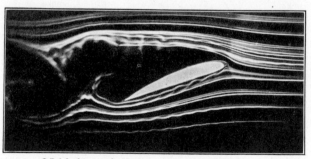

Official photograph, National Advisory Committee for Aeronautics.

FIG. 1:7. Smoke picture, high α.

for the model controls and one for the tunnel. The free-flight tunnel yields information on stability and controllability.

The Gust tunnel comprises a model catapulting rig and a vertical airstream. The model is catapulted through the vertical airstream, and motion pictures are made of its path. A small recording accelerometer in the model furnishes data on its behavior. By varying control screens in the vertical duct, nearly any gradient can be made to appear in the gust. This tunnel furnishes valuable data for structural design.

Official photograph, National Advisory Committee for Aeronautics.

Fig. 1:8. NACA 5-ft Free-Flight tunnel in operation.

The NACA has two free-spinning tunnels, one 15 ft in diameter, the other 20 ft. In these tunnels the models are spun in an airstream that blows vertically upwards. The flow has a lower velocity at the center to keep the models from sliding over to the walls. The speed of the airstream may be rapidly altered and is usually kept equal to the rate of descent of the model, causing it to remain in one location relative to the observers.

Official photograph, National Advisory Committee for Aeronautics.

FIG. 1:9. NACA Free-spinning wind tunnel.

After a specified period, a mechanism changes the control surfaces to make the model recover; moving pictures then record the number of turns necessary to attain a diving condition. A net at the base of the tunnel prevents damage to the model. Correlation between recovery time of properly constructed models and of actual airplanes is good. In general the spin tunnel yields the angle of sideslip, rate of rotation, and angle of attack during a spin. A satisfactory model spins at an angle of attack steeper than 45 degrees and recovers from the spin in less than two turns after the controls are moved.

Another type of test found quite useful is the determination of whether the pilot will clear the tail surfaces if forced to bail out during a spin. For this a dummy pilot is released while the airplane is spinning and the path of the dummy relative to the airplane is observed.

It might be mentioned that the vertical tunnels for testing parachutes differ from the spin tunnels in that they require an even velocity front instead of the dish-shaped front required for a spin tunnel.

1:10. Supersonic Tunnels.

Quite early in the study of aerodynamics, it became apparent that there might be serious changes in the flow patterns about bodies when at any point over the body the local velocity exceeded the local speed of sound. It was a long time, however, before any testing apparatus was available to investigate this field.

The first high-speed tests were made in the direct exhaust of high-pressure tanks, but such arrangements were unsatisfactory, owing to turbulence and general unsteadiness of flow.

Next the induction type of tunnel was tried. As will be seen

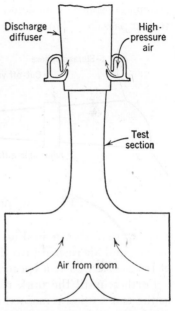

Fig. 1:10. Induction wind tunnel.

in Fig. 1:10 this employs an annular slot from which high-pressure air bleeds. In turn this draft creates a low-pressure region into which atmospheric air rushes. By means of a suitable contraction and a short straight section ahead of the annular slot, excellent flow up to about 700 mph is obtained. But all the early induction-type tunnels received their air from storage tanks and hence had limited time for running. To make available continuous operation and to increase the tunnel speed well into the supersonic range, a very high-speed tunnel was constructed in Zürich, Switzerland. Later a similar but more powerful wind tunnel was built at the Guidonia Laboratories in Milan, Italy (Ref. 1:7). Both were of the single-return type and had larger test sections than the previously constructed tunnels. The jet of the Italian tunnel is 15.6 in. by 28.9 in.

In the last few years the United States has become active in this field, and a few supersonic tunnels have been built. Large supersonic tunnels are being planned at the time of writing.

A new and very promising form of supersonic wind tunnel was disclosed at the end of World War II when inspection of the German wind tunnels became possible. This consisted of a large evacuated sphere connected to the atmosphere by a valve-controlled passage. This passage had a convergent-divergent nozzle

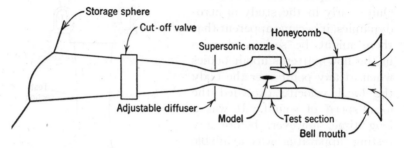

FIG. 1:11.   Intermittent wind tunnel.

such as that shown in Fig. 1:11 so that, when the valve was opened and air rushed into the sphere, a test section downstream of the nozzle was at a speed above that of sound.

Further, until the tank reached a specific pressure, the speed in the test section remained constant owing to a phenomenon of supersonic flow that makes the velocity dependent on the nozzle shape, not on the back pressure. Though such a tank would again limit a run to a few seconds, the automatic speed control of the design made it much more satisfactory than earlier induction types. Several tunnels of this type are also under construction in this country.

Before closing this section on supersonic tunnels, it seems in order to mention some of their design fundamentals and to draw attention to the many difficulties. In the first place, supersonic speeds are obtained not by pressures alone, but by pressures plus specially designed convergent-divergent passages. This means that a supersonic tunnel must have either a separate entrance cone for each speed, or an adjustable one. The power required is considerable, too. One design having a test section 12 in. by

18 in. will require 14,000 hp to reach a speed of two and a half times that of sound.

Above the speed of sound a diverging passage increases the speed of the stream as opposed to the action when the speed is below that of sound. Further, the jump back to subsonic speed occurs abruptly. Unless this jump occurs very close to sonic speed, large losses will result. Hence it will be seen that the combination of directly opposing laws of flow and the possibility of large losses due to a compressibility shock makes the design of a supersonic regain passage extremely difficult. Much more work remains to be done before efficient and reliable supersonic tunnels can be built.

1:11. Open-Circuit Tunnel. The Hispano-Suiza Company of Paris, France, has one of the few large open-circuit wind tunnels in operation today. It is similar in general layout to that shown in Fig. 1:2, having a test section 16.4 ft in diameter and 26.4 ft long. The maximum speed is 205 mph, which requires 4000 hp. A tunnel of this type employing a continuous stream of fresh air is particularly suited for engine testing. In general it may be said that an open-circuit tunnel of given efficiency may be constructed at lower cost than a closed tunnel of the same efficiency, but the open circuit may make the testing dependent upon local weather conditions.

1:12. Low-Turbulence Tunnel. In 1946 the NACA announced the completion of the first very low turbulence tunnel capable of testing three-dimensional models at high Reynolds numbers. The important features of this tunnel include (besides pressurization similar to the Southern California Co-op tunnel) multistage turns instead of four corners, an extraordinarily high contraction ratio (25 to 1), and the use of eight stages of mesh screen across the settling chamber.

All these artifices contribute towards reducing the turbulence in the test section. (For additional information see Sect. 3:6.)

1:13. Stability Tunnel. The only tunnel directly designed for dynamic stability work is located at the Langley Field branch of the NACA. Its most vital feature is its ability to subject the models to curving airstreams that simulate those actually encountered when an airplane rolls, pitches, or yaws. The rotating airstream for simulating roll is produced by a motor-driven paddle just ahead of the test section. Curved air of properly varying velocity for simulating pitch and yaw is produced by a combination of a curved test section and velocity screens. The proper use of this apparatus makes possible the determination of the stability derivatives.

1:14. Two-Dimensional Tunnel. The NACA has several two-dimensional tunnels designed and devoted entirely to section tests. For this type of airfoil research the test section is quite flat, and the model spans the shorter axis from one wall to another. Such a tunnel is shown in Fig. 5:5. This tunnel has a test section 3 ft by 7½ ft, and, like the Low-Turbulence tunnel at Moffett Field, achieves extremely low turbulence through the use of screens in the settling chamber.

Many tunnels of varying jet shapes have alternate two-dimensional jets that may be installed when needed. Some of these special jets consist merely of large endplates for the airfoil models, while others contract the entire stream to a narrow jet and have an additional diffuser downstream. Properly designed, a two-dimensional jet insert can increase the maximum speed of a tunnel by 70 per cent.

1:15. Table of Wind Tunnels. Table 1:1 was originally intended to include all the tunnels now in existence, but restrictions have made this impossible. Possibly some of the tunnels mentioned are no longer used; certainly there are others about which no information has been released. In a general way the table may serve as an index of the research potentialities of the various countries.

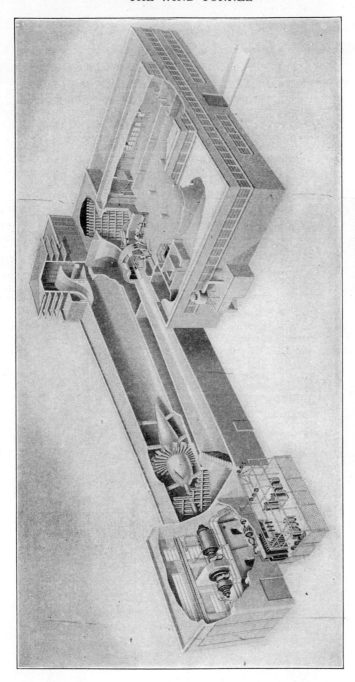

FIG. 1:12. Tunnel and laboratory of the Boeing Aircraft Corp.

TABLE 1:1. WIND TUNNELS

1. The National Advisory Committee for Aeronautics

Tunnel	Located at	Type	Jet Open or Closed	Vmax. mph	Energy Ratio	Turbu-lence Factor	Jet Shape	Jet Length	Con-traction Ratio	Hp	Reference or Remarks
Full-Scale	Langley Field, Va.	Double return	Open	118	2.84	1.1	60 x 30 ft Elliptic	0.93D	4.93	8,000	*TR 459*, 1933
20-ft, Propeller Research	Langley Field, Va.	Double return	Open	110	1.39	1.2	20 ft Round	1.75D	7.97	2,000	*TR 300*, 1928
19-ft, Pressure	Langley Field, Va.	Single return	Closed	200			19 ft Round	1.5D		2,000	
8-ft, High-Speed	Langley Field, Va.	Single return	Closed	500 (700)			8 ft Round	1.8D		8,000 (16,000)	*JAS*, March 1937
Variable-Density	Langley Field, Va.	Annular return	Closed		1.6	2.6	5 ft Round				*TR, 416*, 1932
Atmospheric	Langley Field, Va.	Single return	Closed	80	1.4	1.6	7 x 10 ft Rect.	1.1D	4.0	200	*TR 412*, 1932 *TR 664*, 1939
Rectangular, High-Speed	Langley Field, Va.	Open circuit	Closed	690	1.60		11 x 18 in. Rect.	3.8D	5.9		*TR 463*, 1933
'5-ft, Free Spinning	Langley Field, Va.	Annular return	Closed	40	0.35		12-sided polygon	1.25D	2.9	150	*TR 557*, 1936
24-in., High-Speed	Langley Field, Va.	Open circuit	Closed	695	2.05	1.1	24 in. Round	0.67D			*TR 646*, 1938

16-ft, High-Speed	Langley Field, Va.	Single return	Closed	520			16 ft Round	1.5D	20	16,000	
Two-Dimensional	Langley Field, Va.	Single return	Closed	150	1.4		3 x 7½ Rect.	1.0h	3.37	2,000	TN 1283, 1944
4 x 6 ft, Vertical	Langley Field, Va.	Single return	Closed	76		1.93	4 x 6 ft Rect.	0.75D	10	50	TN 337, 1931 TN 734, 1939
Stability	Langley Field, Va.	Single return	Closed	220		1.08	6 ft Square	3.7D	13	600	
7 x 10 ft No. 1	Langley Field, Va.	Single return	Closed	300	6.8	1.01	7 x 10 ft Rect.	1.5w	13	1,600	
7 x 10 ft No. 2	Langley Field, Va.	Single return	Closed	500	6.9	1.01	7 x 10 ft Rect.	1.5w	10	3,200	
6 x 9 ft, Ice Tunnel	Cleveland, Ohio	Single return	Closed	400	7.0		6 x 9 ft Rect.	2.2w		4,000	
High-Altitude	Cleveland, Ohio	Single return	Closed	500	4.6		20 ft Round	2.0D	6.25	18,000	$Aero\ Digest$, Jan. 15, 1944
7 x 10 ft No. 1	Moffett Field, Calif.	Single return	Closed	300	6.8		7 x 10 ft Rect.	1.4w	13.0	1,600	
7 x 10 ft No. 2	Moffett Field, Calif.	Single return	Closed	300	6.8		7 x 10 ft Rect.	1.4w	13.0	1,600	
Full-Scale	Moffett Field, Calif.	Single return	Closed	250	8.5		40 x 80 ft Rect.			36,000	

TABLE 1:1. WIND TUNNELS (Continued)

1. The National Advisory Committee for Aeronautics (Continued)

Tunnel	Located at	Type	Jet Open or Closed	Vmax. mph	Energy Ratio	Turbulence Factor	Jet Shape	Jet Length	Contraction Ratio	Hp	Reference or Remarks
16-ft, High-Speed	Moffett Field, Calif.	Single return	Closed	680	9.5		16 ft Round	1.6D		27,000	
12-ft, Low-Turbulence	Moffett Field, Calif.	Single return	Closed	750	11.8	1.0	12 ft Round		25	11,000	

(Many new high-speed and supersonic wind tunnels are under construction at the NACA.)

2. Colleges and Industry of the United States

Boeing Aircraft Co.	Seattle, Wash.	Single return	Closed	700			8 x 12 ft Rect.	1.25D		16,000	*Aero Digest,* May 1944
California Institute of Tech.	Pasadena, Calif.	Single return	Closed	250	3.56	1.1	10 ft Round	0.8D	4.5	800	
Consolidated-Vultee Aircraft	San Diego, Calif.	Single return	Closed	300	7.0		8½ x 12 ft Rect.	1.25D	6.55	2,250	*Aero Digest,* Jan. 15, 1944
Cornell Aero Laboratory	Buffalo, N. Y.	Single return	Closed	700	10.0 (est.)		8½ x 12 ft Rect.	1.0D	8.00	14,000	

	Location	Return		Speed			Section			Power	Reference
U. of Detroit	Detroit, Mich.	Single return	Both	150	2.0	1.5	7 x 10 ft Rect.	1.1D	4.9	275	Aircraft Engineering, Oct. 1931
Georgia Institute of Technology, 9 ft	Atlanta, Ga.	Single return	Both	150	3.7	1.7	9 ft Round			375	
Lockheed Aircraft Co.	Burbank, Calif.	Single return	Closed	314			8 x 12 ft Rect.	1.25D		1,250	
MIT Wright Bros.	Cambridge, Mass.	Single return	Closed	250	3.5	1.08	10 x 7.5 ft Elliptic	1.5D		2,000	SAE Journal, Sept. 1941
U. of Michigan	Ann Arbor, Mich.	Single return	Open	100	1.7		8 ft Oct.			300	Aircraft Engineering, June 1931
New York University	New York, N. Y.	Double return	Closed	125	3.5	1.4	7 x 10 ft Rect.	1.0D	4.5	250	
North American Aircraft	Inglewood, Calif.	Single return	Closed	325	7.8		7.75 x 11 ft Rect.	1.09D		3,000	Aero Digest, Aug. 1942
Northrop Aviation	Hawthorne, Calif.	Single return	Closed	165	3.8	1.1 (est.)	10 ft Round	10 ft	5.0	1,000	
Southern California Co-op	Pasadena, Calif.	Single return	Closed	700	10 (est.)		8½ x 12 ft Rect.	1.0D	8.08	12,000	
United Aircraft	East Hartford, Conn.	Single return	Closed	208 to 700	2.3 to 7.3		18 ft or 8 ft Oct.	1.65D or 2.0D	4.8 or 25	7,000	
U. of Washington	Seattle, Wash.	Double return	Closed	250	6.2	1.2	8 x 12 ft Rect.	0.83D	6.0	1,500	JAS, Oct. 1939

TABLE 1:1. WIND TUNNELS (*Continued*)

3. *Armed Services of the United States*

Tunnel	Located at	Type	Jet Open or Closed	Vmax. mph	Energy Ratio	Turbulence Factor	Jet Shape	Jet Length	Contraction Ratio	Hp	Reference or Remarks
Wright Field, 5 ft	Wright Field, Ohio	Open circuit	Closed	270	3.5	1.5	5 ft Round	3.6D	3.7	900	
Wright Field, 10 ft	Wright Field, Ohio	Single return	Closed	750	8 (est.)		10 ft Round	1.6D	16.0	40,000	
Wright Field, 20 ft	Wright Field, Ohio	Single return	Closed	400			20 ft Round		5.05	40,000	*Aero Digest,* April 1941
Supersonic	Wright Field, Ohio	Single return	Closed	1,700	5 (est.)		2 x 2 ft Square	2.0D	8.0	5,000	
Vertical	Wright Field, Ohio	Annular return	Open	136	1.61		12 ft Round	1.25D	9.86	900	
Wash. Navy Yard, 6 ft	Washington, D. C.	Single return	Open	120	2.52	1.67	6.33 ft Round	1.03D	5.15	200	TN 536, 1935
Wash. Navy Yard, 8 x 8 ft	Washington, D. C.	Single return	Closed	70	0.3	2.67	8 x 8 ft Square	2.5D		500	
DTMB,* 8 x 10 No. 1	Carderock, Md.	Single return	Closed	200	4.0	1.01	8 x 10 ft Rect.	1.3D	4.5	1,000	
DTMB,* 8 x 10 No. 2	Carderock, Md.	Single return	Closed	180	4.0	1.01	8 x 10 ft Rect.	1.3D	4.5	700	

4. Other Nations

AUSTRALIA

Name	Location	Return					Test section				Reference
9 x 7	Melbourne, Australia	Single return	Closed	195	5.08	1.15	7 x 9 ft Oct.	1.51D	4.0	550	Aircraft Engineering, Nov. 1943

CANADA

Name	Location	Return					Test section				
John Street	Ottawa, Ont.	Double return	Open	160	2.7	1.24	9 ft Round	1.52D	4.0	600	
New Horizontal	Ottawa, Ont.	Single return	Closed	325	6.0	1.28	6 x 10 ft Ellipse †	1.25D	9.0	2,000	
Spinning	Ottawa, Ont.	Annular return	Open	50	1.85	1.92	15 ft Round	0.67D	4.0	275	

CHINA

Name	Location	Return					Test section				Reference
Tsing Hua University	Nanchang	Single return	Both	130	5.8		12 to 18 ft Round			450	Aircraft Engineering, Sept. 1939

* David Taylor Model Basin.
† To be changed to 7 x 10 ft rect.

TABLE 1:1.   Wind Tunnels (*Continued*)

4. *Other Nations (Continued)*

ENGLAND

Tunnel	Located at	Type	Jet Open or Closed	V max. mph	Energy Ratio	Turbulence Factor	Jet Shape	Jet Length	Contraction Ratio	Hp	Reference or Remarks
RAE, 24 ft	Farnborough	Single return	Open	115			24 ft Round	1.83D	3.53	2,000	R & M 1720, 1936
Fairey Aircraft	Hayes	Single return	Closed	144			10 x 12 ft Elliptic		4.14	350	Aircraft Engineering, Jan. 1939
Handley-Page Aircraft	Radlett	Single return	Closed	132	3.4		7 x 5.3 ft Oct.	1.28D	4.0	220	Aircraft Engineering, July 1940
NPL Open-Jet	Farnborough	Double return	Open	143	2.7		7 x 9 ft Elliptic		3.9	375	Aircraft Engineering, June 1935
NPL Compressed-Air	Teddington	Annular return	Closed	60	2.3	2.0	6 ft Round			500	Flight, June 1, 1932
NPL Low-Turbulence	Farnborough	Single return	Closed				20 in. Oct.	6.0D	13.0		R & M 1843
NPL Duplex	Farnborough	Open circuit	Open	67	0.53		14 x 7 ft Rect.			400	Flight, June 1, 1932
RAE, 5 ft, Low-Speed	Farnborough	Single return	Open	215	2.4	1.5	5 ft Round	1.8D	2.78		R & M 1364, 1930

FRANCE

| Hispano-Suiza | Paris | Open circuit | Open | 205 | 2.94 | 16.4 ft Round | 1.61D | | 4,000 | Aircraft Production, April 1941 |

GERMANY

The list of German wind tunnels is probably the most incomplete of all, owing, of course, to secrecy maintained during the war. Information now (1946) available indicates that in 1943 the Germans had at least 51 wind tunnels of which 8 were for supersonic studies and at least 8 more for the high-speed subsonic range. It can be inferred that in the supersonic range the German equipment exceeded that of our country. In this part of the table it is advantageous to quote speeds as Mach numbers instead of miles an hour. There is no direct relation, but roughly M.N. = 1.0 is 700 mph for tunnel work.

Tunnel	Located at	Type	Jet Open or Closed	Mach No.	Energy Ratio	Turbulence Factor	Jet Shape	Jet Length	Contraction Ratio	Hp	Reference or Remarks
AVA, 0.8 meter	Göttingen		Closed	1.0			2.6 ft Square			Injector	
AVA, 11 x 13 cms	Göttingen		Open	3.0			4.3 x 5.1 in.			Intermittent	
AVA, 21.5 cm	Göttingen		Open	3.0			8.5 in. Square			Intermittent	
DVL, 1.2 meter	Göttingen	Single return	Open	146 mph		1.2	3.94 ft Round			230	TM 734, 1934

TABLE 1:1. WIND TUNNELS (*Continued*)

4. *Other Nations* (*Continued*)

GERMANY (*Continued*)

Tunnel	Located at	Type	Jet Open or Closed	Mach. No.	Energy Ratio	Turbulence Factor	Jet Shape	Jet Length	Contraction Ratio	Hp	Reference or Remarks
DVL, 5 x 7 meter	Göttingen	Single return	Open	145 mph		1.05	16.4 x 23 ft Elliptic	1.26D	4.0	2,700	*TM* 788, 1936
DVL, Spin-Tunnel	Göttingen										
DVL, High-Speed	Göttingen	Single return	Closed	638 mph	10.0	1.02	8.85 ft Round	1.0D	7.0	17,500	
DVL, Cold-Air	Göttingen	Double return	Open	178 mph					12.5		*Aeroplane,* Feb. 23, 1938
Dornier, 3 x 4 meter	Lake Constance	Single return	Open	134 mph			9.8 x 3.1 ft Elliptic			800	*TM* 868, 1938
Focke-Wulf	Kiel(?)	Single return	Open	67 mph			6.9 x 4.3 ft Rect.		3.5	56	*Aircraft Engineering.* Sept. 1932
Kochel, 40 cm No. 1	Kochel		Open	4.4			16 in. Square			Intermittent	
Kochel, 40 cm No. 2	Kochel		Open	4.4			16 in. Square			Intermittent	
Kochel, 17.5 cm	Kochel		Half open	3.3			7 in. Square			1,100	

Kochel, 100 cm	Kochel		Open	10.0	40 in. Square				80,000	Never completed
LFA, 95 cm	Volkenrode		Closed	1.8	37 in. Square				16,000	
LFA, 25 cm	Volkenrode		Closed	4.0	10 in. Square				1,350	
LFA, 40 cm	Volkenrode		Closed	3.0	16 in. Square				Intermittent	
LFA, 100 cm	Volkenrode		Open	1.1	40 in. Round				16,000	
LFA, 9 ft	Volkenrode	Single return	Closed	1.0	9 ft Round				16,000	
Munich, 9 ft	Munich	Single return	Closed	1.0	9 ft Square				16,000	Never completed
Reyerhausen, Low-Turbulence	Reyerhausen	Single return	Closed	220 mph	5.5 x 11 ft Rect.			25	1,350	
St. Otztal, 26 ft	St. Otztal	Single return	Closed	1.0	26 ft Round	1.9D		9.0	100,000	Never completed
					ITALY					
Breda	Milan	Single return	Open	205 mph	6.1 ft Round		2.3	5.0	800	TM 922, 1939
Guidonia	Milan	Single return	Closed		29 x 16 in. Rect.				2,850	JAS, Oct. 1940

TABLE 1:1. WIND TUNNELS (Continued)

4. Other Nations (Continued)

JAPAN

The wind tunnels of Japan were in four major groups: the First Naval Air Technical Arsenal, Yokosuka; Army Air Technical Research Laboratory, Tachikawa; Central Aeronautical Research Institute, Tokyo; and Tokyo Imperial University, Tokyo.

Tunnel	Located at	Type	Jet Open or Closed	V max. mph	Energy Ratio	Turbu-lence Factor	Jet Shape	Jet Length	Con-traction Ratio	Hp	Reference or Remarks
Small Wind	Yokosuka	Open circuit	Open	79			6 ft diam Round			99	
Spin Tunnel 1	Yokosuka	Quadruple return	Closed	100			9.84 ft Round			296	
Spin Tunnel 2	Yokosuka	Single return	Closed	95			13.1 ft Round			395	
Variable-Density Propeller	Yokosuka	Single return	Closed	560			9.84 ft Round				Unfinished
1st Wind Tunnel	Yokosuka	Open circuit	Open	178			4.1 ft Round			197	
2nd Wind Tunnel	Yokosuka	Single return	Closed	134		1.2	8.2 ft Round	1.85D		395	

3rd Wind Tunnel	Yokosuka	Single return	Closed	134	8.2 ft Round	395	
4th Wind Tunnel	Yokosuka	Single return	Closed	178	9.85 ft Round	986	
Variable-Density	Yokosuka	Single return	Closed	291	5.9 ft Round	986	
High-Speed	Yokosuka	Single return	Closed	1,000	3.28 ft Round	1,430	
Middle-Size	Yokosuka	Single return	Closed	90	24.6 ft Round	3,940	
1.2-meter	Tachikawa	Single return	Open	178	3.7 ft Round	118	
2.2-meter	Tachikawa	Single return	Open	178	7.23 ft Round	197	
7-meter	Tachikawa	Double return	Open	134	23 ft Round	2,960	Destroyed during war
2.5-meter	Tachikawa	Single return	Open	178	8.2 ft Round	740	
Supersonic	Tachikawa	Single return	Closed	720	1.3 ft Square	750	
2.5-meter, High-Speed	Tachikawa	Single return	Closed	450	8.2 ft Round	2,960	
CARI, 3-meter	Tokyo	Single return	Closed	119	9.8 ft Round	400	

TABLE 1:1. WIND TUNNELS (*Continued*)

4. *Other Nations* (*Continued*)

JAPAN (*Continued*)

Tunnel	Located at	Type	Jet Open or Closed	Vmax. mph	Energy Ratio	Turbulence Factor	Jet Shape	Jet Length	Contraction Ratio	Hp	Reference or Remarks
CARI, 50-cm	Tokyo	Single return	Closed	750			1.6 ft Round			400	
CARI, 1.5-meter High-speed	Tokyo	Single return	Closed	750			4.9 ft Round			3,600	
CARI, 2.5-meter	Tokyo	Open circuit	Closed	112			8.2 ft Oct.			500	
CARI, Engine	Tokyo	Open circuit	Open	533			13.1 ft Round			30,000	Partially completed
TIU, 3-meter	Tokyo	Single return	Open	111	1.00		9.85 ft Round			494	*Aircraft Engineering,* Oct. 1931
TIU, 1.5-meter	Tokyo	Single return	Open	134	2.32		4.92 ft Round	2.D		99	*Aircraft Engineering,* Oct. 1931
TIU, 2-meter	Tokyo	Single return	Open	123			6.56 ft Round			246	
Variable-Density	Tokyo	Single return	Closed	338			5.25 ft Round			355	
Mitsubishi	Nagoya	Single return	Open	135	2.8	1.2	6.5 ft Round			200	*TIU,* 66, 1930

Name	Location	Type	Jet	Speed	Ratio	Section			Power	Reference
Kawanishi	Kobe	Single return	Open	100	1.14	6.5 ft Round	1.4		200	TIU 66, 1930
RUMANIA										
Bucharest Polytech	Bucharest	Annular return	Closed	93	3.35	4.9 ft Round	1.67D	7.85	50	TM 651, 1931
RUSSIA										
Adamtchik	Moscow	Open circuit	Closed	80.5	1.53	4.9 ft Round			47	TM 386, 1926
Joukowski	Moscow	Open circuit	Closed	112.0	3.1	9.8 ft Round			350	TM 386, 1926
Moscow Technical School	Moscow	Open circuit	Closed	107.3	3.5	4.9 ft Round				
SPAIN										
Cuatro Vientos	Cuatro Vientos	Single return	Open			9.8 ft Round			700	TM 414, 1926
SWITZERLAND										
Zürich ETH 3 x 2 meter	Zürich	Single return	Both	195	6.4	9.8 x 6.7 ft Rect.			550	Aircraft Engineering, Aug. 1935
Zürich ETH	Zürich	Single return	Closed	1,100		15 x 15 in. Square			900	TM 808

PROBLEMS

1:1. What difficulties are encountered when testing in a pressure tunnel that are not met in other types?

1:2. What disadvantages would there be in utilizing natural wind velocities for testing?

1:3. Look up the available references on three similar tunnels, and prepare a short paper discussing them.

1:4. For what type of work is a full-scale tunnel most suited? not suited?

1:5. Discuss some of the necessary features of a smoke tunnel.

1:6. Explain the difference between an Eiffel- and a Prandtl-type tunnel.

REFERENCES

1:1. JOHN R. MARKHAM, The M.I.T. Wright Brothers Wind Tunnel, *SAE Journal*, September, 1941.

1:2. EASTMAN N. JACOBS, The Variable-Density Tunnel, *TR* 416, 1932.

1:3. SMITH J. DEFRANCE, The NACA Full-Scale Wind Tunnel, *TR* 459, 1933.

1:4. C. TOWNSEND LUDINGTON, *Smoke Streams*, Coward-McCann, New York.

1:5. C. H. ZIMMERMAN, Preliminary Tests in the NACA Free-Spinning Tunnel, *TR* 557, 1936.

1:6. JOHN STACK, The NACA High Speed Wind Tunnel and Tests of Six Propeller Sections, *TR* 463, 1933.

1:7. ANTONIO FERRI, Investigations and Experiments in the Guidonia Supersonic Wind Tunnel, *TM* 901, 1939.

1:8. MARIO PITTONI, The Breda Wind Tunnel, *TM* 922, 1939.

1:9. J. ACKERET, High-Speed Wind Tunnels, *TM* 808, 1936.

1:10. W. S. FARRER, Smoke Investigation of Air Flow, *JAS*, July, 1932.

1:11. A. BAILEY, Development of High-Speed Induction Wind Tunnel, *R&M* 1468, 1932.

1:12. A. BAILEY, The Development of a High-Speed Induction Wind Tunnel of Rectangular Cross Section, *R&M* 1791, 1937.

1:13. A BAILEY, Further Development of a High-Speed Wind Tunnel of Rectangular Cross Section, *R&M* 1853, 1938.

CHAPTER II

WIND-TUNNEL DESIGN

It should be borne in mind that no one tunnel will be adequate for the complete testing program of a new type of airplane. Such a program demands not only the conventional fixed model tunnel but also facilities for testing spin and stability models. The design of these special tunnels, some of which are so rare as to be almost unique, is well beyond the scope of this book. Here the subject is simply the general utility tunnel.

Official photograph, National Advisory Committee for Aeronautics.

FIG. 2:1. Typical airplane installation in the test section of the Ames 40-by 80-ft wind tunnel.

The requirements of general utility are perhaps most completely met by the single-return tunnel. The ability to operate with open or closed throat is advantageous too. The wind-tunnel engineer would probably set as a desirable minimum the ability to attain a testing Reynolds number * of at least 1,500,000 to

---

* The Reynolds number = $(\rho/\mu)Vc$, where ρ = air density in slugs per cubic foot, μ = air viscosity in pound-seconds per cubic foot, V = velocity in feet per second, and c = wing chord in feet.

2,500,000. Indeed, it may be seen from Chapter VII that there is little need to have more than 2,500,000 unless about 9,000,000 is attained. The 1,500,000 to 2,500,000 criterion requires roughly a 1-ft wing chord at 150 mph. Yet, with such conditions for the wing, the tail surfaces of a complete model are at an undesirably low Reynolds number. This consideration points to a larger, higher-speed tunnel, and so the circle goes. Somewhere, unless the cost of tunnel construction, tunnel operation, model construction, and testing is of no consequence, a limit must be set. In recent years many tunnels with rectangular test sections 7 ft by 10 ft or 8 ft by 12 ft have been constructed, usually having a tunnel speed of about 250 mph. This seems to be a very satisfactory tunnel size for the determination of drag, stability, and hinge moments.

Ideally, at least, the wind-tunnel design engineer starts a new tunnel by determining its purpose and hence the required jet shape and airspeed. From the testing requirements he also determines whether the tunnel shall have an atmospheric or closed return. The estimated number of hours of operation and local power costs then dictate the optimum tunnel efficiency. This involves the principle frequently applicable in engineering that added first cost can result in high efficiency and lower operating costs. As will be seen later, in wind-tunnel design added efficiency is achieved by increased tunnel length and hence increased cost of construction.

As a final step in the design, the losses in the test section, corners, diffusers, and entrance cone are calculated and summed up to get the input power.

From a practical standpoint, the design may take the amount of money available as the starting point. Various designs in the proper bracket are then considered until the optimum is selected. The physical location may also be a decisive factor. If the tunnel is to be located in a certain building, or on a specific plot of ground, the designer must consider this factor in the layout.

Additional problems arise if the tunnel is of special design. For instance, the pressure-type tunnels may be initially tested by being filled with water under pressure to avoid the danger that would arise if they failed under a compressed-air load. The weight of the water may indeed alter the normal foundation design. Tunnels with atmospheric return require additional studies of their physical surroundings.

The general layout for a tunnel, supposing that no extraneous factors seriously enter into the design, has reached a form generally agreed upon for reasons of construction economy and tunnel efficiency. This usually embraces a diffuser of three or four test section lengths, and two sets of similar corners. The similar corners save a little engineering and construction cost, and making the two turns before the propeller of a constant area assists in getting smooth flow to the propeller, provided that it is located reasonably close to the second corner. The plane of the return passage is almost always horizontal, to save cost and make the return passage easier to get to. The vertical return is justified only when space is at a premium. No rule or general procedure has been agreed upon as regards the shape of the return passage—round or rectangular. Factors governing the choice are given in the appropriate paragraphs.

Factors influencing the design of the test section, corners, return passage, and contraction cone are discussed on the following pages. The actual power losses are covered in Sect. 2:10.

2:1. The Test Section. As has been mentioned previously, most wind-tunnel designs are started with two criteria in mind: (1) the type of testing to be performed; and (2) the tunnel necessary to do the job. The "tunnel necessary" includes considerations of jet dimensions (size and shape), and the desired tunnel wind speed. These items in turn determine (within broad limits) the power that will be needed and largely determine the entire design. In a way, the jet size and wind speed could be interpreted as one criterion: desirable test Reynolds number. In theory, at least, a larger jet using a larger model could operate satisfactorily at a lower speed. But although the same Reynolds number could be obtained in a tunnel of twice a given size at half the power, the original cost of the larger tunnel would be four times that of the smaller. In practice the jet speeds in the larger tunnels are as high as, if not higher than, those in the smaller ones.

Probably the shape of a test section for a stability and control tunnel should be rectangular. This shape offers the flat surfaces required by the disks used in wingtip mounting and a flat floor for the tunnel engineers to stand on when working on the model. (The last feature may not be a design criterion *per se*, but practically it is important.) Moreover, a rectangular jet has a large amount of "useful area." That is, for a given jet area a larger model can be tested in a rectangular (or in an elliptic) jet than in a round or square one. Because it is difficult to construct, the elliptic jet is no longer favored. A circular jet is advantageous for testing propellers, rotors, and engines.

The length of the test section in common practice varies from one to two times the major dimension of the jet. The power losses in the jet (see Sect. 2:10) are sizable owing to the high speed, and an advantage accrues from keeping the length down. If forces are to be determined by reading the pressures on the tunnel walls, the longer jet is desirable.

As the air proceeds along the test section the boundary layer thickens. This action reduces the effective area of the jet and causes an increase of velocity. The velocity increase in turn produces a drop in local static pressure, tending to draw the model downstream. This added drag, called "horizontal buoyancy," is discussed in Sect. 6:1, where corrections may be found.

If the cross-sectional area of the jet is increased enough to allow for the thickening boundary layer, a constant value of the static pressure may be maintained throughout the test section. Unfortunately no exact design method is available that assures the development of a constant static pressure. For a first approximation the walls of a closed jet should diverge about ½ degree each; finer adjustments may be necessary after the tunnel is built and the longitudinal static pressure is measured. Some tunnels whose test sections have corner fillets have these fillets altered until a constant static pressure is obtained. The advantages of such a flow are enough to justify a moderate amount of work in obtaining it.

A practical detail in jet design rarely satisfactorily attained is the installation of sufficient windows for viewing the model. In the course of testing it will become necessary to see all parts of the model: top, sides, bottom, and as much of the front as is reasonably practical.

Adequate lighting is also needed, and separate switches for those lights below eye level should be provided. Permanent flood lights to be used in photographical work should also be installed.

The above paragraphs have been written for the customary closed test section because that type is most generally in use. For propeller and rotor tests, however, the open jet offers considerable advantage, as can be seen by reference to Sects. 6:2

and 6:17, where the corrections for propeller and nacelles are seen to be much smaller if an open jet is employed.

The objections to an open jet are twofold:

1. The wind-tunnel balance usually requires so much shielding for operating with an open jet that approximately one solid boundary is simulated. This confuses the boundary corrections to be applied and raises doubt that the jet is truly open.

2. The power required for a given tunnel with an open jet may easily exceed three times the power required by the same tunnel at the same speed with a closed jet. Further data on this factor may be obtained by comparing energy ratios (see Sect. 3:7) for tunnels with open and closed test sections from Table 1:1.

If an open jet is employed the exit cone should be larger than the entrance cone. An expansion along the test section of 2 degrees will decrease the pressure gradient that occurs without it; Darrius (Ref. 2:12) suggests a 6-degree expansion as more satisfactory overall, considering the increased energy recovered. Some engineers keep the diffuser at constant diameter for about a half jet length to allow the flow to stabilize.

It will easily be seen that an open jet used with an open circuit return is a virtual impossibility unless the open jet is surrounded by a sealed-off chamber, as air would flow into the jet as much as into the entrance cone. Indeed, a sealed-off area around a closed jet is a beneficial item for both open-circuit and closed-return tunnels, reducing leakage, the entry of dust, and outside noise.

2:2. The Return Passage. As the power losses in a wind tunnel vary with the cube of the airspeed, it is desirable to increase the cross-sectional area of the return passage and hence reduce the local tunnel speed as rapidly as possible. This is particularly important in the region before the first corner because (as will be demonstrated) a large percentage of the total power loss occurs therein. The rate of this area increase is limited by the amount of expansion the air will stand without separating from the walls with accompanying large losses. Tests have shown that a reasonable expansion of a round passage is about 5 to 8 degrees between opposite walls. When a rectangular passage is expanded in one direction only, an angle of 12 degrees between opposite walls is permissible.

The smaller expansion angles make for a longer, more expensive tunnel whose flow is the optimum and whose cost of operation slightly lower than that of a large-expansion-angle tunnel.

Crowding the upper limit of expansion to save construction cost has its disadvantages. In the usual three-dimensional test section the model is mounted in the middle of the airstream, and its wake proceeds downstream without seriously impairing the flow in the tunnel. Only a small increase in power is required with increasing angle of attack of the model. In the two-dimensional jet a more serious effect appears. As the model stalls, the turbulent flow, being at the walls (as well as at the middle of the airstream), may start a separated region that can spread downstream along the tunnel sides, stalling the diffuser. The power required for this large separated region may exceed 150 per cent of that required for the tunnel with the model at a low angle. Hence, either a reserve of power must be maintained, or this flow must be controlled through slots in the diffuser emitting air at high velocity. Such an arrangement is called "boundary-layer control." A tunnel whose diffuser is below atmospheric pressure may sometimes obtain boundary-layer control with simple guided slots open to the atmosphere.

One item in the return passage that deserves mention is a strong wire "safety" screen between the test section and the propeller to serve as a catch-all when failure of a model occurs. Though such failures can be reduced by careful design of the model, and the leaving of tools, pieces of material, and model parts in the test section can be reduced by an alert crew, somehow sooner or later, some objects will join the slipstream and go hurrying towards the propeller with calamitous intent. Whether the janitor then sweeps up the propeller along with the now fragmentary model parts is a function of the grid efficiency only. Obviously, the power losses suffered from the addition of such an obstacle may be reduced by having the screen in the lowest-velocity section possible. Additional power may be saved by selecting the largest mesh compatible with the desired degree of protection, and designing the screen to cover only the lower area of the tunnel where any foreign objects are most likely to occur. Placing the screen at the trailing edges of the second set of guide vanes is advantageous because the vanes may act as buffers, and the drag of the screen is reduced by being in the wake of the vanes.

The safety screen can be made to serve a double purpose if separation troubles are encountered in the diffuser. This arrangement embraces a fine wire screen about two-thirds of the distance

from the test section to the first corner. The rapid pressure rise
assists in maintaining flow at the walls, and at the same time the
screen acts as a safety screen.

If the tests to be run include extensive smoke-flow studies or
the operation of internal-combustion engines, an atmospheric
return may be the optimum design.* Even so, a considerable

Courtesy Georgia Institute of Technology.

FIG. 2:2.   Corner vanes and safety screen.

return passage is needed to drop the local airspeed to such a
value that the energy contained in the air "dumped" out the
end is small.

Any return passage should have sufficient airtight doors and
windows so that accessibility and visibility are well provided
for, particularly near the propeller-power plant unit and the
entrance cone.

* Some recent studies indicate considerable promise to the open-circuit
tunnel for almost any type of testing as construction costs are reduced by
eliminating the return passage. Further work must be done, and a large
installation must be constructed and put into service before a definite conclusion can be drawn.

2:3. The Breather. If the tunnel is to be operated with an open jet, due consideration must be given to the possibility of pulsations arising similar to the vibrations in an organ pipe. This phenomenon, believed to be a function of jet length, can be quite serious.

The simplest solution, usually successful, consists of putting a slot (about 0.05 diameter wide) in the diffuser which connects it to the atmosphere. Such an arrangement is called a "breather." If the slot is properly made and adjusted so that it is just large enough to prevent organ piping, the losses can be kept low. In some open-jet tunnels alterations to the exit cone proved sufficient to prevent the vibration, but in others no satisfactory exit cones or breathers have been found that would permit operation above 200 mph.

Closed-jet tunnels usually require breathers too, because the entire return passage is above atmospheric pressure, and some air may leak out. In turn the loss of air would drop the jet pressure below atmospheric unless it were replenished. The proper place for a closed-jet tunnel breather is at the downstream end of the test section (see Fig. 1:1), and like that for an open-jet tunnel a slot about 0.05 diameter wide usually suffices.

2:4. The Propeller-Flow Straightener System. The wind-tunnel propeller,* seemingly similar to the propeller of an airplane, operates under peculiar conditions that put it in a class by itself. For one thing, unlike the airplane propeller, the wind-tunnel propeller is prevented by the law of continuity † from producing an increase of velocity in the slipstream; and, for another, rotation imparted to the flow is of paramount importance instead of being considered a loss to be removed by a second propeller only when high torque is prohibited.

There are three basic propeller-straightener systems in current use:

1. A propeller with straightener vanes behind it.

2. A propeller with prerotating vanes ahead of it, probably also having straightener vanes behind it.

3. Counterrotating propellers in which the second propeller removes the rotation imparted by the first.

---

* Although sometimes called a "fan," the wind-tunnel propeller operates in a moving flow, using a large blade angle, and is more properly called a "propeller." The author hence prefers that word to the more common "fan."

† See p. 41.

The counterrotating propeller can remove all the twist for all tunnel speeds and power inputs. Since two propellers can obviously be designed to develop more thrust than one, the counter-

Courtesy of United Aircraft Corp.

FIG. 2:3. A wind-tunnel propeller installation.

rotating propellers may become essential in high-power installations. The drive is more complicated, however, as equal torque should be applied to both propellers.

Propellers with prerotating vanes can develop more thrust for a given blade area because the initial rotation increases the total velocity of the airstream. Also the increased propeller blade angle used with prerotating vanes may increase the efficiency. If a model should break and parts fly through the tunnel, the prerotating vanes offer a measure of protection to the tunnel propeller. They have the disadvantage that they cannot impart the proper prerotation for different power conditions and hence must be made adjustable or have straightener vanes added behind the propeller.

For tunnels of moderate size and power a single propeller is usually quite satisfactory. If it is properly designed, a straightener system can be devised that will remove the twist for all power inputs and speeds. Such straighteners are discussed in the following paragraphs.

The availability of variable-pitch propellers may be very helpful with any type of propeller-straightener combination as they offer limited means of control of the velocity distribution. Also, when the propeller drive motor is of the synchronous type the propeller can be put in flat pitch for low pull-in torque and then opened out to develop the tunnel speed. This action may lead to greater power outputs from this type of motor as the pull-in torque is often the limiting factor.

The design of wind-tunnel propellers has had considerable discussion (Ref. 2:14), but a method proposed by Patterson (Ref. 2:13) is presented here because it considers the propeller-straightener system as a unit and does not concern itself merely with the propeller. As rotation must be kept low if a fixed straightener system is to remove the twist for all conditions, consideration of the vanes becomes important, and their design will frequently necessitate a propeller vastly different from what the ordinary criteria indicate. The fact that each section of this type of propeller operates at constant efficiency, though of small merit as far as the propeller is concerned, makes the usual graphical integration of the thrust and torque loading curves unnecessary, and hence the design is facilitated.

This theory, however, neglects the loss associated with the necessary tip clearance at the tunnel wall and the radial flow at the propeller encountered due to the centrifugal action. The large boss recommended for use with a wind-tunnel propeller tends to lessen the latter effect. The tip-clearance loss will result in efficiencies slightly lower than indicated by this theory. The loss due to tip clearance adds to both the friction and expansion losses that occur at the walls of a wind tunnel and indicates that instead of constant thrust the wind-tunnel propeller should perhaps have a graded thrust loading curve, greatest at the walls in order to best develop a uniform velocity front. This refinement is beyond the scope of this presentation.

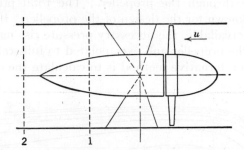

Fig. 2:4. The propeller-straightener combination.

First let us consider the flow in a duct so that the terms and factors encountered later in the propeller theory may be understood when applied.

A. Flow in a Duct

When Bernoulli's equation

$$p + \tfrac{1}{2}\rho V^2 = \text{constant} \tag{2:0}$$

is written between two locations in a duct, it applies only if the losses between the sections are zero. Naturally, in practice, they never are, and one or the other of the two terms at the second section must show a diminution corresponding to the loss in head. The law of continuity for an incompressible fluid, $A_1 V_1 = A_2 V_2$, where A and V are areas and velocities at two stations, makes it impossible for the velocity to fail to follow Bernoulli's rule, and hence the velocity head at the second location will be as predicted. But there will be a drop in static head Δp corresponding to the friction loss. This loss in pounds per square foot appears over the area A_2, so that the product of the two yields the drag of the section between 1 and 2. Multiplying the drag by the velocity yields the power lost. According to familiar experience, the drag of a surface varies with the dynamic pressure q, and it is customary to express the loss of the section in coefficient form, defining

$$k = \frac{\Delta p A}{\tfrac{1}{2}\rho A V^2} = \frac{\Delta p}{q} \tag{2:1}$$

It will be seen that the coefficient k compares with C_D in wing-drag calculations.

Throughout the wind tunnel the losses that occur appear as successive static-pressure drops, to be balanced by the static-pressure rise through the propeller. The total pressure drop Δh must be known for the design of the propeller. If a model of the tunnel is available, the necessary pressure rise may be measured across the propeller and extrapolated to full-scale Reynolds number. An alternative method is to calculate the energy ratio

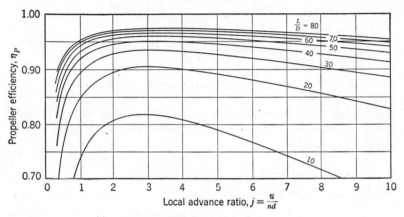

FIG. 2:5. Approximate propeller efficiencies for various advance and L/D ratios.

(see Sects. 2:10 and 3:7) and find the propeller pressure rise coefficient $k = \Delta h / (\frac{1}{2}\rho u^2)$, where u is the velocity through the propeller. It is now in order to consider several design features of the propeller-straightener system.

B. Factors Influencing the General Layout

It will be seen from Fig. 2:5 that high propeller efficiencies are largely determined by proper selection of the advance ratio (see p. 45) and utilization of L/D ratios of the order of 50. It remains to demonstrate the best methods for satisfying these criteria.

Large advance ratios imply lowered speeds of propeller rotation, necessitating a drive motor of low rpm or a geared driving system. The desire for higher rpm for the driving motor indicates that the higher-speed regions of the wind tunnel are best suited for the location of the propeller. Balancing that against the increase of nacelle drag as the local speed is increased, the best compromise usually locates the propeller downstream of the second corner after the test section. Here the airspeed is moderate, and, if a short settling section is provided before the propeller, the flow is excellent. If the propeller is to be driven by a motor outside the tunnel, the corner location offers a short shaft length. The design of a propeller that is to be located well down the return-passage diffuser may be complicated by the uneven velocity front found in such passages.

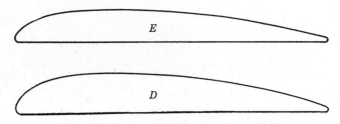

FIG. 2:6. Satisfactory airfoils for propeller sections.

L/D ratios as high as 50 and higher are obtainable only with "infinite" aspect ratio and moderately thin airfoils. Infinite aspect ratio can be simulated by effectively endplating both the propeller blade root and the tip, endplating being accomplished by providing a large nacelle or "boss" for the root and maintaining a small tip clearance so that the tunnel wall becomes the tip endplate. The large nacelle is advantageous from other considerations, too. By decreasing the tunnel cross-sectional area at the propeller a higher velocity is achieved, and higher motor speeds are possible at the same advance ratio. The large boss also encloses the propeller root sections that must be thicker for structural reasons, leaving only the thin, highly efficient sections exposed to the airstream. Frequently it is possible to use an airfoil of constant thickness in the exposed portion, thus facilitating the design. Small gains are to be found from utilizing an L/D of greater than 50, so that the actual airfoil selected is of secondary importance from an aerodynamic standpoint and structural considerations can be entertained. Type E of the RAF propeller sections is satisfactory, as is the slightly thicker Type D (see Fig. 2:6). The ordinates of these airfoils are shown in Table 2:1.

TABLE 2:1. ORDINATES OF PROPELLER PROFILES D AND E

Distance from Leading Edge	Height above Flat Undersurface	
	D	E
0	0.0135	0.0115
0.0125	0.0370	0.0319
0.025	0.0538	0.0442
0.05	0.0780	0.0610
0.075	0.0925	0.0724
0.10	0.1030	0.0809
0.15	0.1174	0.0928
0.20	0.1250	0.0990
0.30	0.1290	0.1030
0.40	0.1269	0.1022
0.50	0.1220	0.0980
0.60	0.1120	0.0898
0.70	0.0960	0.0770
0.80	0.0740	0.0591
0.90	0.0470	0.0379
0.95	0.0326	0.0258
1.00	0.0100	0.0076
L.E. rad.	0.0135	0.0115
T.E. rad.	0.0100	0.0076

Although the optimum boss diameter is from 0.6 to $0.7D_p$, where D_p = diameter of the tunnel at the propeller, a smaller value of 0.3 to 0.5 is more practical for wind-tunnel use. The very large boss requires a large and long nacelle for proper stream-lining, which, in turn, involves costly construction difficulties and greater power losses from the diffusing action as the area of the air passage is increased. It would be possible to prevent the diffusing losses by shaping the tunnel so that the area throughout the propeller-nacelle region remained constant, but such irregularity would also entail expensive construction.

The number of blades on the propeller is somewhat arbitrary, for the product of the number of blades and their chord represents the total area and must be aligned with the thrust requirements. Several factors influence the selection of the number of blades. The minimum number probably is four; at least that number is needed to assure little pulsation in the airstream. The maximum number of blades will doubtless be limited by strength considerations. The maximum value of the sum of the blade chords Nc must not exceed the local circumference at the root if excessive interference is to be avoided. The Reynolds number of the blade chord should be above 700,000 in order to keep the section drag low. Since the number of blades is not critical, a reasonable procedure is to estimate the number needed and examine the final design to see whether alterations are in order.

C. THE PROPELLER ADVANCE RATIO, j

In the simple blade element theory (Ref. 2:15), the angle of attack of a local section of the blade is simply the local blade angle minus the advance angle $\phi = V/(2\pi nr)$, where $V = $ forward speed, $n = $ rps, and $r = $ section radius. This definition, which neglects both the induced indraft and rotation, is permissible only because a second assumption (that the airfoil coefficients should be based on an aspect ratio of 6.0) is made. With a wind-tunnel propeller, no indraft is possible, but rotation exists and the simple blade-element advance angle is seriously changed. Figure 2:8 and eqs. 2:25 and 2:26 demonstrate the proper interpretation of the advance angle for a propeller in a duct.

D. THE ROTATION, e

It has already been demonstrated that in order to meet the requirements of the law of continuity there can be no increase of axial velocity in a duct of constant area. However, the propeller imparts twist or rotation to the airstream and hence increases its absolute velocity. This added speed is removed, not turned, by the straightener vanes, and its energy appears as a rise in static pressure.

Increasing the diameter of the propeller boss will decrease the amount of rotation for a given installation, as will increasing the propeller rpm.

E. THE STRAIGHTENER VANES

Experiments at the NPL have shown that satisfactory anti-twist or straightener vanes can be made by using the NACA symmetrical airfoils set with their chords parallel to the tunnel centerline provided that the amount of twist to be removed is small compared with the axial velocity. The limiting twist is that required to stall the vanes; i.e., $e = \omega r/u = \tan \tau$ (where

τ = angle of twist in the slipstream and ω = angular velocity in the slipstream at radius r) must correspond to an angle less than α_{stall} of a symmetrical section at infinite aspect ratio including multiplane interference. The interference is an advantage here as with the type of straighteners to be employed it decreases the lift curve slope by a factor of 0.75. That is, α_{stall} with interference is 33 per cent above the free-air stall angle.

The chord for the proposed straightener may be found from

$$c_s = \frac{2\pi r}{N_s} \qquad (2:2)$$

where N_s = number of straightener vanes.
$\quad\;\; c_s$ = chord of vane at radius r.

If a constant thickness ratio is assumed for the straightener vanes, the actual thickness at the wall would be large owing to the large chord. Hence it is advantageous to select a constant thickness (not thickness ratio). A reasonable value is that $t_s/c_s = 0.15$ at $x = r/R = 0.8$. (R = tunnel radius at propeller section.) Hence from eq. 2:2

$$\frac{t_s}{c_s} = \frac{N_s t_s}{2\pi R x} \qquad (2:2a)$$

A value of 7 comes to mind for N_s, as in order to avoid periodic interference with the propeller the straightener should have a number of blades that is no multiple of the even number of propeller blades.

There will be a loss through the straightener, of course, and this loss will be greater than the skin friction of the vanes in free air as the straightener is a diffuser, changing the rotational velocity ωr to static head. The pressure loss coefficient of a straightener composed of symmetrical NACA airfoil sections has been empirically determined as

$$k_s = 0.045 \frac{t_s}{c_s} + 0.003 \qquad (2:2b)$$

Substituting from eq. 2:2 we have

$$k_s = \frac{0.045}{2\pi r} t_s N_s + 0.003 \qquad (2:3)$$

F. PROPELLER-STRAIGHTENER THEORY

The theory for the design of a wind-tunnel propeller-straightener system is as follows:

Letting the total cross-sectional area at the plane of the propeller be A_p and the area of the propeller boss be A_b, the power input becomes (Fig. 2:4)

$$\text{Power in} = \Delta h \cdot (A_p - A_b) \cdot u = \eta_t \, \text{bhp} \cdot 550$$

where η_t = propeller-straightener efficiency.

Hence

$$k = \frac{\eta_t \, \text{bhp} \cdot 550}{\frac{1}{2}\rho u^3 (A_p - A_b)} = \frac{\eta_t \, \text{bhp} \cdot 550}{\frac{1}{2}\rho V_t^3 A_t} \frac{V_t^2}{u^2}$$

where A_t and V_t are the test section area and velocity, respectively.

Applying the definition of the energy ratio and the law of continuity,

$$k = \eta_t \frac{1}{\text{E.R.}_1} \frac{(A_p - A_b)^2}{A_t^2} \qquad (2:4)$$

The efficiency of the propeller-straightener unit is derived from the basic relation

$$\eta_t = \frac{\text{Power out}}{\text{Power in}} \qquad (2:5)$$

The power out produces a rise in static pressure Δh over the area A and may be written

$$\text{Power out} = \Delta h \cdot A \cdot u$$

where u = local velocity (axial).

$$\text{Power in} = 2\pi n Q$$

where Q = torque.

$$n = \text{revolutions per second.}$$

It will be convenient to consider the efficiency of a blade element in the development later, so rewriting η for an annulus of width dr at radius r we have:

$$\eta_t = \frac{\Delta h \cdot 2\pi r \cdot dr \cdot u}{2\pi n \, dQ}$$

In differential form

$$dQ = 2\pi r \cdot dr \cdot \rho u \cdot \omega r^2$$

and, as $\Delta h = k \cdot \tfrac{1}{2}\rho u^2$, and $\Omega = 2\pi n$,

$$\eta_t = \frac{ku^2}{2\Omega r^2 \omega}$$

Defining the local advance ratio

$$j = \frac{u}{nd} = \frac{u\pi}{2\pi nr} = \frac{u\pi}{\Omega r} \qquad (2:6)$$

and expressing the rotation of the flow e as a fraction of the axial velocity,

$$e = \frac{\omega r}{u} \qquad (2:7)$$

and

$$\eta_t = \frac{kj}{2\pi e} \qquad (2:8)$$

Writing the loss in head due to the straightener as Δp_s and proceeding as in the derivation of eq. 2:8, we find

$$\eta_s = \frac{k_s j}{2\pi e} \qquad (2:9)$$

We may determine e from

$$e = \frac{kj}{2\pi \eta_t} \qquad (2:10)$$

And hence η_p becomes determined through

Propeller efficiency = Total efficiency + Straightener efficiency

loss or, in symbols,

$$\eta_p = \eta_t + \eta_s \qquad (2:10a)$$

Writing the elemental thrust as the pressure rise times the elemental area, we have

$$dT = \Delta p \cdot 2\pi r \cdot dr \qquad (2:10b)$$

Expressing the local radius as a fraction of the tip radius R by the relation $x = r/R$, and dividing the expression for the elemental thrust by $\frac{1}{2}\rho u^2 \cdot \pi R^2$ to reduce it to coefficient form, we have

$$\frac{dT_c}{dx} = \frac{\Delta p \cdot 2\pi r \cdot R}{\frac{1}{2}\rho u^2 \pi R^2} = \frac{2\,\Delta p \cdot x}{\frac{1}{2}\rho u^2} \qquad (2{:}11)$$

The total pressure rise required is

$$\Delta h = k \cdot \tfrac{1}{2}\rho u^2 \qquad (2{:}12)$$

$$= \text{Propeller rise} + \text{Rotation} - \text{Straightener loss}$$

$$= \Delta p + \tfrac{1}{2}\rho\omega^2 r^2 - k_s \cdot \tfrac{1}{2}\rho u^2$$

Solving, the necessary rise through the propeller is

$$\frac{\Delta p}{\frac{1}{2}\rho u^2} = k + k_s - e^2 \qquad (2{:}13)$$

And eq. 2:11 becomes

$$\frac{dT_c}{dx} = (k + k_s - e^2) \cdot 2x \qquad (2{:}14)$$

Elemental torque dQ = Rate of change of moment
of momentum

$$= \rho u \cdot 2\pi r \, dr \cdot \omega r \cdot r \qquad (2{:}15)$$

or, in coefficient form, letting

$$dQ_c = \frac{dQ}{\frac{1}{2}\rho u^2 \cdot \pi R^2 \cdot R}$$

$$\frac{dQ_c}{dx} = 4x^2 e \qquad (2{:}16)$$

Finally,

$$Q_c = \frac{kJ}{\pi\eta_t}(1 - x_0{}^2) \qquad (2{:}17)$$

where x_0 = radius ratio at the root section.
J = advance ratio of propeller tip.

Equation 2:17 determines the input torque necessary and hence the power required to realize the total pressure rise Δh.

By approaching the problem in a slightly different manner it is possible to get a relation between j, η_p, and e such that the local L/D is determined.

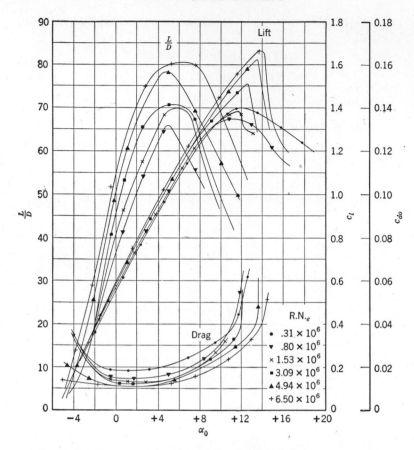

FIG. 2:7. Characteristics of propeller airfoil D, infinite aspect ratio.

We proceed as follows: The total pressure rise due to the propeller is

$$\Delta h_p = \text{Static rise} + \text{Rotational dynamic head}$$

$$\Delta h_p = \Delta p + \tfrac{1}{2}\rho\omega^2 r^2 \tag{2:18}$$

and

$$\text{Power output} = \Delta h_p \cdot 2\pi r \, dr \cdot u$$

$$= 2\pi r \, dr \cdot u \, \Delta p + \tfrac{1}{2}\rho\omega^2 r^2 \cdot 2\pi r \, dr \cdot u$$

$$= u \cdot dT + \tfrac{1}{2}\omega \, dQ \qquad \text{(eq. 2:15; 210}b\text{)}$$

The propeller efficiency $\eta_p = \dfrac{u \, dT + \frac{1}{2}\omega \, dQ}{2\pi n \, dQ}$, or, in coefficient form,

$$\eta_p = \frac{u \, dT_c}{2\pi n \cdot dQ_c \cdot R} + \frac{1}{2}\frac{\omega}{2\pi n}$$

$$= \frac{J \, dT_c}{\pi \, dQ_c} + \frac{1}{2}\frac{ej}{\pi} \tag{2:19}$$

Substituting from 2:14 and 2:16

$$\eta_p = \frac{j}{2\pi e}(k + k_s) \tag{2:20}$$

Expressing the elemental thrust in a form similar to conventional wing coefficients we have

$$dT = \tfrac{1}{2}\rho W^2 \cdot c \, dr \cdot N C_t \tag{2:21}$$

where $W = \dfrac{u}{\sin \phi}$,

N = number of blades, and

$$C_t = \text{thrust coefficient} = c_l \cos \phi + c_{d0} \sin \phi$$
$$\tag{2:22}$$
$$C_x = \text{torque force coefficient} = c_l \sin \phi + c_{d0} \cos \phi$$

Reducing Eq. 2:21 to the T_c form, we have

$$\frac{dT_c}{dx} = \frac{N C_t \frac{1}{2}\rho u^2 \cdot cR}{\frac{1}{2}\rho u^2 \sin^2 \phi \pi R^2} = \frac{N C_t \cdot c}{\pi R \sin^2 \phi} \tag{2:22a}$$

$$\frac{dT_c}{dx} = \frac{y C_t}{\sin^2 \phi} \tag{2:22b}$$

where $y = \dfrac{Nc}{\pi R}$ by definition. $\tag{2:22c}$

The corresponding elemental torque is

$$dQ = N C_x \cdot \tfrac{1}{2}\rho W^2 \cdot c \, dr \cdot r$$

$$\frac{dQ_c}{dx} = \frac{yx C_x}{\sin^2 \phi} \tag{2:23}$$

Substituting in 2:19, the propeller efficiency

$$\eta_p = \frac{j}{\pi} \frac{C_t}{C_x} + \frac{1}{2} \frac{ej}{\pi} \qquad (2:24)$$

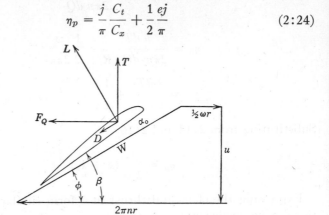

FIG. 2:8.

From Fig. 2:8,

$$\tan \phi = \frac{u}{2\pi nr - \frac{1}{2}\omega r}$$

$$= \frac{u}{\pi nd - \frac{1}{2}\frac{\omega r}{u}\frac{u}{nd}\frac{\pi}{\pi}nd} \qquad (2:25)$$

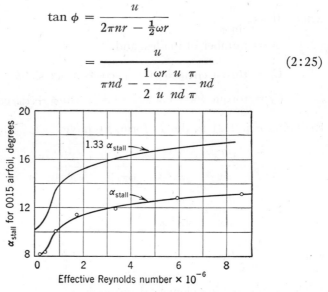

FIG. 2:9. Effect of interference.

Hence from eqs. 2:2a and 2:3

$$\tan \phi = \frac{j}{\pi} \frac{1}{1 - \frac{1}{2}ej/\pi} \qquad (2:26)$$

Hence from eqs. 2:22, 2:24, and 2:26

$$\eta_p = \frac{\dfrac{j}{\pi}\left(\dfrac{L}{D} - \dfrac{j}{\pi}\right) + \dfrac{1}{2}\dfrac{ej}{\pi}\left(1 - \dfrac{1}{2}\dfrac{ej}{\pi}\right)}{\dfrac{L}{D}\dfrac{j}{\pi} + 1 - \dfrac{1}{2}\dfrac{ej}{\pi}} \qquad (2:27)$$

With η_p and j known, eq. 2:27 can be employed to yield the L/D desired at each corresponding radius, but the values of c_l, c_{d0}, and α_0 cannot be determined accurately until the local Reynolds number is known. (See footnote p. 31.) Hence it is necessary to determine an approximate Reynolds number as follows:

1. Using calculated L/D, read approximate lift coefficient $c_{l\ \text{approx.}}$ in Fig. 2:7.

2. From $\dfrac{dT_c}{dx} = 2x(k + k_s - e^2)$ find $\dfrac{dT_c}{dx}$.

3. Calculate yC_t from

$$\frac{dT_c}{dx} = \frac{yC_t}{\sin^2 \phi} \qquad (2:27a)$$

4. Calculate $y_{\text{approx.}}$ from

$$y \cong \frac{yC_t}{c_{l\ \text{approx.}} \cos \phi} \qquad (2:27b)$$

5. Get approximate c from

$$c_{\text{approx.}} = \frac{\pi R y_{\text{approx.}}}{N} \qquad (2:28)$$

6. $$\text{R.N.} = \frac{\rho}{\mu} cW \qquad (2:29)$$

where μ = viscosity of the air = $(340.8 + 0.548(°F))10^{-9}$. Having the Reynolds number, we now use the characteristic curves of the selected airfoil section to determine c_l, c_{d0}, and α_0.

The values of the advance angle ϕ may be determined from eq. 2:26. The blade angle is determined from

$$\beta = \phi + \alpha_0 \qquad (2:30)$$

Since dT_c/dx is known for each value of x from eq. 2:14, C_t may be found from eq. 2:22, sin ϕ from eq. 2:26, and y from eq. 2:22b. From

$$c = \frac{\pi R y}{N} \qquad (2:31)$$

the local chord may be computed.

G. Design Procedure

1. Select a desired overall efficiency η_t, and add to it the estimated straightener loss (2 to 4 per cent) to get the required propeller efficiency η_p.

2. From the plot of approximate propeller efficiencies vs. advance ratios (Fig. 2:5) determine the required L/D and j range to attain η_p. If the available range is excessive, select the advance ratio for the tip speed as low as possible, as this will yield maximum rpm and minimum rotation. Determine n from

$$n = \frac{u}{jd}$$

Check to see that a tip speed of 550 ft/sec is not exceeded so that compressibility losses will not be encountered.

3. Calculate k from eq. 2:4, and e from eq. 2:8. Check that e at the root is less than $1.33\alpha_{stall}$ from Fig. 2:9.

4. Calculate t_s/c_s and k_s from eqs. 2:2a and 2:2b.

5. Calculate η_s from eq. 2:9, and η_p from eq. 2:10a.

6. Determine L/D from eq. 2:27.

7. Calculate ϕ from eq. 2:26.

8. Read approximate c_l from Fig. 2:7.

9. Find dT_c/dx from eq. 2:14.

10. Calculate yC_t, y, c, and R.N. from eqs. 2:27a, 2:27b, 2:28, and 2:29.

11. Using approximate R.N., read accurate c_l, c_{d0}, and α_0 from Fig. 2:7.

12. Calculate y from eq. 2:22b.

13. Calculate c from eq. 2:22c.

14. Determine β from eq. 2:30.

15. Determine Q from eq. 2:17.

Example 2:1

A propeller is required for a wind tunnel whose energy ratio is 5.0. The area of the test section is 56.4 ft², and the testing velocity is 193 mph = 284 ft/sec. The wind-tunnel diameter at the propeller is 13 ft.

A boss diameter of $0.6D$ and 12 blades are values selected for preliminary calculations. Hence $A_p - A_b = 133 - 47.8 = 85.2 \, \text{ft}^2$, and $u = 284 \times 56.4/85.2 = 188$. Let $\eta_t = 0.93$.

Step 1. Estimating the straightener loss at 3 per cent, it is seen that the propeller efficiency must therefore be 96 per cent.

Step 2. From Fig. 2:5 it is seen that $\eta_p = 96$ per cent may be reached from $j = 2.2$ to $j = 4.8$, using $L/D = 50.0$, which is a reasonable value.

$$n = \frac{u}{JD} = \frac{188}{2.2 \times 13} = 6.58$$

$$\Omega = 2\pi n = 41.4 \, \text{rad/sec}$$

$$V_{\text{tip}} = 2\pi n R = 2\pi \times 6.58 \times 6.5 = 269 \, \text{ft/sec}$$

which is well below 550 ft/sec, the approximate limit to avoid compressibility.

Step 3.

$$k = \frac{\eta_t}{ER}\left(\frac{A_p - A_b}{A_t}\right)^2 = \frac{0.93}{5.00}\left(\frac{85.2}{56.4}\right)^2 = 0.425$$

$$e = \frac{kj}{2\pi\eta_t} = \frac{0.425}{2\pi(0.93)}j = 0.0729j$$

$$j = \frac{u}{nd} = \frac{u}{n\,Dx} = \frac{188}{(6.58)(13.0)x} = \frac{2.20}{x}$$

$$e_{\text{root}} = \frac{0.220}{0.6} \times 0.0729 = 0.267$$

$$\tau = \tan^{-1} 0.267 = 14.9°$$

This is below $1.33\alpha_{\text{stall}}$ from Fig. 2:9, using an estimated $RN = 2,000,000$.

Step 4. The thickness of the straightener vanes (to be held constant) is $t_s/c_s = 0.15$ at $x = 0.8$. From eq. 2:2 we have

$$c_{s(x=0.8)} = \frac{2\pi Rx}{N_s} = \frac{2\pi(6.5)(0.8)}{7.0} = 4.67 \, \text{ft}$$

Hence from eq. 2:2a

$$\frac{t_s}{c_s} = \frac{N_s t_s}{2\pi Rx} = \frac{7 \times 0.70}{2\pi(6.5)x} = \frac{0.12}{x}$$

$$k_s = 0.045\frac{t_s}{c_s} + 0.003 \tag{2:2b}$$

$$= \frac{0.0054}{x} + 0.003$$

The remaining steps are indicated and tabulated below.

x	0.6	0.7	0.8	0.9	1.0
j	3.67	3.14	2.75	2.44	2.20
e	0.267	0.229	0.200	0.178	0.160
t_s/c_s	0.20	0.171	0.15	0.133	0.12
k_s	0.0120	0.0107	0.0098	0.0090	0.0084
$\eta_s = \dfrac{k_s j}{2\pi e}$	0.026	0.023	0.021	0.020	0.018
η_t	0.930	0.930	0.930	0.930	0.930
η_p (eq. 2:10a)	0.956	0.955	0.951	0.950	0.948
j/π	1.17	1.00	0.875	0.777	0.700
$\frac{1}{2}ej/\pi$	0.156	0.1145	0.0875	0.0692	0.056
L/D (eq. 2:27)	40.6	38.8	36.1	36.5	37.0
$\tan\phi$	1.39	1.13	0.960	0.835	0.742
ϕ, degrees	54.3	48.5	43.8	39.8	36.6
c_l approx.	0.53	0.51	0.50	0.52	0.51
$k + k_s - e^2$	0.366	0.384	0.395	0.402	0.406
$\dfrac{dT_c}{dx}$	0.440	0.538	0.633	0.724	0.812
$\sin^2\phi$	0.660	0.560	0.475	0.410	0.360
yC_t	0.290	0.301	0.301	0.296	0.292
$\cos\phi$	0.584	0.663	0.725	0.769	0.800
$y_{\text{approx.}}$	0.937	0.890	0.755	0.742	0.715
$c_{\text{approx.}}$	1.59	1.52	1.285	1.264	1.21
$W = u/\sin\phi$	231	251	273	293	313
R.N.approx.	2.13×10^6	2.22×10^6	2.04×10^6	2.08×10^6	2.21×10^6
c_l	0.55	0.53	0.51	0.51	0.51
c_{d0}	0.0140	0.0140	0.150	0.140	0.0130
α_0	−0.2	−0.2	−0.6	−0.5	−0.5
β, degrees	54.1	48.3	43.2	39.6	35.8
C_t (eq. 2:22)	0.32	0.352	0.369	0.432	0.408
y	0.873	0.834	0.795	0.738	0.700
c	1.483	1.418	1.350	1.250	1.190

The usual requirement that the propeller blade section be thin (especially at the tips) does not rigidly hold in wind-tunnel propellers. The reasons are twofold: the airspeed at the propeller is rarely very high and compressibility effects are not serious; and high enough L/D ratios are obtained so easily that straining for small increments through the use of thin sections is unnecessary. The thicker sections are stronger, too, but peculiar high-frequency vibrations that occur in many wind-tunnel propellers and the possibility of the propeller's being struck by airborne objects make it advisable to incorporate margins of safety of the order of 5.0 into their design. These vibrations are best damped by laminated wood propeller blades. An additional advantage accrues from having removable blades, as a damaged blade may be replaced without rebuilding the entire propeller.

Propeller vibrations are often caused by an asymmetrical velocity front reaching the propeller, due to improper turning in the corners and/or flow detachment from the walls. Surveys ahead of the propeller can determine whether this condition exists, and adjustments of the corner vanes or any abrupt places in the tunnel can be made.

2:5. The Drive Motor. Since both the drag of the various items inside the wind tunnel and the thrust of the propeller vary as the square of the propeller rpm it is seen that an even velocity front may be maintained in the tunnel only if speed changes are made by varying the propeller rpm, not by changing the pitch of the propeller. This indicates that either the driving motor should be capable of continuous variation in speed control or an infinitely variable coupling should be provided. Further requirements include no "hunting," low maintenance, and accuracy of speed control to 0.2 per cent from zero to maximum. In practice the speed range is usually not as great as this.

The possibilities in the electric motor field narrow down to three types capable of speed variation: the d-c motor, the variable-frequency motor, and the wound-rotor induction motor. Of these, the d-c motor offers the simplest type of control but has the added complication of usually requiring an a-c motor driving a d-c generator to supply the current, as high-wattage direct current is not generally available. Such a system of a-c motor, d-c generator, and d-c tunnel drive motor is called a Ward-Leonard system.

In order to slow down the wound-rotor induction motor, part of the rotor voltage must be dissipated in a resistance. This means that the total power consumed is nearly constant for all motor (and tunnel) speeds. If the tunnel is to be run at full speed for almost all tests (not an unusual procedure) the wound-rotor induction motor may be perfectly acceptable.

The variable-frequency motor and variable-frequency generator are more expensive than the d-c set-up, but they are available in higher powers for a given drive motor size.

When limitations of first cost preclude the more complicated systems outlined above, the multiple-pole induction motor may be used. It offers the ability to provide several speeds in regular steps, 600, 900, 1200, and 1800 rpm being the usual rating. Further, this motor is smaller than a d-c motor of the same horsepower and would offer less air resistance if the motor is to be installed in the tunnel.

A combination Ward-Leonard and synchronous motor is another good compromise when economy is a limiting factor. For this installation the d-c exciter required for the synchronous motor is oversize. For low tunnel speeds the exciter is run as a d-c motor. A single invariable high speed is provided by the synchronous motor. This arrangement provides continuously varying speeds in the range needed for rotor and powered model tests, etc., but only a single high speed. Further, unless a variable-pitch propeller is available for use at synchronous speed each change of angle of attack of the model varies the tunnel speed slightly, and the dynamic pressure must be read for each point and used in the data work-up. All this greatly complicates the calculations. The use of a relatively small d-c motor reduces the size of the motor-generator set needed for the tunnel.

For medium-speed tunnels of moderate turbulence there are probably more advantages in having the driving motor in the return passage than mounted exteriorly with a shaft to the propeller. The former is the simpler arrangement, and sometimes the flow of the air over the motor enables it to deliver overload power without overheating. Probably a better system is to cool the motor with a separate air source and pump. This system permits a sealed and more streamline motor nacelle, which in turn may improve the flow.

Occasionally the variable propeller speed is obtained by means of either a magnetic clutch or a fluid drive, both devices being satisfactory in the high speed range if the added length of the drive shaft does not interfere with the layout. Less satisfaction is noted for these devices at low speeds as they sometimes exhibit poor response and stability.

The use of an internal-combustion engine is undesirable both from the standpoint of operating cost and lack of longtime dependability.

2:6. The Corners. It is not practical in wind-tunnel design to make the corners of the return passage so gradual that the air can follow the curve with but small loss. Such corners would require more space than is usually allotted to a tunnel and also would increase the costs of construction. Abrupt corners * are therefore usually in order, and their losses are kept to a minimum through the use of proper turning vanes.

The nature of losses in a straight duct have been discussed on page 41, and the corners of a duct behave in a similar manner: the law of continuity assures the same airstream velocity after the turn as before it if no area change has occurred, while the drag of the corner due to both skin friction and separation losses appears as a drop in static pressure Δp. Again this loss is usually referred to the velocity in the duct by

$$\eta = \frac{\Delta p}{q}$$

where η = corner loss coefficient and q = dynamic head in the corner.

An abrupt corner without vanes may show a loss of 100 per cent of the velocity head ($\eta = 1.00$). With carefully designed vanes an η of 0.15 is reasonable. The basic idea is to divide the corner into many turns of high aspect ratio. In this application, then, the rectangle formed by any two vanes should have a width-height ratio of at least 6. In general, this criterion defines the vane gap since the height is known. The vane chord should then be about 2½ times the gap. Where a choice remains, allowance should be made for the fact that the vane drag goes down as the Reynolds number goes up. Here the Reynolds number is based on the vane chord, and larger chords are hence preferable.

Several vane profiles are shown in Fig. 2:10, and each is labeled with the loss realized under test conditions by the various experimenters (Refs. 2:6, 2:7, 2:8, and 2:9) at Reynolds numbers of about 40,000. Equation 2:39 yields values slightly higher than Fig. 2:10 would indicate, but it is felt that the increase is justified for the usual installations.

The hollow vanes offer the opportunity of contributing to the

---

* A promising approach to the problem of turning the air in a wind tunnel has been made by Szczeniowski. In his paper (Ref. 2:3) a special corner of unusual cross section is proposed. The design is expected to yield a uniform velocity without the need of guide vanes, and should have very low losses. A second approach, used successfully by the NACA in two tunnels, is to have many turns of small angles on the theory that three turns of, say, 30 degrees yield more even flow and less loss than one of 90. This construction is, of course, more expensive.

tunnel cooling as they have room for a coolant to be circulated
internally. Any of these guide vanes can be used in conjunction
with horizontal vanes to form a honeycomb.

As the velocity is highest at the guide vanes just downstream
of the tunnel test section, they are the most critical and should
receive the most careful workmanship. All vanes should have
adjustable trailing edges for minor corrections to the flow angle.

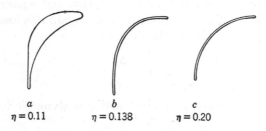

$$a$$
$$\eta = 0.11$$

$$b$$
$$\eta = 0.138$$

$$c$$
$$\eta = 0.20$$

Fig. 2:10. Corner vanes.

2:7. The Honeycomb. Many wind tunnels can achieve a
reduction of turbulence in the jet by the addition of a honeycomb just ahead of the entrance cone. The honeycomb should
preferably be of airfoil sections, built into square cells with a
length 5 to 10 times their width. If the contraction ratio of the
tunnel is large, and a good honeycomb is installed, the turbulence can be low indeed.

A second and more modern method that both improves the
velocity distribution and decreases the turbulence consists of
adding screens of 16 mesh or smaller in the settling section ahead
of the entrance cone.

2:8. The Entrance Cone. The shape of the entrance cone is
not critical. Curves producing either sinusoidal or constant
acceleration of the air are satisfactory, as are almost any smooth
curves. In general the entrance cone should be about a large
diameter long, faired very gradually at the downstream end so
that the flow has time to even out. The upstream end may contract abruptly, but pressure rises rapid enough to cause separation (i.e., corners) should be avoided. Windows should be provided so that the flow can be observed. In high-speed tunnels
the entrance cone curve must be such that no velocities exist
anywhere that are higher than the final jet velocities. Such
curves are discussed by Tsien (Ref. 2:4), and several are shown
in Fig. 2:11.

A settling chamber about 0.5 diameter long ahead of the entrance cone seems to aid materially in improving the flow in the test section. Since this point is the lowest in the entire tunnel a water drain capable of being sealed should be provided.

The contraction ratio of the entrance cone determines the overall size and hence the cost of a closed-circuit wind tunnel so that consideration of the cone entirely by itself is not rational.

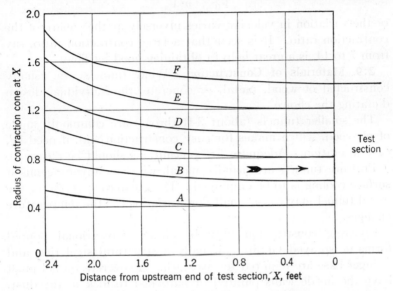

Fig. 2:11. Curves suitable for entrance cones.

However, an important item to consider when selecting the contraction ratio is the effect that it has in decreasing the velocity variation in the test section.

Let us suppose that the variation of the velocity ahead of the contraction is v_n from the average velocity V_n, and in the test section it is v_0 from the mean value V_0. Writing Bernoulli's equation between the two sections we have

$$p_n + \tfrac{1}{2}\rho(V_n + v_n)^2 = p_0 + \tfrac{1}{2}\rho(V_0 + v_0)^2$$

Expanding, and making the good approximation that there is little loss of head between the two stations so that

$$p_n + \tfrac{1}{2}\rho V_n{}^2 = p_0 + \tfrac{1}{2}\rho V_0{}^2$$

we have

$$v_n{}^2 + 2v_n V_n = v_0{}^2 + 2v_0 V_0$$

Dividing through by $V_n{}^2 V_0{}^2$ and neglecting as small $(v/V)^2$

$$\frac{v_0}{V_0} = \frac{V_n{}^2 v_n}{V_0{}^2 V_n}$$

But $V_n{}^2/V_0{}^2 = 1/n^2$, where n = area contraction ratio. Hence

$$\frac{v_0}{V_0} = \frac{1 v_n}{n^2 V_n} \qquad (2:31b)$$

or the variation in velocity varies inversely as the square of the contraction ratio. It is seen that a large contraction ratio, say from 7 to 14, is a great help in obtaining good jet flow.

2:9. Materials of Construction. Wind tunnels are usually constructed of wood, metal, or concrete, the individual design dictating the choice.

The smaller tunnels (about 3-ft throat) are commonly made of plywood, which makes for easy construction and, if need be, easy alteration. Adequate fire precautions should be observed.

Pressure tunnels are usually metal, which is advantageous if surface cooling is to be employed. The greater expansion of the metal tunnel may cause small flow variations as the temperature changes.

Concrete construction may be either conventional poured forms or sprayed Gunite. Usually a structural steel ring and stringer base are required for strength. A concrete tunnel must have the inside walls painted or hardened to lock in the dust. Steps in the construction of a poured-concrete tunnel are shown in Fig. 2:12.

2:10. Power Losses. Wattendorf (Ref. 2:10) has pointed the way towards a logical approach to the losses in a return-type wind tunnel. The procedure employed is to break the tunnel down into (1) cylindrical sections, (2) corners, (3) expanding sections, and (4) contracting sections, and calculate the loss for each.

In each of the sections a loss of energy occurs, usually written as a drop in static pressure, Δp, or as a coefficient of loss, $K = \Delta p/q$. Wattendorf refers these local losses to the jet dynamic pressure, defining the coefficient of loss as

$$K_0 = \frac{\Delta p}{q} \frac{q}{q_0} = K \frac{q}{q_0} \qquad (2:32)$$

or, since the dynamic head varies inversely as the fourth power

Courtesy of United Aircraft Corp.

FIG. 2:12a. Steps in the construction of a poured-concrete wind tunnel. Steel rings and wood forms.

Courtesy of United Aircraft Corp.

FIG. 2:12b. Steps in the construction of a poured-concrete wind tunnel. Exterior of partly finished return passage.

of the tunnel diameter,

$$K_0 = K \frac{D_0{}^4}{D^4} \qquad (2:32a)$$

where D_0 = jet diameter.

D = local tunnel diameter.

Using the above definitions, the section energy loss ΔE = $K\frac{1}{2}\rho A V^3$ may be referred to the jet energy by

$$\Delta E = K \frac{1}{2} \rho A V^3 \frac{A_0 V_0 \cdot V_0{}^2}{A_0 V_0 \cdot V_0{}^2}$$

$$= K \frac{1}{2} \rho A_0 V_0{}^3 \frac{D_0{}^4}{D^4}$$

and, finally,

$$\Delta E = K_0 \cdot \tfrac{1}{2} \rho A_0 V_0{}^3$$

where A_0 = test section area.

A = local area.

$$\text{Energy ratio} = \frac{\text{Jet energy}}{\Sigma \text{ circuit losses}} = ER_2$$

(See eq. 3:6.)

$$ER_2 = \frac{\tfrac{1}{2}\rho A_0 V_0{}^3}{\Sigma K_0 \tfrac{1}{2} \rho A_0 V_0{}^3} = \frac{1}{\Sigma K_0} \qquad (2:33)$$

It will be noted that the above definition of the energy ratio excludes the propeller and motor efficiency.

The magnitude of the losses in a circular wind tunnel may be computed as follows:

In the *cylindrical sections* the pressure drop in length L is $\Delta p/L = (\lambda/D)(\rho/2)V^2$, and $K = \Delta p/q = \lambda(L/D)$. Therefore

$$K_0 = \lambda \frac{L}{D} \frac{D_0{}^4}{D^4} \qquad (2:34)$$

For smooth pipes at high Reynolds numbers von Kármán gives (Ref. 2:11)

$$\frac{1}{\sqrt{\lambda}} = 2 \log_{10} R\sqrt{\lambda} - 0.8 \qquad (2:35)$$

where D = local tunnel diameter, ft.

V = local velocity, ft/sec.

R.N. = $\rho/\mu VD$.

As eq. 2:35 is tedious of solution, a plot is shown in Fig. 2:13.

For open cylindrical sections such as an open jet, a reasonable value for skin-friction coefficient is

$$\lambda = 0.08 \qquad\qquad (2:36)$$

For an open jet of $\dfrac{\text{length}}{\text{diameter}} = 1.5$, the loss becomes 0.08×1.5 = 12 per cent as compared to about one-tenth that value for a closed jet.

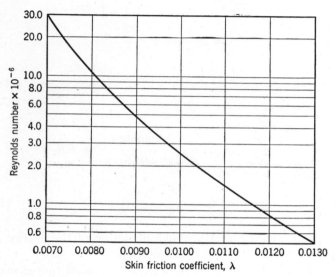

Fig. 2:13.

In the *divergent sections*, both wall friction and expansion losses occur. The combined loss of the two is summed up by

$$K_0 = \left(\frac{\lambda}{8\tan(\alpha/2)} + 0.6\tan\frac{\alpha}{2}\right)\left(1 - \frac{D_1{}^4}{D_2{}^4}\right)\frac{D_0{}^4}{D_1{}^4} \quad (2:37)$$

where α = divergence between opposite walls (not over 10 degrees).

D_1 = smaller diameter.

D_2 = larger diameter.

It will be seen that the smaller expansions yield smaller losses up to the point where the skin friction of the added area becomes excessive. This, it will be seen by differentiating eq. 2:37, occurs when

$$\tan \frac{\alpha}{2} = \sqrt{\frac{\lambda}{4.8}} \qquad (2:38)$$

For reasonable values of λ the most efficient divergence is therefore about 5 degrees. However, available space limitations for the tunnel as well as the cost of construction usually dictate that a slightly larger divergence be employed at a small increase in cost of operation.

It will be noted that the losses in a divergent section are two to three times greater than the corresponding losses in a cylindrical tube, although the progressively decreasing velocity would seem to indicate losses between that of a cylindrical section with the diameter of the smaller section and that of one with the diameter of the larger section. The reason for the added loss is that the energy exchange near the walls is of such a nature that the thrust expected from the walls is not fully realized. Effectively, a pressure force is thereby added to the skin-friction forces.

In the *corners*, friction in the guide vanes accounts for about one-third of the loss, and rotation losses for the other two-thirds. For corners of the type shown in Fig. 2:10 the following partly empirical relation is reasonable, being based on a corner pressure drop of $\Delta p/q = 0.15$ at R.N. $= 500,000$.

$$K_0 = \left(0.10 + \frac{4.55}{(\log_{10} \text{R.N.})^{2.58}}\right) \frac{D_0{}^4}{D^4} \qquad (2:39)$$

In the *contraction cone* the losses are friction only, and the pressure drop is:

$$\Delta p_f = \int_0^L \lambda \frac{\rho}{2} V^2 \frac{dL}{D}$$

where $L =$ length of contraction cone.

$$K_0 = K \frac{D_0{}^4}{D^4} = \frac{\Delta p_f}{q} \frac{D_0{}^4}{D^4} = \int_0^L \lambda \frac{dL}{D} \frac{D_0{}^4}{D^4} \frac{D_0}{D_0}$$

$$= \lambda \frac{L}{D_0} \int_0^L \frac{D_0{}^5}{D^5} \frac{dL}{L} \qquad (2:40)$$

Assuming a mean value for λ,

$$K_0 = 0.32\lambda\,\frac{L}{D_0} \qquad\qquad (2{:}41)$$

As the total loss in the contraction cone usually runs below 3 per cent of the total tunnel loss, any errors due to approximations in the cone losses become of small importance.

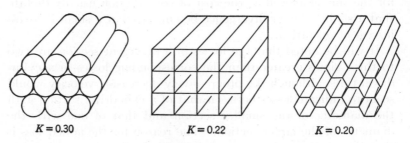

$K = 0.30$ $K = 0.22$ $K = 0.20$

FIG. 2:14.   Some honeycombs and their losses.

Losses in *honeycombs* have been reported by Roberts (Ref. 2:17).   Values of K suitable for use in eq. 2:32a are given in Fig. 2:14 for honeycombs with a $\dfrac{\text{length}}{\text{diameter}} = 6.0$, and equal tube areas.   Roughly speaking, the loss in a honeycomb is usually less than 5 per cent of the total tunnel loss.

The losses incurred in the single-return tunnel of Fig. 2:15

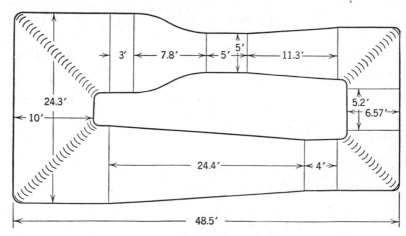

FIG. 2:15.

based on a tunnel temperature of 100° F (ρ/μ = 5560) and a
test section velocity of 100 mph are as follows:

Section	K_0	% Total Loss
1. The jet	0.0093	5.1
2. Divergence	0.0391	21.3
3. Corner	0.046	25.0
4. Cylinder	0.0026	1.4
5. Corner	0.046	25.0
6. Cylinder	0.002	1.1
7. Divergence	0.016	8.9
8. Corner	0.0087	4.7
9. Corner	0.0087	4.7
10. Cylinder	0.0002	0.1
11. Cone	0.0048	2.7
	0.1834	100.0

$$\text{Energy ratio, } ER_2 = \frac{1}{\Sigma K_0} = \frac{1}{0.1834} = 5.45$$

Probably this figure should be reduced about 10 per cent for
leaks and joints.

The effect of varying the angle of divergence or the contraction ratio for a tunnel similar to the one of Fig. 2:15 may be
seen in Figs. 2:16 and 2:17.
These are replotted from Ref.
2:10.

The possibility of attaining higher energy ratios has
several promising leads. One
fundamental is the increase
of efficiency that accompanies larger Reynolds numbers.
That is, a large tunnel similar to a small tunnel will have
the greater efficiency of the
two.

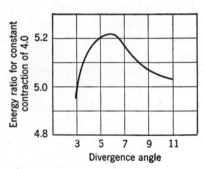

Fig. 2:16. Effect of divergence angle
on energy ratio.

Reduction of the losses in the divergent passage is limited, as
previously stated, to a certain minimum angle between opposite
walls. The use of this minimum angle would, however, yield
smaller losses than are customarily encountered. Corner losses
may be reduced through the use of two previously mentioned
innovations. The first is to break the four 90-degree turns into

several vaned turns of less than 90 degrees (Ref. 2:12). The second is to employ potential elbows (Ref. 2:3) for the turns. Increasing the contraction ratio through a longer return passage will also increase the energy ratio but at an added cost in tunnel construction. Increased length before the first turn is particularly effective.

An entirely different approach, particularly useful for high-speed tunnels, is to reduce the power required for a given speed by reducing the air density through partly evacuating the entire tunnel. This procedure greatly complicates model changes as

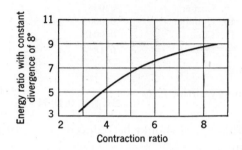

FIG. 2:17. Effect of contraction ratio on energy ratio.

the tunnel pressure must be relieved before the tunnel crew can enter. (Some of the newer tunnels propose to overcome this difficulty by having pressure doors that will seal off the test section from the rest of the tunnel and greatly reduce the pumping between runs.) As the power required is a function of ρV^3, by reducing the pressure to one-fourth its former value the speed may be increased by the ratio $\sqrt[3]{4}$ to 1 for the same power input. Stated differently, a 59 per cent higher Mach number will be attained with the lower pressure. Another method of saving power is to have the tunnel filled with a gas in which the speed of sound is lower than in air so that high Mach numbers may be obtained at lower speeds (Ref. 2:2).

When figuring power requirements for a proposed design, consideration must also be given to (a) the power required to overcome model drag under the most extreme cases and (b) the power required to overcome the increased tunnel losses due to parts of the diffuser stalling from the model effects.

For (a) the power required to fly a model whose span is 0.8 tunnel diameter, $AR = 5$, and $C_D = 0.5000$ is probably sufficient.

Item (b) for conventional tests is covered in (a) above, but for wingtip mounting or section tests as much as 150 per cent *more* power may be needed if the diffuser is seriously stalled and large rotational and diffusion losses are created.

2:11. Cooling. All the energy supplied to the propeller driving a wind tunnel finally emerges as an increase of heat energy in the windstream. This increases the temperature of the tunnel air until the heat losses finally balance the input. For low-power tunnels (and particularly those with open jets) this balance is realized at reasonable temperatures, the heat transfer

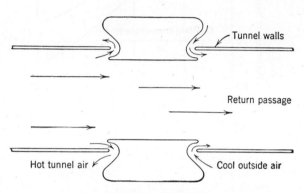

FIG. 2:18. An air exchanger.

through surface cooling and air exchange being sufficient. For tunnels with high power inputs and high jet velocities this low-temperature balance no longer occurs. For example, the heat rise incurred by bringing air to rest at 450 mph is about 36° F. With an energy ratio of 8.0, the heat rise in the airstream would be 4.5° F per circuit, leading in a very short while to prohibitive temperatures. Obviously, tunnels in this class require cooling arrangements to augment the inherent heat losses.

Additional cooling may be accomplished by four means: (1) an increase of surface cooling by running water over the tunnel exterior; (2) interior cooling by the addition of water-cooled turning vanes or (3) a water-cooled radiator in the largest tunnel section; (4) a continual replacement of the heated tunnel air with cool outside air by means of an air exchanger.

Most high-speed tunnels use an air exchanger (Figs. 2:18 and 2:20) to replace the lower-energy boundary layer with cool outside air, having exchange towers to assure adequate dispersion of the heated air and fresh air that is free from surface contamination. Assuming the previously mentioned rise of 4.5° F per circuit, a 10 per cent exchange would limit the rise to 45° F,

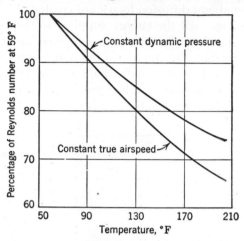

FIG. 2:19. Effect of temperature on test Reynolds number.

Courtesy United Aircraft Corp.

FIG. 2:20. Air exchange towers.

excluding heat losses elsewhere. (Ten per cent is a fairly average amount of exchange.)

One difficulty associated with an air exchanger is that it puts the highest-pressure section of the tunnel at atmospheric pressure, and hence the jet pressure is below atmospheric. This leads to troublesome but by no means insoluble problems of sealing off the balance room. (The same low jet static pressure is present in open-circuit tunnels.) Another difficulty that must be considered is the possible effects of weather conditions on a tunnel with a large amount of air exchanged.

It should be mentioned that a breather slot at the downstream end of the test section can be used in conjunction with the air exchanger to get the jet up to atmospheric pressure and hence avoid balance sealing troubles. However, this arrangement with the air going in the breather and out the exchanger requires as much as 20 per cent of the total power input.

The other methods of cooling seem to offer less advantage than the air exchanger. The unknowns of internal and external boundary-layer thicknesses make the problem of cooling through the walls quite difficult. In discussing internal cooling, Tifford (Ref. 2:5) states that a radiator has possible advantages over cooled turning vanes.

The obvious disadvantages of high temperatures in the wind tunnel include added trouble cooling the drive motor (if it is in the tunnel and does not have separate cooling), the rapid softening of the model temporary fillets, and increased personnel difficulties. Another deleterious effect is the drop in Reynolds number that occurs with increasing temperatures whether the tunnel is run at constant speed or at constant dynamic pressure. Figure 2:19 illustrates this effect.

As most electric motors have high efficiencies, placing the motor outside the tunnel is probably not justified by the small amount of tunnel heating saved thereby.

PROBLEMS

2:1. What percentage of the power supplied to a wind-tunnel motor appears as heat energy in the air? (The motor itself is in the tunnel.)

2:2. State four methods of cooling a tunnel.

2:3. In what sections of the tunnel do the largest losses occur?

2:4. Explain why there is no increase of axial speed across the propeller disk.

2:5. What are the objections to a double-return tunnel?

2:6. Discuss materials that could be used in the construction of a wind tunnel.

2:7. Check the loss calculations for the tunnel of Fig. 2:15.

REFERENCES

2:1. FELIX NAGEL, Static and Dynamic Model Similarity, *JAS*, September, 1939.

2:2. IVAN A. RUBINSKY, The Use of Heavy Gases or Vapors for High Speed Wind Tunnels, *JAS*, September, 1939.

2:3. BOLESLAW SZCZENIOWSKI, Design of Elbows in Potential Motion, *JAS*, January, 1944.

2:4. TSIEN, HSUE-SHEN, On the Design of a Contraction Cone for a Wind Tunnel, *JAS*, February, 1943.

2:5. ARTHUR N. TIFFORD, Wind Tunnel Cooling, *JAS*, March, 1943.

2:6. G. KROBER, Guide Vanes for Deflecting Fluid Currents with Small Loss of Energy, *TM* 722, 1932.

2:7. A. R. COLLAR, Some Experiments with Cascades of Airfoils, *R&M* 1768, 1937.

2:8. G. N. PATTERSON, Note on the Design of Corners in Duct Systems, *R&M* 1773, 1937.

2:9. D. C. MCPHAIL, Experiments on Turning Vanes at an Expansion, *R&M* 1876, 1939.

2:10. F. L. WATTENDORF, Factors Influencing the Energy Ratio of Return Flow Wind Tunnels, p. 526, 5th International Congress for Applied Mechanics, Cambridge, 1938.

2:11. T. VON KÁRMÁN, Turbulence and Skin Friction, *JAS*, January, 1934.

2:12. G. DARRIEUS, Some Factors Influencing the Design of Wind Tunnels, *Brown-Boveri Review*, July-August, 1943.

2:13. G. N. PATTERSON, Ducted Fans: Design for High Efficiency, *ACA* 7, July, 1944.

2:14. A. R. COLLAR, The Design of Wind Tunnel Fans, *R&M* 1889, August, 1940.

2:15. W. C. NELSON, *Airplane Propeller Principles*, John Wiley & Sons, New York, p. 9.

2:16. G. N. PATTERSON, Ducted Fans: High Efficiency with Contra-Rotation, *ACA* 10, October, 1944.

2:17. H. E. ROBERTS, Considerations in the Design of a Low Cost Wind Tunnel, Paper presented at 14th Annual Meeting of the Institute of Aeronautical Sciences, January, 1946.

CHAPTER III

CALIBRATION OF THE WIND-TUNNEL JET

After the tunnel is constructed, the next step is to determine the flow characteristics, i.e., the variation of flow angle across the jet, the variation in dynamic pressure across the jet, the variation in static pressure along the longitudinal axis of the jet, and the degree of turbulence in the air.

3:1. Speed Setting. First, however, it is in order to discuss the methods employed in setting the speed of wind tunnels. It is not practical to insert a pitot-static tube (see Sect. **3:4**) into the tunnel jet when there is a model in place because (1) it would interfere with the model, and (2) it would not read true owing to the effect of the model on it.

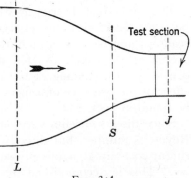

FIG. 3:1.

The solution comes from a consideration of Bernoulli's equation written between two points in the tunnel, preferably the large section, L, and a small section, S. The small section can be just ahead of the jet, far enough upstream to avoid any effects when the model is installed or moved (Fig. 3:1).

The total head at the two points will be nearly the same; the downstream head will be slightly smaller on account of the pressure drop between the two stations. Hence we have

$$p_L + q_L = p_S - q_S K_1 + q_S$$

where K_1 is the loss coefficient of the section between the static readings, and p and q are static and dynamic pressures. That is,

$$p_L - p_S = q_S - K_1 q_S - q_L$$

75

Now, if A is the section area,

$$A_S V_S = A_L V_L \qquad (3:0)$$

Squaring, and multiplying through by $\rho/2$, we have

$$\frac{\rho}{2} A_S^2 V_S^2 = \frac{\rho}{2} A_L^2 V_L^2$$

Letting $q = (\rho/2)V^2$, and $K_2 = A_S^2/A_L^2$, we get $q_L = K_2 q_S$. This leads to

$$p_L - p_S = q_S - K_1 q_S - K_2 q_S = (1 - K_1 - K_2)q_S$$

Also, as

$$q_S = q_J \frac{A_J^2}{A_S^2} = K_3 q_J$$

where $K_3 = A_J^2/A_S^2$,

$$p_L - p_S = (1 - K_1 - K_2)K_3 q_J \qquad (3:1)$$

The tunnel can be run at various speeds, and $(p_L - p_S)$ can be read along with the jet dynamic pressure q_J. (The last is read by means of a pitot-static tube in the empty jet.) This evaluates $(1 - K_1 - K_2)K_3$, and future desired values of q_J can be set by running at the proper value of $(p_L - p_S)$. The effect of the presence of a model on the clear jet calibration may be found in Sect. 6:2.

Since the coefficients vary only slightly with small changes of Reynolds number, but directly with q, it is much preferable to run at constant dynamic pressure rather than at constant velocity. This is accomplished by operating at constant values of $(p_L - p_S)$ (see eq. 3:1). The constant dynamic pressure used should be noted on the data sheet, or else the speed that would produce that dynamic pressure at sea level, i.e., the "indicated airspeed," should be stated.

The velocities of high-speed tunnels may be set with the aid of an instrument that measures the temperature, total head, and static head and delivers the final answer as the Mach number of the flow. Such an instrument is called a Machmeter.

3:2. Pressure Measurements. As many of the pressures encountered in wind-tunnel testing are indicated by fluid columns, a short description of suitable fluids is needed. (See also p. 297.)

The most commonly used liquid is alcohol. It is popular because it is cheap, easy to obtain, good as to viscosity, and low in specific gravity, hence productive of a higher fluid column than water.

The specific gravity of alcohol varies a moderate amount with temperature. Corrections for this effect may be found from Fig. 3:2. It follows, for example, that if alcohol is labeled either

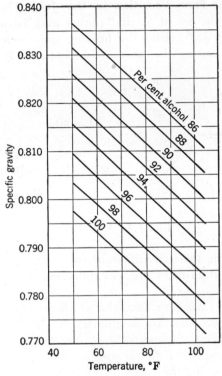

FIG. 3:2. Temperature corrections for alcohol density.

by its specific gravity at some temperature ("sp. gr. = 0.801 at 80° F") or by its water content ("94.0 per cent alcohol") it will be completely defined and its proper curve for temperature correction may be determined.

The method of correcting the specific gravity of alcohol for changes in temperature is explained in the following example.

Example 3:1

An alcohol-water mixture has a specific gravity of 0.805 at 68° F. What is the percentage of alcohol, and what will be the specific gravity at 77° F?.

1. Locate the point (0.805, 68° F), and draw a line through it parallel to the other lines of the figure. Estimate the distance between the lines 94 and 96 per cent, and read 94.6 per cent alcohol.

2. Follow down the newly constructed 94.6 per cent line until it intersects 77° F. Read sp. gr. = 0.802.

3:3. Angular-Flow Variation in the Jet.

The variation of flow angle in the jet of a wind tunnel may be measured by a yawhead (Fig. 3:3), either by holding the yawhead in a fixed plane and measuring the pressures in opposite holes separately

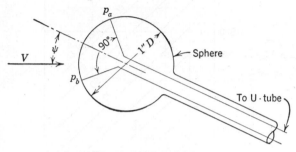

FIG. 3:3. A yawhead.

or by connecting the two orifices across a manometer and rotating the yawhead until the pressure difference between the orifices is zero.

It is usually easiest to have the yawhead fixed in the tunnel and to determine the flow angularity by reading the pressure difference between the two orifices Δp and comparing with a previous calibration of the instrument. The calibration may be made by rotating the yawhead at a single location in the airstream and plotting $\Delta p/q$ against angle of yaw.

Theoretical and actual values for a spherical yawhead are compared in Fig. 3:4. This calibration is independent of Reynolds number from at least 40 mph to 120 mph, standard air.

Though many wind tunnels exhibit an angular variation of ±0.75 degree or even ±1.0 degree, it is not believed that accurate testing can be done with a variation greater than ±0.50 degree. The larger angles of flow distort the span load distribution excessively. Unfortunately, the variation of the flow angle across the jet may change with the tunnel speed. If such a change is noted, a testing speed must be selected and the guide and anti-twist vanes adjusted to give smooth flow at that speed.

If it is not possible to correct the angularity to a satisfactorily small value, an average value for a given model may be found by measuring the flow angle at numerous stations and multiplying it by the model chord at the proper station. If the above product is plotted against the wing span and the area under the curve is divided by the total wing area the resultant will be a fair approximation of the average angle.

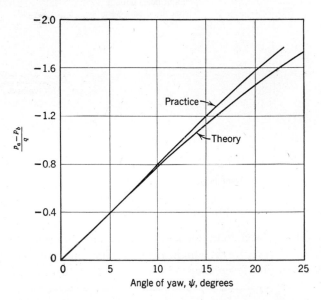

Fig. 3:4. Calibration of yawhead.

3:4. Velocity Variation in the Jet. The variation of the dynamic pressure, $q = (\rho/2)V^2$, may be measured across the test section by means of a pitot-static tube. The local velocities may then be obtained from

$$V = \sqrt{\frac{2q}{\rho}} \qquad (3:2)$$

The following paragraphs will discuss the methods of making the survey and presenting the results. Suggestions are also made for improving a poor velocity distribution. First, however, it is in order to consider the pitot-static tube in some detail in order to understand its construction and use.

A "standard" pitot-static tube is shown in Fig. 3:5. The orifice at A reads total head $(p + \frac{1}{2}\rho V^2)$, and those at B read the static pressure, p. If the pressures from the two orifices are

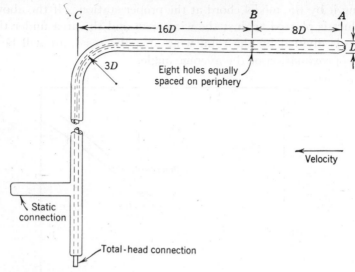

FIG. 3:5. Pitot-static tube.

connected across a manometer, the pressure differential will, of course, be $\frac{1}{2}\rho V^2$, from which the velocity may be calculated. (For determining ρ see Ex. 3:3.)

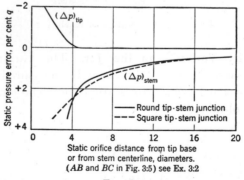

FIG. 3:6.

The pitot-static tube is easy to construct, but it has some inherent errors. If due allowance is made for these errors, a true reading of the dynamic pressure within about 0.1 per cent may be obtained.

It has been amply demonstrated that a total head tube with a hemispherical tip will read the total head accurately independent of the size of the orifice opening as long as the yaw is less than 3 degrees. Hence the total head reading introduces no difficulties.

The static holes suffer from two effects: (1) The crowding of the streamlines near the tip reduces the pressure along the shank

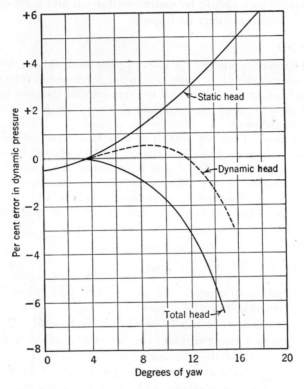

FIG. 3:7.   Performance of standard pitot tube in yaw.

of the pitot-static tube so that the static pressure at the static orifices will be low. The amount of error is seen in Fig. 3:6. (2) A high-pressure region exists ahead of the stem that tends to make the indicated static pressure too high. Also see Fig. 3:6.

The two effects may block each other out if the static holes are properly located. The "standard" pitot-static tube does not employ this principle as it would require the static holes to be so close to the tip that small deviations in tip construction or damage to the tip could make a relatively large error in the static reading.

Hence: (1) If a new pitot-static tube is to be built it may either be designed as per Fig. 3:5 and its static pressure readings corrected as per Fig. 3:6; or a 2.5D tip length and 9D stem length may be used. The 2.5-9D arrangement should require no correction but should be checked for accuracy. (2) Existing pitot-static tubes should be examined for tip and stem errors so that their constants may be found.

Example 3:2

Space limitations preclude the use of a pitot-static tube of "standard" dimensions, and one whose static orifices are 3.2 diameters from the base of the tip and 8.0 diameters from the centerline of the stem is chosen. Find the error in velocity and dynamic pressure if the joint between the stem and tip is round.

(a) *Tip error.* From Fig. 3:6 it is seen that static orifices located 3.2 diameters from the base of the tip will read 0.5 per cent q too low.

(b) *Stem error.* From Fig. 3:6 it is seen that static orifices located 8.0 diameters from the stem will read 1.13 per cent q too high.

(c) *Total error.* The static pressure therefore will be $1.13 - 0.5 = 0.63$ per cent q too high, and hence the indicated dynamic pressure will be too low. The data should be corrected as follows:

$$q_{\text{true}} = 1.0063 q_{\text{indicated}}$$

$$V_{\text{true}} = 1.0032 V_{\text{indicated}}$$

The accuracy of a standard pitot-static tube when inclined to an airstream is shown in Fig. 3:7.

The pitot-static tube can be used only in free air. When the tube is close to a lifting surface, the pressure gradient will totally nullify the worth of the reading as an indication of free stream velocity. It is possible to place the pitot-static tube in such a place relative to an airplane wing that it makes the airspeed indicator read high at high speed and low at low speed, or vice versa.

For the pitot survey the pitot-static tube is moved around the jet, and the dynamic pressure is measured at numerous stations. The velocities as calculated from the dynamic pressures or the pressures themselves are then plotted, and the points are connected by "contour" lines of equal values. The variation of q in the working range of the jet should be less than 0.50 per cent from the mean, which is a 0.25 per cent variation in velocity.

A plot of the dynamic-pressure distribution in a rectangular test section is shown in Fig. 3:8. Of interest is the asymmetry usually found, and the maximum variation well above satisfactory limits. The survey should have been carried to the walls.

The correction of an excessive velocity variation is not as serious a problem as the correction of excessive angular variation.

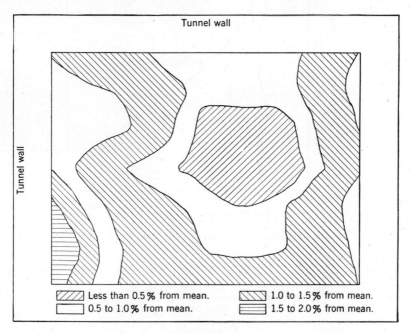

FIG. 3:8.

There are more methods of attack, for one thing, and less probability that the variation will change with tunnel speed, for another.

It is not correct to think of the tunnel as having uniform flow. The same particles of air do not reappear in a plane of the testing section. Slowed by the wall friction, the particles closest to the walls are constantly being overtaken and passed by the particles of the central air. The greater loss near the walls would be expected to yield a lowered velocity near the perimeter of the test section, and doubtless this would occur if the contraction cone did not tend to accelerate the air nearest its walls more than that near the central part, and if the tunnel propeller, through proper design, did not provide additional energy near the walls.

If satisfactory velocity distribution is not obtained, there still remain several minor adjustments for improving the situation.

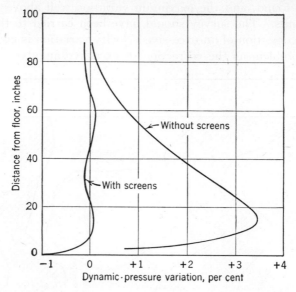

Fig. 3:9.   Effect of screens on velocity distribution in the jet.

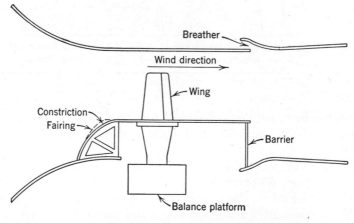

Fig. 3:10a.   Alteration to a contraction cone.

The guide vanes may be adjusted * to move added air into the low-velocity regions.   If the velocity variation is annular, a change of the propeller blade angle accompanied by a change in

* This method is very uncertain and unpredictable.

propeller hub fairing diameter may be tried. Screens may be added in the largest section of the tunnel, so located radially that they cover the sections that correspond to high-velocity regions in the jet. The improvement in velocity distribution by such screens is shown in Fig. 3:9. The loss in energy ratio due to them is quite small and far outweighed by the improvement in testing conditions.

Profound changes in flow near the walls can also be made by alteration of the entrance cone; an interesting example is shown in Fig. 3:10, *a* and *b*. For a special test a round jet was constricted into a semicircular one. Two opposite effects then occurred: (1) the constriction of the air in the lower part of the tunnel tended to make a high-velocity region over the lower part of the jet; (2) the abrupt expansion at the exit cone decreased the energy of the air in the lower part of the jet. Actually the abrupt expansion resulted in severe turbulence and complete mixing, instead of affecting only the lower half. The tunnel energy ratio dropped from 3.2 to 0.7. The velocity distribution showed a higher-speed region near the jet floor. A change in

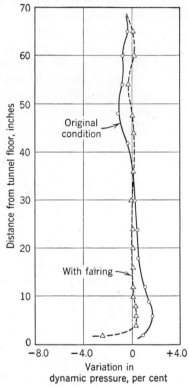

FIG. 3:10*b*. Velocity gradient due to alteration.

the shape of the entrance cone (shown dotted in Fig. 3:10*a*) altered the velocity survey from the original (shown solid in Fig. 3:10*b*) to the dotted curve. The latter proved to be satisfactory.

3:5. Longitudinal Static-Pressure Gradient. The static-pressure gradient along the test section must be known in order to make the necessary buoyancy corrections. (See Sect. 6:1.) It may be obtained by reading the local static pressure with a pitot-static tube that is progressively moved from entrance cone to exit cone. Care must be taken that the pitot tube is headed directly into the wind and that no extraneous static pressure is created by the bracket holding the pitot tube. Also see Sect. 2:1.

3:6. Turbulence. The disagreement between tests made in different wind tunnels at the same Reynolds number and between tests made in wind tunnels and in flight indicated that some correction was needed for the effect of the turbulence produced in the wind tunnel by the propeller, guide vanes, and tunnel walls. It developed that this turbulence caused the flow pattern in the tunnel to be similar to the flow pattern in free air at a higher Reynolds number. Hence the tunnel test Reynolds number could be said to have a higher "effective Reynolds number." The increase ratio is called the "turbulence factor" and is defined by:

$$R.N._e = T.F. \times R.N. \tag{3:3}$$

The turbulence may be found with a "turbulence sphere" as follows:

The drag coefficient of a sphere is affected greatly by changes in velocity. Contrary to the layman's guess, C_D for a sphere *decreases* with increasing airspeed since the result of the earlier transition to turbulent flow is that the air sticks longer to the surface of the sphere. This action decreases the form or pressure drag, yielding a lower total drag coefficient. The decrease is so rapid in one range that both the drag coefficient and the drag go down. Obviously, the Reynolds number at which the transition occurs at a given point on the sphere is a function of the turbulence already present in the air, and hence the drag coefficient of a sphere can be used to measure turbulence. The method is to measure the drag, D, for a small sphere 5 or 6 in. in diameter, at many tunnel speeds. After subtracting the buoyancy (see Sect. 6:1) the drag coefficient may be computed from

$$C_D = \frac{D}{(\rho/2)\pi(d^2/4)\,V^2} \tag{3:4}$$

where d = sphere diameter.

The sphere drag coefficient is then plotted against the calculated Reynolds number, R.N. (Fig. 3:12), and the Reynolds number at which the drag coefficient equals 0.30 is noted and termed the "critical Reynolds number," R.N.$_c$. The above particular value of the drag coefficient occurs in free air at a R.N. = 385,000, so it follows that the turbulence factor

$$\text{T.F.} = \frac{385,000}{\text{R.N.}_c} \qquad (3:5)$$

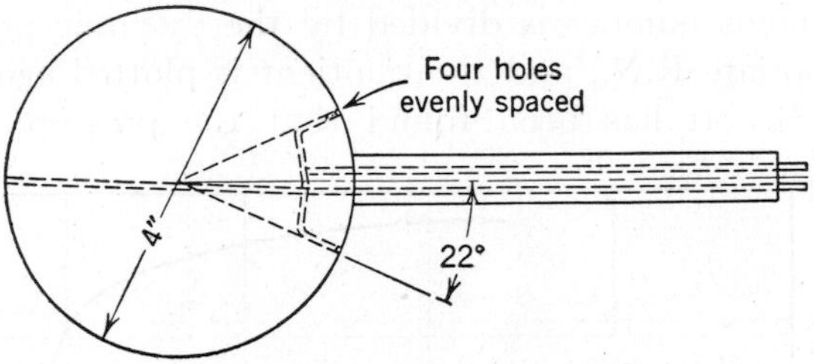

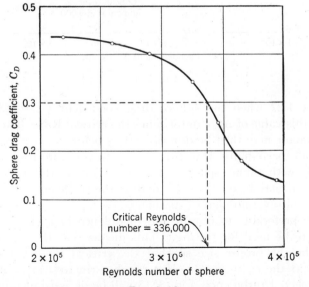

Four holes evenly spaced

4"

22°

FIG. 3:11. Turbulence sphere.

The effective Reynolds number, R.N.$_e$, may then be found from eq. 3:3.

A second method of measuring the turbulence in a wind tunnel makes use of a "pressure sphere." No force tests are necessary,

Sphere drag coefficient, C_D

0.5

0.4

0.3

0.2

0.1

0

Critical Reynolds number = 336,000

2×10^5 3×10^5 4×10^5

Reynolds number of sphere

FIG. 3:12.

and the difficulties of finding the support drag are eliminated. The pressure sphere (an ordinary duckpin ball will do) has an orifice at the front stagnation point and four more interconnected and equally spaced orifices at 22 degrees from the theoretical rear stagnation point.   A lead from the front orifice is connected across a manometer to the lead from the four rear orifices.   After the pressure difference due to the static longitudinal pressure gradient is subtracted, the resultant pressure difference, Δp, for each Reynolds number is divided by the dynamic pressure for the appropriate R.N., and the quotient is plotted against R.N. (Fig. 3:13).   It has been found that the pressure difference

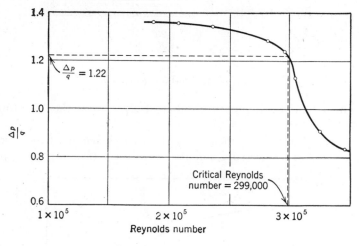

FIG. 3:13.

$\Delta p/q = 1.22$ when the sphere drag coefficient $C_D = 0.30$, and hence this value of $\Delta p/q$ determines the critical R.N.   The turbulence factor may then be determined as before.

In all probability the turbulence factor will itself change slightly with tunnel speed.   If information on this variation is needed, it may be obtained by finding the turbulence factor with spheres of several different diameters.

It is preferable to obtain the turbulence of a tunnel at the speed to be used for testing.   This means that the sphere used must be the proper size so that the critical Reynolds number occurs at the right speed.   If a rough estimate can be made of the expected turbulence, Fig. 3:15 will be of assistance in determining the proper size of the sphere.   All turbulence spheres must be absolutely smooth to be successful.

The turbulence will also vary slightly across the jet and probably diminish as the distance from the entrance cone is increased.

Particularly high turbulence is usually noted at the center of the jet of double-return tunnels because this air has scraped over the walls in the return passage.

Turbulence factors vary from 1.0 to about 3.0. Values above 1.4 possibly indicate that the air has too much turbulence for good testing results. Although it appears from the above discussion on turbulence factors that high turbulence yields high

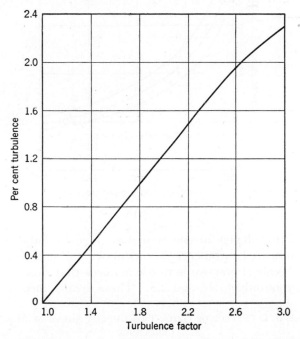

FIG. 3:14. The variation of the turbulence factor with turbulence.

effective Reynolds numbers, the truth is that the correction is not exact and that excessive turbulence makes the test data difficult of interpretation. Certainly very low turbulence is necessary for research on low-drag airfoils. The relation of the turbulence factor to the degree of turbulence present is shown in Fig. 3:14.

Low turbulence may be "designed in" by (1) incorporating a large contraction ratio of 15 or 20 to 1 (or as large as circumstances permit); (2) providing for six or eight 16-mesh screens in the settling chamber, about 0.01 tunnel diameter apart; and (3) breaking the turns into many (say 9) turns of 20 degrees each, each with its own turning vanes. A tunnel already built may have the turbulence reduced by adding the screens.

Bars 1 in. in diameter placed perpendicular to the model wing and about two to five chords ahead of it will increase the turbulence, as will coarse grids of heavy wire, or fishnets. The amount

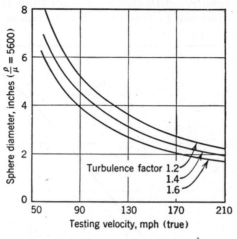

FIG. 3:15.

of turbulence change in one tunnel is given in Table 3:1. Although indicated turbulence factors above 5.0 may be obtained, the more general practice is to use artifices that raise the turbulence factors only to around 2.5. These arrangements are used

TABLE 3:1. EFFECT OF GRIDS TWO CHORDS AHEAD OF MODEL ON TURBULENCE

Tunnel Condition	Turbulence Factor
Clear jet	1.60
$\frac{1}{4}$-in. hardware cloth	2.24
$\frac{1}{2}$-in. hardware cloth	2.46
$\frac{3}{4}$-in. hardware cloth	3.00

solely for maximum lift measurements. (For the use of the turbulence factor and effective Reynolds number in extrapolating wind-tunnel results, see Sect. 7:1.)

The explanation of how the addition of screens may either increase or decrease the turbulence lies in the manner in which the screens act. Fine screens break the existing turbulence into smaller vortices. If a sufficient distance is provided, these small disturbances die out before they reach the model, or they are squeezed out by the contraction cone. Screens or grids to increase turbulence must both create turbulence and be close enough to the model so that the turbulence created does not have time to die out.

Below the degree of turbulence that corresponds to a turbulence factor of about 1.05 and above Mach numbers of 0.4, it is indicated that the turbulence sphere is not sufficiently accurate to get good results. Recourse is then had to more complicated devices. Though the design and operation of these devices are beyond the scope of this book, their principles are of interest. Further information is available in the references listed.

1. The hot-wire anemometer (Refs. 3:2, 3:3, 3:4). The hot-wire anemometer consists of a small-diameter platinum wire (about 0.015 mm) of short length (about 10 mm) which is placed in the airstream so that its length is perpendicular to the mean airflow direction. It is heated to a suitable temperature by an electric current. Fluctuations in the airstream produce fluctuations in the temperature of the wire and hence in its resistance. The ensuing voltage drops across the wire may be amplified by vacuum-tube amplifiers, and mean values of the current changes may be read by sensitive milliammeters. Sometimes the wave patterns are examined with cathode-ray oscillographs.

Fundamentally, the hot-wire anemometer is supposed to indicate the rapidity of the fluctuations by an identical frequency of current changes, and the amplitude of the fluctuations by the amount of current change. Actually, neither is directly accomplished, the fluctuating voltage of the anemometer being neither proportional to the amplitude nor in phase with the fluctuations in the airstream. Most of the difficulties are traceable to the heat-storing qualities of the wire which make it impossible for the temperature changes of the wire to follow the small high-frequency variations in the air. As expected, smaller wires exhibit less lag than large ones. Special compensating circuits further improve the accuracy of the anemometer.

2. The ultramicroscope (Ref. 3:5). A second device for determining the amount of variation of velocity in an airstream is called the ultramicroscope. Its principle of operation is as follows:

When viewed by an observer traveling at the speed of an airstream, particles of dust appear as specks of light. If the observer's speed is less or greater than that of the airstream, the particles become invisible. The ultramicroscope possesses a rotating objective so designed that the speed of rotation may be varied in small increments both above and below the mean tunnel airspeed. The limiting speeds at which particles appear define the maximum and minimum speeds present.

The entire discussion so far has dealt with small high-frequency turbulence. Another form consisting of larger turbulence of a much lower frequency may also exist. This type, to which no name has been assigned, appears with a random frequency of 0.1 to 1.0 second—too fast to appear in the fluid columns of yawheads or pitot-static tubes as surging, and not fast enough to be picked up by hot-wire anemometers set for high-frequency oscillations. A test for this low-cycle disturbance can best be made with a light weather vane about 6 in. long, the turbulence causing random oscillations of the vane. It appears likely that this type of turbulence is associated with flow separation somewhere in the tunnel.

3:7. Energy Ratio. The ratio of the energy of the air at the jet to the input energy is a measure of the efficiency of a wind tunnel, though by no means a measure of the value of the tunnel for research. It is nearly always greater than unity, indicating that the amount of stored energy in the windstream is capable of doing work at a high rate before being brought to rest. The energy ratio, E, is from 1.5 to 3.5 for most closed-throat tunnels. A few of the newer tunnels have values fully twice the larger value. Complete information on these tunnels has not yet been released, but some are briefly covered in Sect. 1:15.

It is unfortunate that an exact agreement on the definition of energy ratio has not been reached. Some engineers use the motor and propeller efficiency, η_1, in their calculations; some do not. This disagreement results in two definitions, as follows:

$$\text{E.R.}_1 = \frac{qAV}{550 \text{ hp}} \quad \text{and} \quad \text{E.R.}_2 = \frac{qAV}{550\eta_1 \text{ hp}} \tag{3:6}$$

where q = dynamic pressure in the jet, pounds per square foot.

A = jet area, square feet.

V = jet velocity, feet per second.

The employment of η_1 separates out the motor and propeller efficiency and gives a truer measure of the wind-tunnel design.

This type of energy ratio varies only slightly with tunnel speed and is about 10 per cent higher than the maximum calculated with η_1 neglected.

On the other hand, motor and propeller efficiencies at rated output do not vary greatly, and the form without η_1 can be obtained more directly from wattmeter readings and can be used more directly in estimating input requirements. It is also useful in tunnel-cooling problems, for all the input energy appears as heat in the airstream if the driving motor is in the tunnel and is not separately cooled.

In general, the highest energy ratios are associated with the largest entrance-cone contractions. (See also Sect. 2:10.)

For completeness, two more terms frequently used instead of energy ratio are defined.

$$\text{Energy factor} = \frac{1}{\text{E.R.}_2} \qquad (3:7)$$

and

$$\text{Tunnel efficiency} = 1 - \frac{1}{\text{E.R.}_2} \qquad (3:8)$$

Example 3:3

A wind tunnel with a test section 7 ft by 10 ft has an indicated airspeed of 100 mph at a pressure of 740 mm Hg and a temperature of 85° F. If input power is 25 amperes at 2300 volts, three-phase alternating current at an electrical power factor of 1.0, find (1) the true airspeed; (2) the Reynolds number of a 1-ft chord wing; (3) the energy ratio (E.R.$_1$) of the tunnel, assuming the drag of the wing to be negligible.

Answer. (1) We first determine the air density ρ.

$$\rho = 0.002378 \frac{518}{(459 + 85)} \frac{740}{760}$$

$$= 0.002204 \text{ slug/cu ft}$$

(See p. 314 for standard conditions.) Hence

$$\sigma = \frac{\rho}{\rho_0} = 0.927$$

and

$$V_{\text{true}} = \frac{V_i}{\sqrt{\sigma}} = \frac{100}{0.962} = 103.9 \text{ mph}$$

(2) From p. 314 the viscosity of the air

$$\mu = [340.8 + 0.548(°F)]10^{-9}$$
$$= [340.8 + 0.548(85)]10^{-9}$$
$$= 387.4 \times 10^{-9}$$

and hence

$$\text{R.N.} = \frac{\rho}{\mu} Vl = \frac{0.002204 \times 103.9 \times 1.467 \times 1.0}{387.4 \times 10^{-9}}$$

$$= 868,000$$

(3) $$\text{E.R.}_1 = \frac{qAV}{550 \text{ hp}} = \frac{\frac{1}{2}\rho A V^3}{550 \dfrac{\sqrt{3EI}}{746}}$$

$$= \frac{\frac{1}{2}(0.002204)(7 \times 10)(1.467)^3(103.9)^3}{550 \times \dfrac{(1.732)(25)(2300)}{746}}$$

$$= 3.721$$

PROBLEMS

3:1. An alcohol-water mixture has a specific gravity of 0.802 at 23° C. Find (a) the water content and (b) the specific gravity at 26° C.

3:2. Sketch a pitot-static tube, locating the orifice to read (a) total head, (b) static head; (c) show the connections for reading dynamic pressure.

3:3. Assuming the critical Reynolds number of a sphere to be 235,000, find the turbulence factor of the tunnel.

3:4. A tunnel using 200 hp has a 10-ft-diameter round jet which is at standard atmospheric conditions. Find the energy ratio E.R.$_1$ if a speed of 100 mph is attained.

REFERENCES

3:1. E. R. SPAULDING and KENNETH G. MERRIAM, Comparative Tests of Pitot-Static Tubes, *TN* 546, 1935.

3:2. H. L. DRYDEN and A. M. KUETHE, Effect of Turbulence in Wind Tunnel Measurements, *TR* 342, 1930.

3:3. ROBERT C. PLATT, Turbulence Factors of NACA Wind Tunnels as Determined by Sphere Tests, *TR* 558, 1936.

3:4. F. L. WATTENDORF and A. M. KUETHE, Investigations of Turbulent Flow by Means of the Hot-Wire Anemometer, *Physics*, January-June, 1934.

3:5. L. F. G. SIMMONS, A. FAGE, and H. C. H. TOWEND, Comparative Measurements of Turbulence by Three Methods, *R&M* 1651, 1935.

3:6. H. L. DRYDEN and A. M. KUETHE, The Measurement of Fluctuations of Air Speed by the Hot-Wire Anemometer, *TR* 320, 1929.

3:7. W. C. MOCK, JR., and H. L. DRYDEN, Improved Apparatus for the Measurement of Fluctuations of Airspeed in Turbulent Flow, *TR* 448, 1932.

CHAPTER IV

MODEL FORCE, MOMENT, AND PRESSURE
MEASUREMENTS

The purpose of the load measurements of the model is to make available the forces, moments, and pressures so that they may be corrected for tunnel boundary, scale, and Mach number effects (Chapters VI and VII) and utilized in predicting the performance of the full-scale airplane.

The loads may be obtained by any of three methods: (1) measuring the actual forces and moments with a wind-tunnel balance; (2) measuring the effect that the model has on the airstream by wake surveys and tunnel-wall pressures; or (3) measuring the pressure distribution over the model by means of orifices connected to pressure gauges.

These methods are considered in detail in the following sections.

4:1. Balances. Besides lift, drag, and pitching moment, the airplane is subjected to rolling moment, yawing moment, and side force. This makes a total of six measurements in all: three forces, mutually perpendicular, and three moments about mutually perpendicular axes. The wind-tunnel balance must separate out these forces and moments and accurately present the small differences in large forces, all without appreciable model deflection. Further, the forces and moments vary widely in size. It is seen that the balance becomes a problem that should not be deprecated; in fact, it might truthfully be said that balance design is among the most trying problems in the field. The cost of a balance reflects these difficulties, ranging from $30,000 for a simple balance for a 7 by 10 ft 150 mph tunnel to $200,000 for a more complex apparatus for a larger tunnel.

In order to picture the situation most clearly, an impractical wire balance based on readings made with spring scales is shown in Fig. 4:1. The model, supposedly too heavy to be raised by the lift, is held by six wires, and six forces are read by the scales A, B, C, D, E, and F.

1. Since the horizontal wires A, B, and F cannot transmit bending, the vertical force (the lift)

$$- L = C + D + E$$

2. The drag

$$D = A + B \qquad (4{:}0)$$

3. The side force

$$Y = F$$

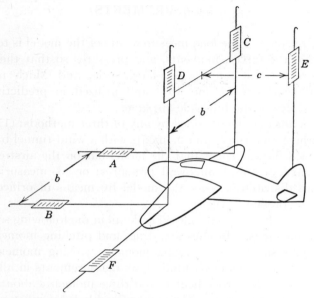

FIG. 4:1. Diagrammatic wind-tunnel balance.

4. If there is no rolling moment, scales C and D will have equal readings. A rolling moment will appear as

$$\text{R.M.} = (C - D) \times \frac{b}{2}$$

5. Similarly, the yawing moment

$$\text{Y.M.} = (A - B) \times \frac{b}{2} \qquad (4{:}1)$$

6. The pitching moment

$$M = E \times c$$

Exact perpendicularity between the components must be maintained. For instance, if the wire to scale F (Fig. 4:1) is not exactly perpendicular to wires A and B, a component of the drag will appear (improperly, of course) as side force. A similar situation exists in regard to lift and drag and lift and side force. Since the lift is the largest force by far in conventional wind-tunnel work, extreme care should be taken to assure its perpendicularity to the other components. (See Sect. 4:11.)

Before proceeding to more complicated balances, Fig. 4:1 should be studied until a clear picture is obtained of the forces and moments to be measured.

Four types of wind-tunnel balance are in general use today, each possessing certain advantages over the others. These balances are named from their main load-carrying members—wire, platform, yoke, and pyramidal—which are discussed in the following paragraphs.

A different approach to the problem of measuring the forces on the model is the incorporation of electric strain gauges (see Sects. 4:8 and 8:6) directly into the model at the mounting points. At the present time this set-up is in the development stage.

4:2. Wire Balances. One approach to the problem of the wind-tunnel balance is to support the model by wires whose loads are in turn measured by as many scales * as necessary. The whole system is usually preloaded to assure adequate tension in all members. Such an arrangement is called a wire balance. An elementary one is outlined in Fig. 4:2.

With wire balances, models are tested inverted so that their "lift" adds to the weight. This precludes the chance of unloading the wires, which could lead to large shock loads. As shown, the forces are brought up to simple laboratory beam balances equipped with dashpots which must be brought into equilibrium by individual operators, using weights. The balancing arrangement described above is satisfactory for student instruction, but the manpower cost would be prohibitive for commercial work.

The wire balance shown in Fig. 4:2 is called a six-component balance because it measures the three forces (lift, drag, and side force) and the three moments (yaw, pitch, and roll). By locking off C, E, and F this would become a three-component balance measuring lift, drag, and pitching moment only.

---

* Spring scales are not satisfactory as any deflection in the system may change the model's angle of attack or the location of the moment center of the balance.

The mounting bracket shown in Fig. 4:2 is by no means standard. Such arrangements are used only in the smallest tunnels where very small models preclude a satisfactory internal mount. Larger tunnels usually mount to locations about half-way out the wing span. The 45-degree wire is used by some to get the drag force vertically into a beam balance.

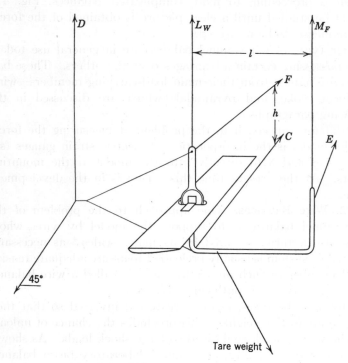

FIG. 4:2. A six-component wire balance.

Wire balances are probably the simplest and easiest to build, but they have several serious disadvantages. They have large tare drags that cannot be accurately determined. The wires usually have a tendency towards crystallization and corrosion, and probably every wire balance in existence has at one time or another broken a wire. Breakage of a wire can lead to loss of the model and other disastrous results.

This particular balance shown in Fig. 4:2 mounts the models at the quarter-chord. The results are ·ead as follows:

$$\text{Lift} = L_W + M_F$$

$$\text{Drag} = D$$

$$\text{Side force} = C + E + F$$

$$\text{Pitching moment} = -M_F \times l \qquad (4\!:\!2)$$

$$\text{Rolling moment} = (C - F)\frac{h}{2}$$

$$\text{Yawing moment} = -E \times l$$

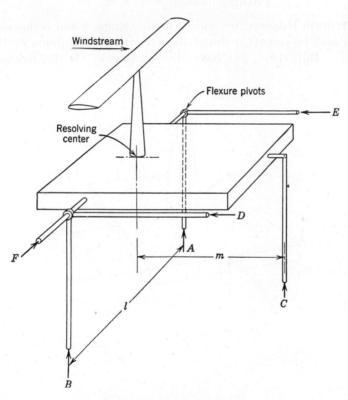

Fig. 4:3. Platform balance.

4:3. Platform Balance. The platform balance (Fig. 4:3) utilizes either three or four legs to support the main frame. For the three-legged type, the forces and moments are:

$$\text{Lift} = -(A + B + C)$$

$$\text{Drag} = D + E$$

$$\text{Side force} = -F$$

$$\text{Rolling moment} = (A - B)\frac{l}{2} \qquad (4\!:\!3)$$

$$\text{Yawing moment} = (E - D)\frac{l}{2}$$

$$\text{Pitching moment} = C \times m$$

Platform balances are widely used. Rugged and orthogonal, they may be constructed and aligned with the minimum of difficulty. But they also have disadvantages: (1) the moments

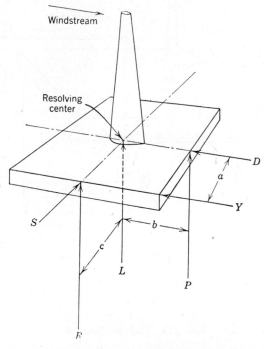

FIG. 4:3a. Asymmetrical platform balance.

appear as small differences in large forces, an inherently poor arrangement; (2) the six components are not read directly but must be summed up mechanically through extra calculating-machine complications or by the computing staff at additional cost; (3) the balance resolving center is not at the airplane, and the pitching moments must be transferred.

Sometimes the platform balance is rigged in an asymmetrical manner as shown in Fig. 4:3a, thus dividing the forces more advantageously as far as the measuring system is concerned. For instance, instead of roll being measured as the small difference between two large forces, it comes out as a single force, the major part of the lift being carried through the center strut. Similar relations exist between drag and yaw, and lift and pitch. We then have:

$$\text{Lift} = -(L + R + P)$$
$$\text{Drag} = D + Y$$
$$\text{Side force} = -S$$
$$\text{Roll} = -R \times c$$
$$\text{Pitch} = P \times b$$
$$\text{Yaw} = -Y \times a$$

$$(4:4)$$

4:4. Yoke Balance. The yoke balance offers an advantage over the platform balance in that moments are read about the model. However, the inherent design of the yoke leads to bigger deflections than the platform balance, particularly in pitch and side force. Because the balance frame must span the test section in order to get the two upper drag arms in their proper positions, the yaw lever arm is exceptionally long. The high supporting pillars are subject to large deflections. Once again the final forces must be summed up: the drag is the addition of three forces, and the lift is the sum of two. The yoke balance brings out the pitching moment in the drag system instead of in the lift.

$$\text{Lift} = -(A + B)$$
$$\text{Drag} = C + D + E$$
$$\text{Side force} = -F$$
$$\text{Rolling moment} = (B - A)\frac{l}{2}$$
$$\text{Pitching moment} = -E \times m$$
$$\text{Yawing moment} = (D - C)\frac{l}{2}$$

$$(4:5)$$

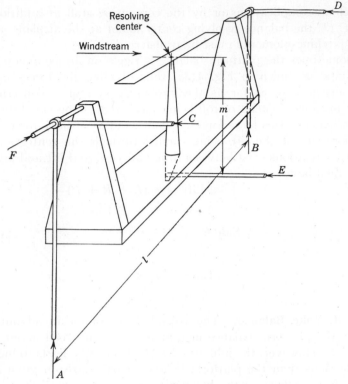

FIG. 4:4. Yoke balance.

The yoke balance may also be rigged asymmetrically, as shown in Fig. 4:4a. This rigging reduces the yaw and roll lever arms by 50 per cent. Furthermore, the moment forces are more properly divided like those of the asymmetrical platform balance. This arrangement preserves the characteristic of the yoke balance to read the moments about the model, but it may yield a framework that is slightly less rigid than the platform type.

With the asymmetrical yoke balance we have:

$$\text{Lift} = -(L + R)$$
$$\text{Drag} = D + Y + P$$
$$\text{Side force} = S$$
$$\text{Pitching moment} = -(Y + D)h \qquad (4:6)$$
$$\text{Rolling moment} = R \times n$$
$$\text{Yawing moment} = -(Y + P)n$$

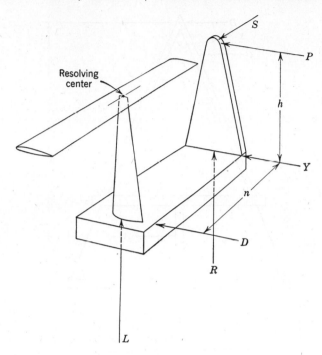

Fig. 4:4a.   Asymmetrical yoke balance.

4:5. Pyramidal Balance. The complaints usually heard against the platform and yoke balances are largely overcome by the ingenious engineering of the pyramidal type. However, as usually happens, additional difficulties are added.

These are the advantages: the pyramidal balance reads the moments about the airplane, and the six components are inherently separated out and read directly by six measuring units. No components need be added, subtracted, or multiplied. The difficulties involved in reading the small differences in large forces are eliminated, and direct reading of the forces and moments simplifies the calculating equipment.

Several criticisms of the pyramidal balance are warranted. The alignment of the inclined struts is so critical that both the construction and calibration of the balance are greatly complicated. Further (and this appears quite serious), deflections of the inclined struts may so change their alignment that the moments are not accurate. This effect must be thoroughly investigated during the calibration of the balance.

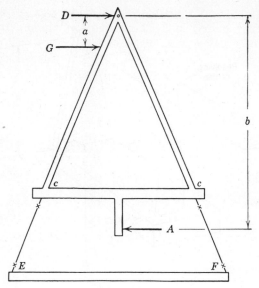

FIG. 4:5.

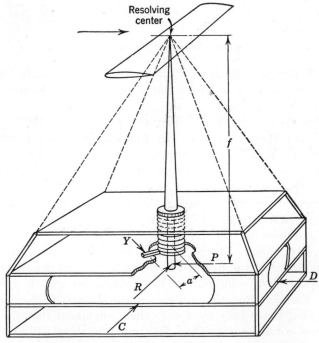

FIG. 4:6.   Pyramidal or virtual center balance.

The manner in which the pyramidal balance separates out the moments is not simple, and it behooves the student to approach the set-up using an elementary truss system. Consider a truss in which two legs are jointed (Fig. 4:5). The force D, acting through the pin joint O, produces only tension in OE and compression in OF. No force is registered at A. However the force G, not acting through O, produces bending in OE, and OE would collapse unless the force $A = aG/b$ were present. If G and b are known, the size of the force A determines the point of action of G. In this manner, if G were a known drag force, its pitching moments about the resolving center O would be determined by the force A.

Though the above example illustrates the principle of the pyramidal balance, in actual practice a considerable revision is required. In order to prevent the legs of the pyramid from being in the airstream, they are cut off at what would be C in Fig. 4:5. The truncated legs are then carefully aligned so that their extensions pass through the common point O. The complete set-up is illustrated in Fig. 4:6.

$$\text{Lift} = \text{total weight on lowest table}$$
$$\text{Drag} = D$$
$$\text{Side force} = -C$$
$$\text{Pitching moment} = -P \times f \qquad (4:7)$$
$$\text{Rolling moment} = R \times f$$
$$\text{Yawing moment} = Y \times a$$

4:6. Mounting the Model. Any strut or wire connecting the model to the balance will add three quantities to the forces read. The first is the obvious drag of the exposed strut or wire; the second is the effect of the strut's presence on the free air flow about the model; and the third is the effect of the model on the free air flow about the strut. The last two items are usually lumped together under the term "interference," and their existence should make clear the impossibility of evaluating the total tare by the simple expedient of measuring the drag on the struts with the model out.

The earliest attachments were by means of wires or streamline struts. The ruling criterion was to add the smallest possible drag and then either estimate it or neglect it. With the advent of the image system of evaluating the tare and interference (Sect. 4:12), wires became obsolescent; they were rarely adaptable for image tests and had the added hazard of occasionally failing as the result of crystallization.

The mounting struts employed at first still tended towards the minimum drag criterion and were of airfoil shape. More recently, however, many mounting struts have been made of elliptic cross section with longitudinal grooves. The idea behind this trend is that the Reynolds number of the mounting struts will always be very low and they may therefore have not only a large drag but also a drag that varies widely under minute changes. The elliptic strut may indeed have even more drag, but that shape, particularly with grooves, is not as susceptible to unsteady flow.

Only a minimum of strut is exposed to the airstream, the remainder being shielded by fairings not attached to the balance. In this way the tare drag of the mounting is decreased, sometimes being only 50 per cent of the minimum drag of an average wing. It is not advisable to try to decrease the tare drag of the "bayonets" by continuing the windshields up close to the model because a fairing close to the model can increase the interference effects more than it decreases the tare. The proper balance between amount of exposed strut and proximity of the windshield to the model may be found by having adjustable sleeves at the windshield top. The sleeve location at which $C_{d0\,min.}$ for model plus tare and interference is a minimum is the best, as this indicates that the tare plus interference is a minimum too.

Some balances yaw the model support struts oppositely to the model, so that the struts always remain parallel to the airstream and hence contribute the smallest possible effect when the model is yawed. Another useful but not necessary arrangement is to have several sets of supports of varying size from which the smallest can be selected according to the load range.

One feature may be considered necessary for the ordinary support system: a rubber diaphragm seal that prevents flow from around the balance up between the supports and shields into the tunnel. There are two types of pressures that may cause this flow. The first is due to the basic tunnel design which not infrequently results in a jet static pressure below the atmospheric pressure, and hence a pressure differential, sometimes quite large, between the balance chamber and the jet. The cure for this trouble is to seal off the balance room and allow sufficient time after the tunnel has reached speed for the excess air to drain into the tunnel.

The second pressure is that due to the attitude of the model. This is much smaller than the first and can be taken care of simply by a light diaphragm seal. Closing off the balance room in no way changes the necessity for the support column seal.

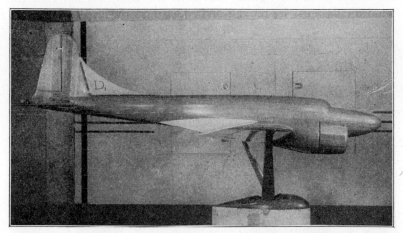

FIG. 4:7. Single-strut mounting.

The attachment fittings usually come into the wing about the 30 to 50 per cent chord point. In complete airplanes, the most rearward center of gravity location is used to give maximum room for the fittings. If a model of a multiengined airplane is to be tested, the mounting strut interference will be smallest if the struts do not attach at a nacelle point.

The various arrangements of mounting are enumerated herewith:

1. Single-strut mounting. This arrangement is by far the simplest. Only a single windshield is needed, and it need not move as the model is rotated in yaw. The single strut is satisfactory for small models and nacelles (see Fig. 5:36) and may be used in conjunction with wingtip supports to evaluate tare and interference. Unfortunately, the usual model size is such that one strut is not rigid enough, particularly in torsion.

2. Single strut with fork.   An increase in resistance to roll deflections may be gained by splitting the single strut into a fork at the top (Fig. 4:8).   However, this method does not appreciably increase the torsional rigidity of the mounting.   The fork has increased interference as compared with the straight strut and does not lend itself to inverted mounting for image tests.

3. Two-strut mounting.   The two-strut mounting surpasses the single strut for rigidity but adds the complication that the windshields must be moved and rotated as the model is yawed.

FIG. 4:8.   Model on fork-type mounting.

4. Three-point mounting.   The conditions of rigidity, tare, and interference evaluation and the ease of varying the angle of attack are all met most satisfactorily by the three-point supporting system.   It is also the most complex and requires that two and sometimes three windshields be arranged to yaw with the model (Fig. 4:9).   The rear strut introduces side forces that complicate the yawing moment measurements of a yawed model.

5. Wingtip mounting.   When it becomes necessary to determine the pressure distribution of regions close to the mounting struts, the models are frequently mounted from the wingtips, leaving the fuselage and nacelles in air unobstructed by support

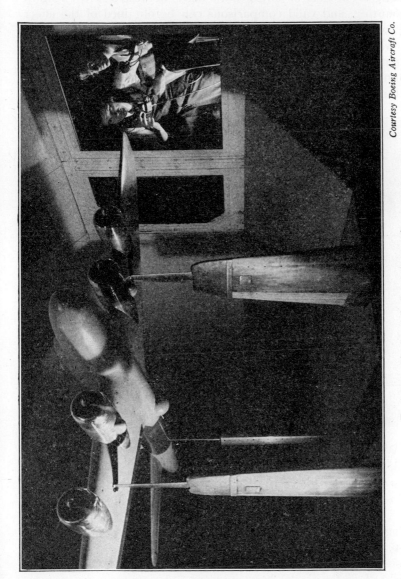

Courtesy Boeing Aircraft Co.

FIG. 4:9. Model of B-17 on three-point support.

fittings. Models of larger scale may be tested with wingtip mounting, and valid comparisons can be obtained of the effect of component parts.

When testing at high speed, wingtip mounting avoids severe interference effects as the actual mountings are deep in the tunnel-wall boundary layer where critical velocities will not be attained.

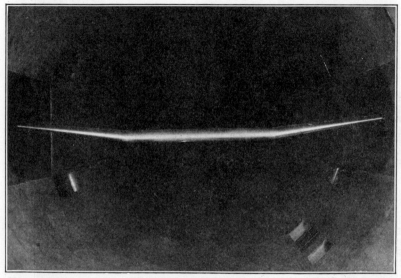

Official photograph, National Advisory Committee for Aeronautics.

FIG. 4:10. Example of wingtip mounting. DC-3 wing in 8-ft high-speed tunnel.

Whether the wingtip mounted model is a constant-chord airfoil, or a complete airplane, the data obtained will be free from downwash and hence similar to the section data obtained in a two-dimensional tunnel. Care must be taken to seal the tip to prevent leakage both from the lower to the upper surface of the wing and from the outside into the tunnel, and vice versa.

6. Plate mounting. The very largest-scale models may be tested by having them split down the plane of symmetry, only one-half of the model being present. Asymmetric flow is prevented by a large plate at the plane of symmetry, just clearing the model. Such an arrangement, though obviously being unsuited for yaw tests, yields accurate pitch, lift, and downwash data at the maximum Reynolds number.

It should be noted that any device that increases the model size also increases the size of the tunnel-wall corrections, sometimes extending them into a range where their accuracy is most doubtful.

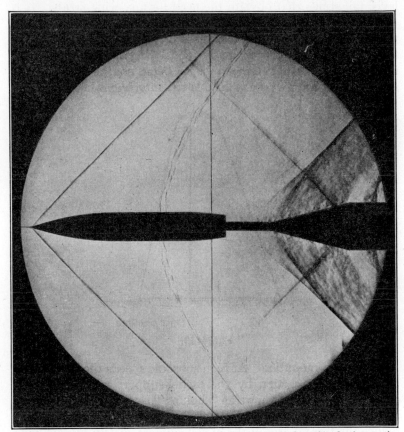

Official photograph, National Advisory Committee for Aeronautics.

FIG. 4:11. Example of tail sting mounting. Schlieren photograph of rocket body at M.N. = 1.5 in Moffett Field 1 by 3 ft supersonic tunnel.

7. Mounting from the tunnel roof. A few balances mounted above the tunnel support the model in an inverted position for "normal" running. As far as can be gathered, this arrangement is a holdover from early wire balances that supported the model similarly so that the lift forces would put tension in the wires. No particular advantage seems to accrue from inverted testing. On the contrary, such a balance position hinders the use of a

crane to install models, and the terminology of testing "normal" and "inverted" becomes obscure.

8. Mounting from a tail sting. Engineers using small supersonic tunnels initiated a system of mounting the models on cantilever tail stings that obviate the need for any wing struts. It is too early to say whether this is superior to the other mounting methods or whether it will be satisfactory for large models. Certainly tail stings tend to make the model drag appear low through stabilizing the wake. Other mounts being considered for high-speed testing have sweepback to lessen interference.

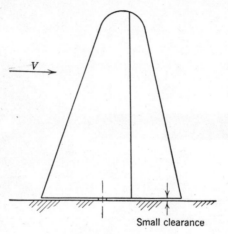

Fig. 4:12.

9. Tension mounting. At high subsonic speeds the blocking of the tunnel test section by the model-support windshields can cause a phenomenon known as "choking" as well as seriously augment the interference effects. A way around these difficulties is to reduce the frontal area of the model support system by removing the windshields and replacing the usual supporting members by thin tie rods from both jet ceiling and floor.

The use of large-scale panel models for investigation of control surfaces is discussed in Sects. 5:4–5:7. These panels require mounting arrangements different from those for wings and complete models. Several mountings are discussed below.

1. Mounting on a turntable. When the model is mounted on a turntable flush with the tunnel wall, the forces and moments on the turntable are included in the data and are difficult to

separate out. Fortunately, for the type of tests usually sought with this arrangement, the absolute value of the drag is not needed, and the effect of the endplate on lift is negligible. (See Fig. 5:14.)

2. Mounting on a single strut. Mounting the panel model on a short strut has the advantage of decreasing the tare drag of the set-up, but it is hard to evaluate the effect of the slot. (See Fig. 4:12.)

3. Mounting as a wing with an endplate. Mounting the panel as a wing with a small endplate to assist in keeping the

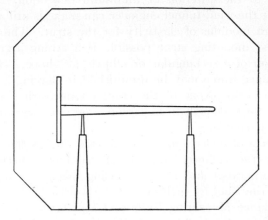

FIG. 4:13. Panel mounted as a wing with endplate.

spanwise lift distribution as it should be is discussed in Sect. 5:5. No endplate of reasonable size will prevent tip flow; hence the spanwise load distribution with this mounting will be greatly in error.

The last paragraphs draw attention to the advantage of having a yoke-type balance frame, whether the balance is a yoke balance or not. The presence of lateral brace members to which bracing wires may be attached is a great convenience. Such members are obviously necessary for wingtip mounting.

Some balances have a ring that completely encircles the tunnel jet. Though the ring offers a number of brace points, the part of the ring above the test section interferes with the installation of the image system.

4:7. Deflections. One of the most troublesome problems of wind-tunnel balances is rigidity. Deflections in the balance may move the model from the resolving center and invalidate the moment data or nullify the balance alignment so that part of the lift appears as drag or side force.

The answer to the problem is obvious: either the deflections must be kept down to where they are negligible, or they must be evaluated and accounted for in the work-up. Of course, keeping them down is preferable.

The largest source of deflection is the mounting system. This must be long to reach out of the test section and thin to avoid excessive interference. Both these requirements are in direct antitheses to the criterion of minimum deflection. The only attack that the wind-tunnel engineer can make is utilizing materials of high modulus of elasticity for the strut. The desire for the shortest mounting strut possible is a strong argument for the selection of a rectangular or elliptic jet shape. Deflections in the balance frame may be diminished by having a deep and rigid framework. None of the common measuring units have deflections large enough to be serious, and so they rarely cause this type of trouble.

The effects of deflections are evaluated during the process of calibrating the balance, and the corrections if necessary are either incorporated into the calculating machinery or given to the computing staff for inclusion in the work-up.

4:8. Balance Measuring Units and Linkages. So far, except for stating the impossibility of directly using deflecting scales for the measuring units of the wind-tunnel balance, no mention has been made of the types of units that are employed. These are usually either mechanical beam balances, hydraulic cells, springless scales, or electric devices. First let us consider how the forces are brought to the measuring units.

Most measuring units operate best with loads that are brought to them vertically. Hence horizontal forces must be led through linkages that rotate them 90 degrees, and usually the vertical forces must also be brought out to a more convenient location. Each link in the system and particularly each joint represents a potential source of friction and deflection. Obviously the number of joints must be kept to a minimum, and those absolutely unavoidable must be designed with the utmost care. Friction also must be kept to a minimum. Surprisingly, ball bearings are almost never used. Their type of construction is better suited to apparatus having large motion between the parts. Instead, the joints of a wind-tunnel balance are either knife edges or flexure plates.

Knife edges are poorly named, for they are not sharp. They are actually wedges whose working edges have a small radius. They are of hardened steel, and their seats are hardened, too. Trouble with knife edges is more likely to result from too sharp a "knife" than too dull a one.

The flexure plates are steel plates that have been milled down very thin at one section, so that they have very small resistance to bending in one direction while good rigidity is maintained in the other. Flexure plates (or pivots) have the added advantage

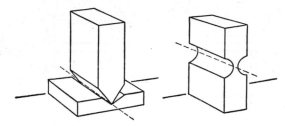

Fig. 4:14.   Knife edge and flexure pivot.

that they can take tension as well as compression and are not subject to the troubles of corrosion and dirt as are the knife edges.

The measuring unit should have, besides the ability to measure small variations in large forces, two added qualities: it should maintain an invariable slope of the curve of applied load vs. indicated load, and it should return to zero when the load is removed very gradually. Of the two, occasional failure to return to zero is the lesser evil. Such action is instantly spotted by an alert tunnel crew, and runs are repeated or corrected as the evidence demands. A change of the balance constant is far more difficult to catch. Almost the only simple methods are to repeat a basic run occasionally or to calibrate the balance. It goes without saying that no measuring system is supposed to "slip calibration," but probably every wind-tunnel engineer has had that very thing occur at one time or another.

It is a fundamental of measuring that a device can be made to read more accurately if it is subject only to loads up to 100 lb than if it must accommodate loads up to 1000 lb. In order to maintain the greatest accuracy, most measuring units have small capacities, and large loads are measured by balancing out the preponderance of the load with "unit" weights. Thus a load of 457 lb might be read by adding unit weights of 400 lb and reading 57 lb with the measuring unit. Depending on the balance design, the unit weights may be added either manually or automatically.

A short discussion of the four most popular types of measuring units follows.

1. The automatic beam balance. The automatic beam balance is shown in Fig. 4:15. It consists of a weighing beam that has an electrically driven rider. When the beam drops down, a

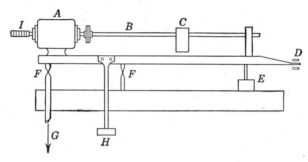

FIG. 4:15. Beam balance. *A*. Driving motor. *B*. Threaded rod. *C*. Rider. *D*. Reversing contacts. *E*. Dashpot. *F*. Flexure pivot. *G*. Applied load. *H*. Pendulum weight. *I*. Counter.

contact is made that causes the driving motor to move the rider in the direction that will balance the beam. A counter on the motor shaft locates the rider and may be calibrated to read the force weighed. The pendulum *H* (see Fig. 4:15) can be adjusted to balance out the destabilizing component due to the weight of the beam.

2. Hydraulic capsules. The hydraulic capsule is a device that measures forces through the pressures they exert on pistons of known area. They are not exactly null, but the amount of deflection of the piston is so small as to be negligible.

The operating principle of the hydraulic capsule is as follows (see Fig. 4:16).

Oil from a pressure source enters the cylinder part of the capsule through an inlet tube and leaks out through a gate directly behind the piston. A load on the piston deflects the diaphragm so that the exit area is decreased, allowing the pressure in the cylinder to build up until the piston location and pressure balance out. The resulting pressure is a function of the size of the load and is measured through accurate pressure gauges.

3. Electric measuring devices. Electric strain gauges of the wire gauge type (see Sect. 8:6) have been tried as measuring devices in several balances but apparently without much success. The electromagnetic arrangement that measures the forces by the amount of current needed to maintain zero deflection in the unit has been very successful. These systems also have a unit weight addition set-up in order to extend their range with maximum accuracy.

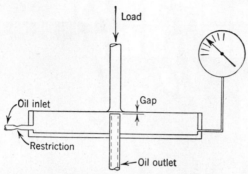

FIG. 4:16. Hydraulic capsule.

4. Springless scales. Although it has been previously mentioned that spring scales or the familiar weight-and-lever systems known as "springless" scales are unsatisfactory because of their large deflections under load, it is important to note that some wind-tunnel balances are being redesigned to utilize such devices as measuring units. Their deflection is taken out of the system by having automatically extending links (called "compensators") in the balance so that the model does not move.

Any measuring system must be checked under vibratory load to obtain the damping and balance that yield the greatest accuracy.

4:9. Automatic Calculation. The data from a wind-tunnel balance are usually presented on counters or dials and are taken down by the tunnel operators for later use of the computing staff. In order to assure simultaneous reading of all the components, the indicators may be so arranged that they may be "frozen" to remain still as long as the operator desires. Though this is advantageous when reading many components, it is pos-

sibly a little more accurate to let the indicators swing and estimate the mean value.

Sometimes the visual indicators are augmented by a printing
system so that reading the data directly may not be necessary,
but a visual check is kept anyhow. The printer takes one reading at a time, and as the forces may be fluctuating this reading
may not be the mean. To overcome the difficulty several readings are taken of each point and averaged.

Fig. 4:17. Typical control table for automatic printing balance. Dials
usually read dynamic pressure q, angle of attack α, angle of yaw ψ, lift, drag,
side force, and rolling, pitching, and yawing moments.

A third refinement is the use of automatic calculating machines built into the balance in such a manner that the moments
and forces when not read directly are calculated. In a platform
balance this procedure would require not only the summation
of the four lift forces, etc., but also the transferring of the pitching moment to the airplane center of gravity. With calculating
machines, the movement of the model due to deflection can frequently be accounted for as the results are presented.

For some of the larger balances where the utmost speed of data
presentation is desired, the calculating machines are so arranged
that the constants of the model being tested can be set into the
system, and the data are presented in final coefficient form.

Though each degree of refinement has its proponents, there is certainly some reason to prefer the simplest type of data presentation possible. The increased complexity and cost plus the difficulty of repairs should make the tunnel engineer think twice before adding anything to the apparatus that he himself cannot fix, if need be.

4:10. Calibrating the Balance. Whatever the balance type and whatever the type of mounting employed, the rigging of the balance must be checked to ascertain that the elements are

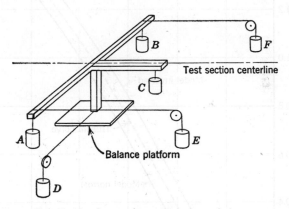

Fig. 4:18. Set-up for calibrating a balance.

mutually perpendicular and that the forces remain properly separated. An arrangement that will accomplish this checking is shown in Fig. 4:18. With this rig, the various loads and moments can be applied separately, and the independence of the readings as well as the accuracy can be determined. For example, weights added at A, B, or C should produce no drag or crosswind force, and a weight moved from E to F should produce no indicated change in drag.

The weights should be progressively added to one component, and all six components should be read. In this way the amount of, say, the lift in the other components may be noted. Then a large load should be added to, say, the drag, and the effect on the lift should be noted. With the added load still on, the lift should be recalibrated; this will indicate changes in calibration due to extraneous loads. At various times during the calibration, very small weights should be added to evaluate the changes of sensitivity due to load.

The above process should be repeated with all the components, and adjustments and corrections should be made until the accuracy and calibration are known.

The process of getting the forces and the moments properly separated is entirely different from aligning the balance with the airstream (Sect. 4:11) and correcting for misalignment.

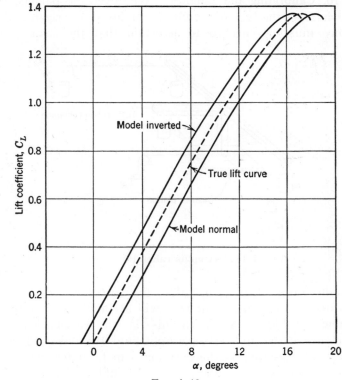

FIG. 4:19.

4:11. Balance Alignment. In order to have the drag scales read pure drag without including any component of lift, the wind-tunnel balance must be properly aligned with the airstream: lift perpendicular to it and drag parallel with it.

The difficulties come under four heads:

1. The air flow will have some variation of angularity, and hence an average perpendicular must be assumed. It will be the true average for one wing planform only.

2. The variation of q will cause the change in angularity to have more effect at some places than others. Again, an average

must be assumed; and again it can be the average for one plan-form only.

3. The mean air flow will in all probability not be horizontal or parallel to the tunnel centerline, and alignment to these criteria is not sufficient.

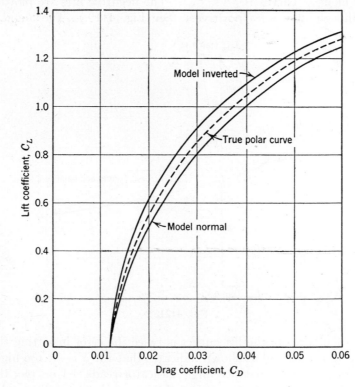

Fig. 4:20.

4. Variation in q and angle may change with airspeed, and hence the alignment will too.

One item simplifies the alignment: the lift for most tests is from 5 to 25 times larger than the drag, and it is usually suffi-cient to align so that no lift appears in the drag-reading appara-tus without checking to see whether any drag appears in the lift-reading mechanism beyond ascertaining that the drag sys-tem is perpendicular to the lift.

The balance alignment is generally accomplished by running a wing both normal and inverted from zero lift to stall.   To assure equal support strut interference for both normal and inverted runs, dummy supports, identical to the conventional ones, are installed downward from the tunnel roof. They are then as shown in Fig. 4:24. The data from both normal and downward lift are plotted as lift curves (C_L vs. α), polars (C_L vs. C_D), and moment curves (C_L vs. C_m). The negative lifts are plotted as though they were positive. (See Fig. 4:19.) The angular

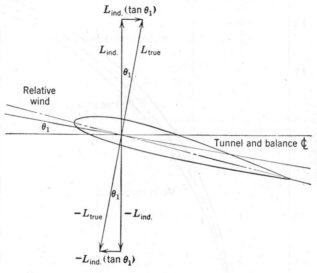

FIG. 4:21.

variation between the lift curves is twice the error in setting the angle of attack and as shown indicates that the α is set too high. That is, when the balance angle indicator reads $+1$ degree, the model is really at 0 degrees to the average wind. The polar shows that the lift is not perpendicular to the relative wind, part of it appearing as drag. Here the balance is tipped forward in reference to the relative wind, for a component of the lift is increasing the drag when the lift is positive and decreasing it when the lift is negative (Figs. 4:20 and 4:21).

The same procedure outlined above for a wing must be followed for each complete model: runs with the image system in; model both normal and inverted. These runs yield the true angle of zero lift and alignment correction. The additional runs needed for tare and interference are discussed in the next section.

If angular and velocity variations in the airstream are large, the above alignment would apply only to wings whose span and chord approximate the test wing.   In the section on angularity (Sect. 3:3), a compromise method is outlined.

It is impracticable to align the balance for each model, and hence the misalignment correction is applied in the data work-up as follows:

Suppose that the polars of the normal and inverted runs appear as in Fig. 4:20.   With the wing in the normal position the balance reads

$$C_{D \text{ indicated}} = C_{D \text{ true}} + C_{L \text{ indicated}} (\tan \theta_1) \qquad (4:8)$$

where θ_1 = angle of misalignment (Fig. 4:21).
Hence,

$$C_{D \text{ ind.}} - C_{D \text{ true}} = C_{L \text{ ind.}} \cdot \tan \theta_1 \qquad (4:9)$$

The correct $C_D (C_{D \text{ true}})$ lies halfway between the $C_{D \text{ normal}}$ and $C_{D \text{ inverted}}$ curves.   Let the difference between the curves at some C_L be ΔC_D.   Then

$$C_{D \text{ ind.}} - C_{D \text{ true}} = \frac{\Delta C_D}{2} \qquad (4:10)$$

and, if the difference between the curves is read at $C_L = 1.0$, the angle of misalignment, θ_1, may be found from

$$\tan \theta_1 = \left(\frac{\Delta C_D}{2} \right)_{C_L = 1.0} \qquad (4:11)$$

When working up the data, the correct drag may then be found from

$$C_{D \text{ true}} = C_{D \text{ ind.}} - (C_{L \text{ ind.}}) \tan \theta_1 \qquad (4:12)$$

A second and simple method is to plot $\Delta C_D / 2$ against C_L and pick off the proper values during the data work-up.   True C_L is close enough to C_L indicated so that usually no correction to C_L is needed.

Two further important points in regard to the evaluation of the alignment correction remain.   First, it should be realized that, in order to have the tare and interference effects identical for both the model normal and inverted runs, the image system must be installed and the dummy struts arranged as per Fig. 4:24.   Second, the misalignment corrections found necessary for a certain model will not suffice if the same model is to be tested at a later date, for expansion of the tunnel due to weather conditions may cause variations of the mean flow angle in the jet.

The error in setting the angle of attack, $\Delta\alpha'$, is found from the normal and inverted lift curves as per Fig. 4:19, the corrected angle in this case being

$$\alpha = \alpha_N - \Delta\alpha' \qquad (4:13)$$

where α_N = angles of attack read with model in normal position.

$\Delta\alpha'$ = half the angular difference between lift curves for normal and inverted positions.

The angular correction for misalignment is usually incorporated into the work-up of the data.

In order to correct for misalignment of the side-force balance, two runs must be made, with both the tare and interference dummies in. The model in normal position should be yawed in one direction and then inverted and yawed in the same direction relative to the tunnel. The correct side-force curve will be halfway between the curves made by model normal and model inverted. The inversion is necessary to nullify effects of the model's irregularities.

Side-force corrections as outlined are rarely made as they entail a set of dummy supports that can be yawed; moreover, extreme accuracy in side force is not usually required. The principles of the correction, however, are important.

It should be recalled that changes in the shape of a polar curve may be due to scale effects and that comparisons of various tests of similar airfoils must be made from readings at the same effective Reynolds number. (It has been shrewdly noted that, if the section selected is one of the more "popular" types that have been frequently tested, it is nearly always possible to find some results that will "agree" with yours.)

4:12. Tare and Interference Measurements. Any conventional wind-tunnel set-up requires that the model be supported in some manner, and, in turn, the supports will both affect the free air flow about the model and have some drag themselves. The effect on the free air flow is called "interference"; the drag of the supports, "tare." Although tare drags could be eliminated entirely by shielding the supports all the way into the model (with adequate clearances, of course), the added size thus necessitated would probably increase the interference so that no net gain would be realized.

The evaluation of the tare and interference is a complex job, requiring thought as well as time for proper completion. The student invariably suggests removing the model to measure the forces on the model supports. This procedure would expose parts of the model support not ordinarily in the airstream (although the extra length could be made removable) and would fail to record either the effect of the model on the supports or the effect of the supports on the model.

First let us consider a method rarely used that evaluates the interference and tare drag separately. Actually the value of the sum of the two will nearly always suffice without determining the contribution of each, but, besides being fundamental, this long method may offer suggestions for determining interference for certain radical set-ups. The procedure is as follows:

The model is first tested in the normal manner, the data as taken including both the tare and interference. In symbolic form we have:

$$D_{\text{measured}} = D_N + I_{LB/M} + I_{M/LB} + I_{LSW} + T_L \quad (4:14)$$

where D_N = drag of model in normal position.

$\quad I_{LB/M}$ = interference of lower surface bayonets on model.

$\quad I_{M/LB}$ = interference of model on lower surface bayonets.

$\quad I_{LSW}$ = interference of lower support windshield.

$\quad T_L$ = free air "tare" drag of lower bayonet.

Next the model is supported from the tunnel roof by the "image" or "mirror" system. The normal supports extend into the model, but a small clearance is provided (Fig. 4:22). The balance then reads the drag of the exposed portions of the supports in the presence of the model. That is:

$$D_{\text{measured}} = T_L + I_{M/LB} \quad\quad (4:15)$$

For the interference run the model is inverted and run with the mirror supports just clearing their attachment points (Fig. 4:23). We then get

$$D_{\text{measured}} = D_{\text{inv.}} + T_U + I_{UB/M} + I_{USW} + I_{M/UB} + I_{LB/M} +$$
$$I_{LSW} \quad (4:16)$$

where $D_{\text{inv.}}$ = drag of model inverted (should equal the drag of the model normal, except for misalignment) (see Sect. 4:11) and the symbol "U" refers to the upper surface

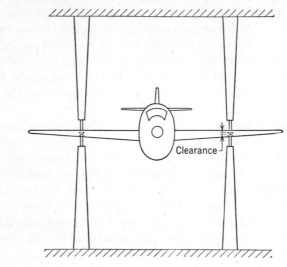

FIG. 4:22.

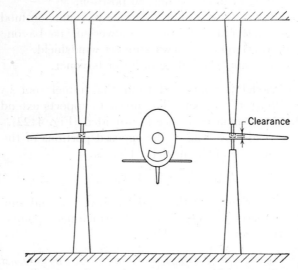

FIG. 4:23. Mirror (or "image") method of determining the effect of the supports on the model.

Then the mirror system is removed and a second inverted run is made.   This yields

$$D_{\text{measured}} = D_{\text{inv.}} + T_U + I_{UB/M} + I_{M/UB} + I_{USW} \quad (4{:}17)$$

The difference between the two inverted runs is the interference of supports on the lower surface.   That is, eq. 4:16 less eq. 4:17 yields

$$I_{LB/M} + I_{LSW} \quad (4{:}18)$$

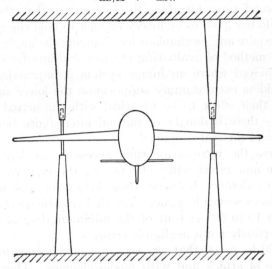

FIG. 4:24.   Arrangement for determining tare and interference simultaneously.

By subtracting eqs. 4:18 and 4:19 from the first run (eq. 4:14), the actual model drag is determined if the balance is aligned.   As explained more fully in Sect. 4:11, the difference between runs made in the normal and inverted position with the mirror system in can be used to find the proper corrections for alignment.

The support tare and interference effects can be found in three runs instead of four by using a slightly different procedure.   In this case the normal run is made, yielding

$$D_{\text{measured}} = D_N + T_L + I_L \quad (4{:}19)$$

Where $I_L = I_{M/LB} + I_{LB/M} + I_{LSW}$

Next the model is inverted and we get

$$D_{\text{measured}} = D_{\text{inv.}} + T_U + I_U \quad (4{:}20)$$

Then the dummy supports are installed.   Instead of the clearance being between the dummy supports and the model, the exposed length of the support strut is attached to the model, and the clearance is in the dummy supports (Fig. 4:24). This configuration yields

$$D_{\text{measured}} = D_{\text{inv.}} + T_L + I_L + T_U + I_U \qquad (4:21)$$

The difference between eq. 4:20 and eq. 4:21 yields the sum of the tare and interference $T_L + I_L$.

The second procedure has the advantage that the dummy supports do not have to be heavy enough to hold the model, nor do they require any mechanism for changing the angle of attack.

A third method of evaluating the tare and interference, sometimes employed where an image system is impracticable, consists of adding extra dummy supports on the lower surface and assuming their effect to be identical with the actual supports. Sometimes there is danger of mutual interference between the dummies and the real supports.

Doubtless the increase of runs necessary to determine the small tare and interference effects and the concern expressed about the difference between those effects on the upper and lower surfaces seem picayune. Yet their combined effect represents from 10 to 50 per cent of the minimum drag of the whole airplane—clearly not a negligible error.

It should be noted that the tare and interference forces vary with angle of attack and with model changes. They must be repeatedly checked and evaluated, particularly for major changes of wing flaps, cowling flaps, and nacelle alterations close to the support attachment. With many models every configuration must have its own support interference evaluated, a long and tiresome test procedure.

The image-system method of tare and interference evaluation assumes that there is no mutual interference between the real and image supports. Also, unless added struts are placed on the lower surface to evaluate the lower strut effect, it must be assumed that $C_{L\,\text{max.}}$ is unaffected by the lower surface mounting struts.

As the model angle of attack is changed, its center of gravity will probably change, producing a pitching moment. This moment must be evaluated by pitching the model with the tunnel wind off and by subtracting the pitching-moment tare from the wind-on runs. Or it must be balanced out by weights hung on the pitch-measuring system to bring the total ship-plus-weights center of gravity on the balance resolving center.

The tare and interference evaluations for the tail support have been omitted from the above discussion because they are generally treated in a slightly different manner.   The reason for this new treatment is that the length of the tail support varies as the angle of attack is changed.   This factor so complicates the dummy arrangements that a system is usually employed that does not require a complete dummy tail support.

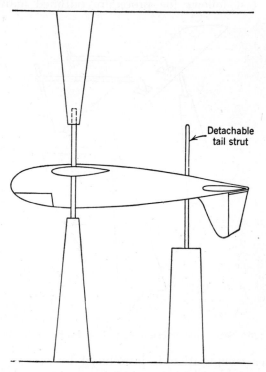

Detachable
tail strut

FIG. 4:25. Set-up for determining the tare and interference of the tail support.

The procedure is as follows: Consider the second method of evaluating the tare and interference.   When the image system is brought down to the inverted model, a short support is added to the then upper surface of the model where the tail support would attach in a normal run.   The piece attached corresponds in length to the minimum exposed portion of the tail support and increases the drag of the model by the interference and tare drag of a tail support on the model's lower surface.   For angles of attack other than that corresponding to minimum length of exposed tail support, the drag of the extra exposed tail support length must be evaluated and subtracted.

A rear support windshield that moves with the rear support to keep a constant amount of strut in the airstream could be employed as long as the added interference of the moving shield is evaluated by a moving shield dummy set-up.

The evaluation of the tare, interference, and alignment of a wing-alone test follows the procedure outlined above, except

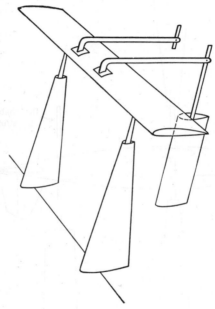

Fig. 4:26. Set-up for determining tare and interference of sting.

that further complication is introduced by the presence of a "sting" that must be added to the wing to connect it to the rear strut of the support system. The tare and interference caused by the sting may be found by adding a second sting during the image tests. As may be noted in Fig. 4:26, the attachment of the sting to the rear support includes a portion of the strut above the connection, and the dummy sting has a section of support strut added both above and below its connection point. This complication is needed to account for the interference of the strut on the sting, as follows.

When the wing is held at a high angle of attack, there will be an obtuse angle below the sting. When the wing is inverted and held at a high angle relative to the wind, there will be an acute angle below the sting, for the rear strut will then be extended to its full length. To eliminate this difference between the normal and inverted tests the support strut is extended above the sting attachment point, so that the sum of the angles between the sting and the support is always 180 degrees. Similarly, the

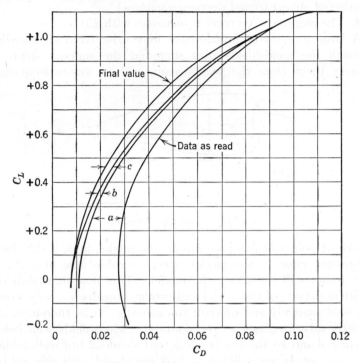

FIG. 4:27. Corrections for a wing-alone test. *a.* Sting and support tare and interference. *b.* Drag of exposed incidence strut. *c.* Alignment.

image sting has the same arrangement. It is noted that, although the angles between the sting and the rear support vary with the angle of attack, the image sting is always at right angles to its short "rear support strut." Further, the image rear support strut does not remain vertical but changes its angle with the wing. The error incurred by failing to have the sting image system simulate the exact interference and rear strut angle is believed to be negligible.

Figure 4:27 shows a wing-alone test for a NACA 0015 wing of aspect ratio 6.0. The wing in this particular test was small, and the corrections for tare, interference, and alignment are correspondingly large, but the variation of the corrections is typical. The following points are of interest.

1. The correction for tare and interference decreases as C_L (and α) increases.

2. The incidence strut drag decreases with increasing α. (The amount of strut exposed decreases with α.)

3. The alignment correction increases with C_L.

A large amount of interference may arise from air bleeding through the windshields that surround the support struts to protect them from the windstream. These struts frequently

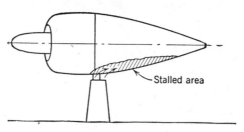

Fig. 4:28.   Effect of "bleeding."

attach at points of low pressure on the model, and, if the shield is brought close to the model, a considerable flow may be induced that will run along the model. This flow may stall the entire underside of the model and produce results not only wrong but also unsteady and difficult to evaluate. It is, therefore, frequently advantageous to terminate the windshields well below the model and let the test be subjected to added but well-defined tare drag or, better still, to seal off the shield with thin rubber balloons so that no inflow is possible.

4:13. Profile Drag by the Momentum Method. It should be noted that a balance is not always required in a wind tunnel. The drag may be obtained by comparing the momentum in the air ahead of the model with momentum behind the model, and the lift may be found by integration of the pressures on the tunnel walls. These artifices are most generally employed in airfoil section research in a two-dimensional tunnel. Spanwise integration is unnecessary then, and section coefficients may be directly obtained.

The basic theory of the wake survey measurement is as follows. Consider the flow past an airfoil (Fig. 4:29). It may be

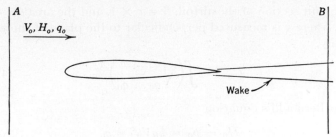

FIG. 4:29.

seen that the part of the air that passes over the model suffers a loss of momentum, and this loss is evidenced by and equal to the profile drag of the airfoil, or

$$D = \frac{\text{Mass}}{\text{Sec}} \times \text{Change in velocity}$$

$$D = \iint \rho V \, da(V_0 - V)$$

where D = drag.
V_0 = initial airspeed (at A).
V = final airspeed in the wake (at B).
da = small area of the wake perpendicular to airstream.

Hence

$$D = \iint (\rho V V_0 \, da - \rho V^2 \, da)$$

and

$$C_D = 2 \iint \left(\frac{V}{V_0} \frac{da}{S} - \frac{V^2}{V_0{}^2} \frac{da}{S} \right)$$

Also

$$V_0 = \sqrt{\frac{2q_0}{\rho}}$$

and

$$V = \sqrt{\frac{2q}{\rho}}$$

Therefore

$$C_D = 2 \iint \left(\sqrt{\frac{q}{q_0}} - \frac{q}{q_0} \right) \frac{da}{S} \qquad (4:22)$$

For a unit section of the airfoil, $S = c \times 1$, and the area $da = dy \times 1$, where y is measured perpendicular to the plane of the wing. Finally,

$$C_D = 2 \int \left(\sqrt{\frac{q}{q_0}} - \frac{q}{q_0} \right) \frac{dy}{c} \qquad (4:23)$$

From Bernoulli's equation

$$H_0 - p_0 = \tfrac{1}{2}\rho V_0^2 = q_0$$

and

$$H - p = \tfrac{1}{2}\rho V^2 = q$$

where H and H_0 = total head in wake and free stream respectively.

p and p_0 = static head in wake and free stream respectively.

Hence we have

$$C_D = 2 \int \left(\sqrt{\frac{H - p}{H_0 - p_0}} - \frac{H - p}{H_0 - p_0} \right) \frac{dy}{c} \qquad (4:24)$$

The ordinary pitot-static tube reads $(H - p)$ directly, but practical difficulties usually prevent the construction of a bank of them. The customary method of obtaining values for eq. 4:23 is to use a wake survey rake (Fig. 4:30). This is simply a bank of total head tubes spaced about a tube diameter apart

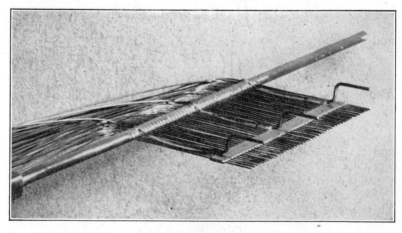

FIG. 4:30. A wake survey rake. For high-speed work the construction shown is not rigid enough.

with the total head orifice about one chord ahead of the rake body. The tubes are individually connected in order to the tubes of a multiple manometer; and, since only the ratio q/q_0 is needed, the readings are independent of the specific gravity of the fluid in the manometer and its angle.

The manometer will appear as in Fig. 4:31. In actual practice many more readings will be available through shimming up the rake in small increments. A small amount of "splash" outside the wake proper may also appear, caused probably by the lateral static-pressure gradient present in the tunnel. The engineer must fair the curve according to his experience.

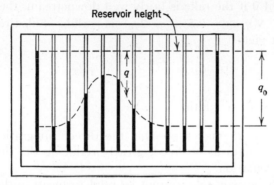

FIG. 4:31. The wake as it appears on the multiple manometer.

The constant readings of the outside tubes indicate that they are out of the wake and hence may be used to determine q_0. It should be noted that q_0 should be used from the manometer reading, not from the tunnel q at the model location, as the longitudinal velocity gradient in the tunnel invalidates q calibrations made upstream. The other tubes read the values of q corresponding to their position on the rake.

It will be seen that the proper values of q can be obtained only if the rake is situated far enough behind the wing so that the wake has returned to tunnel static pressure since a difference in static pressure across the wake will void the values for q. A solution to this problem is to locate the rake at least 0.7 chord behind the trailing edge of the wing, by which time the wake will be approximately at tunnel static pressure. A second solution is to equip the rake with static orifices, the usual practice being to employ three, one at each end and one in the middle, which are averaged. Since the measurement of freestream static

pressure close to a body is a difficult thing a best, extreme caution must be exercised in locating the static holes. A satisfactory procedure is to locate them out of the plane of the rake
body as in Fig. 4:30, and calibrate them with a standard pitot-
static tube, adjusting the tip length of each static tube until
true static is read. If the tunnel is not at atmospheric static
pressure normally, reference tubes on the multiple manometer
should be connected to tunnel static pressure.

It is a tedious job to measure the pressure in each tube, divide
it by q_0, take the square root, and perform the other measures
necessary for the calculation of Eq. 4:23. Since the ratio q/q_0
is close to 1.0 if the rake is fairly well downstream, the assumption that $\sqrt{q/q_0} = 0.5 + q/(2q_0)$ is valid. Substituted into
eq. 4:23 it yields

$$C_D = \frac{Y_w}{c} - \frac{1}{q_0 c} \int q\, dy \qquad (4:25)$$

where Y_w = wake width.

Equation 4:25 makes possible the direct integration of the
wake survey data as received, greatly reducing the time necessary for calculation.

The wake survey rake cannot be used to measure the drag of
stalled airfoils or of airfoils with flaps down. Under these conditions a large part of the drag is caused by rotational losses and
does not appear as a drop in linear momentum.

If practical reasons prohibit the location of the rake far enough
downstream so that the wake has not yet reached tunnel static
pressure, additional corrections are necessary (Ref. 4:1), and
if tests are made at large Mach numbers still further changes
are required.

It has been found that a round total head tube will not read
the true pressure at its centerline if it is located in a region where
the pressure is varying from one side of the tube to the other.
An allowance may be made for this (Ref. 4:1), or the total head
tubes may each be flattened at the tip. The latter procedure is
recommended, although the usual correction for the lateral pressure variation is quite small.

4:14. Integrating Wake Survey Rake. An ingenious integrating rake that can be calibrated to read the drag coefficient
directly on a single pressure tube has been proposed by Silver-

stein (Ref. 4:3). It consists of a simple bank of total head tubes connected to a reservoir (Fig. 4:32). The drag is a function of the average pressure in the reservoir, assuming that the wake curve is similar to a (cosine)^2 curve. Though the integrating wake survey rake is a wonderful timesaver when many tests of similar airfoils are to be made, it is sometimes difficult to get accurate results without calibrating the integrating rake to each new set-up. Unless the rake is attached to the wing being tested, the usual non-integrating rake must be present so that the integrating rake can be centered.

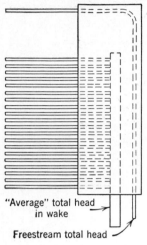

"Average" total head in wake

Freestream total head

Fig. 4:32. Wake rake with integrating head.

Several types of integrating or averaging manometers have been used in an effort to eliminate the laborious calculations of eq. 4:24. With any of them, extreme caution is needed in interpreting the results.

4:15. Lift and Drag by Pressure Distributions. Still a third method exists whereby the lift and drag may be measured: the integration of the static pressures over the wing. For these tests the airfoil is equipped with many flush orifices, each individually connected to a tube of a multiple manometer. For lift determinations the pressures are plotted perpendicular to the chord, yielding the normal force coefficient C_N. When plotted parallel to the chord, they give the chord force coefficient, C_C. The approximate C_L may be found from

$$C_L = C_N \cos \alpha \qquad (4:25a)$$

The actual static-pressure distribution over a wing is shown in Fig. 4:33a. The same pressure distribution plotted normal to the chord for the determination of normal force is shown in Fig. 4:33b, and parallel to the chord for chord force determination in Fig. 4:33c. Several of the pressure readings are labeled so that their relative positions may be followed in the various plots.

The growth of the pressure distribution with angle of attack is shown for a typical airfoil in Fig. 4:34; in this figure may also be found a partial answer to the oft-repeated question "Which lifts more, the upper or the lower surface?" At zero lift, both surfaces have both positive and negative lift. With increasing

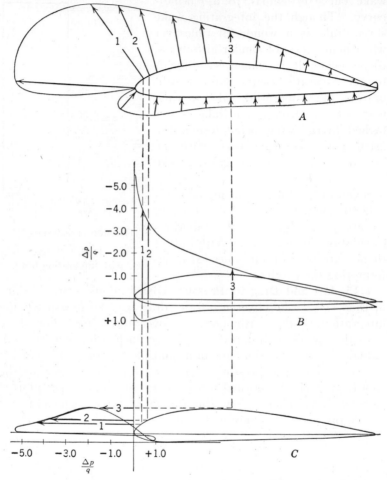

FIG. 4:33. The actual pressure distribution and its presentation.

angle of attack the upper surface increases its proportion until it finally is lifting about 70 per cent of the total.

Many interesting observations may be made from pressure distributions. These include:

1. The location of the minimum pressure point and its strength. (See Sect. 7:5.)

2. The load that the skin is to withstand and its distribution.

3. The location of the point of maximum velocity and its value.   This follows from item 1.

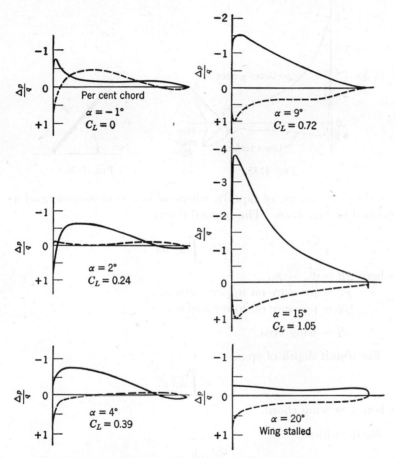

FIG. 4:34.   Growth of static-pressure distribution with angle of attack.

4. The location of the maximum pressure point and its strength.

5. The probable type of boundary-layer flow and its extent. (See Sect. 7:1.)

6. The center of pressure location.

7. The critical Mach number.   This follows from item 3.

Pressure distributions are usually plotted as follows.

Pressures are read with a multiple manometer that may or may not be inclined. The true head in any one tube, p, equals

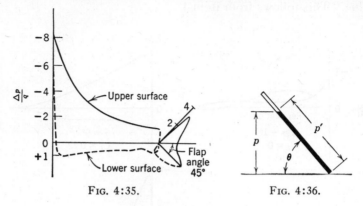

FIG. 4:35. FIG. 4:36.

$(p' \sin \theta) \times$ (sp. gr. of liquid), where p' is the measured head as defined in Fig. 4:36. The normal force,

$$N = \int \Delta p \, ds$$

where $\Delta p = p_u - p_l$.

p_u = pressure on upper surface.

p_l = pressure on lower surface.

S = wing area.

For a unit depth of span,

$$N = \int \Delta p \, dc$$

where c = wing chord.

By definition,

$$N = \frac{\rho}{2} S V^2 C_N$$

and hence

$$C_N = \frac{N}{qc} = \frac{1}{c} \int \frac{\Delta p}{q} \, dc \tag{4:26}$$

It follows that the pressures may be plotted in units of dynamic pressure against their respective locations on the chord. Further, the area under such a curve divided by the chord is the normal force coefficient, and the moment of area about the leading edge divided by the area is the center of pressure.

When a trailing edge flap is lowered, it is customary to show the flap pressures normal to the flap chord in its down position. (See Fig. 4:35.) For finding the total C_N due to the main wing and flap we have

$$C_N = C_{N \text{ wing}} + C_{N \text{ flap}} \cos \delta_F \qquad (4:27)$$

where δ_F = flap angle.

It should be noted that, though good agreement between C_N and C_L can be obtained, the drag measured by the pressure distribution, $C_{D \text{ press.}} = C_C \cos \alpha + C_N \sin \alpha$, does not include skin friction or induced drag.

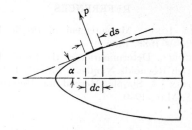

FIG. 4:37.

The point is sometimes raised that a fallacy is involved in plotting the pressures that act normal to the curved surface of the wing as though they were normal to the chord. Actually there is no error. A simple analogy is observable in the pressure in a pipe acting radially but whose force trying to split the pipe is the pressure times the section area made by a plane that contains a diameter.

The mathematical explanation is as follows. Consider a small element of surface ds, which is subjected to a static pressure p acting normal to it. The total force on the element is $p \, ds$, directed along p, and the component of this force normal to the chord line is $p \, ds \cos \alpha$.

But $ds \cos \alpha = dc$, where dc is a short length of the chord, so that the total force normal to the wing chord line is $N = \int \Delta p \, dc$.

It will be noted in Fig. 4:34 that a maximum stagnation pressure of $\Delta p/q = +1.0$ is usually developed near the leading edge of a wing. This may be accepted as the rule for section tests, but swept-back panels will show less than $\Delta p/q = +1.0$ at all stations except at the plane of symmetry.

PROBLEMS

4:1. Define balance alignment.

4:2. Explain how to attain alignment.

4:3. Explain the situation and suggest the necessary corrections if the drag is less when the wing lifts normally than when it is inverted.

4:4. Discuss the difference between the effect of the model on the supports and the effect of the supports on the model.

4:5. State several difficulties inherent in a wire balance.

4:6. Sketch an airplane, and show the forces and moments on it.

4:7. Under what conditions does a wake survey fail to read the drag?

REFERENCES

4:1. B. MELVILLE JONES, Measurement of Profile Drag by the Pitot-Traverse Method, *R&M* 1688, 1936.

4:2. JOSEPH BICKNELL, Determination of the Profile Drag of an Airplane Wing in Flight at High Reynolds Numbers, *TR* 667, 1939.

4:3. A. SILVERSTEIN, A Simple Method for Determining Wing Profile Drag in Flight, *JAS*, May, 1940.

CHAPTER V

TESTING PROCEDURE

Depending on the innovations incorporated and terms of the development contract or program, a new model airplane may require from one to six models (or more) and up to six different wind tunnels. A typical program is as follows:

After the preliminary layout of the proposed new airplane has been made, a "complete" model is designed and constructed. This first model, usually of 6 to 16 per cent scale, is a solid-mahogany breakdown model; that is, the different configurations of the airplane may be built up progressively through additions to the wing alone, enabling the relative effect of each component to be evaluated. Testing this model requires measurement of all six forces and moments: lift, drag, side force, and rolling, yawing, and pitching moments. The important criteria of maximum lift (stalling speed), minimum drag (high speed), and static stability are evaluated. The breakdown model aids in determining the exterior configuration of the airplane so that the specialized models can be designed.

The second model (after the first breakdown model there is no specific order for the additional ones) may be a small-scale spin model for determining the spin-recovery characteristics in a spin tunnel. Here the model is put into a tailspin in the vertical airstream of the tunnel, and a remotely operated mechanism moves the control surfaces as desired to bring the plane out of the spin. Moving pictures of the recovery can be examined to see whether the procedure is satisfactory.

A third model, also light and fragile, may be flown in a free-flight tunnel where moving pictures record its stability and maneuverability.

A fourth model, so constructed that its rigidity is related to the full-scale airplane, may be tested for critical flutter speed (Ref. 2:1).

If the design appears satisfactory or can be made so after these preliminary tests, larger models of component parts are tested. Aileron panels and tail surfaces to perhaps 40 per cent scale may be tested, and nacelles to a similar scale may be investigated for cooling and drag. Compressibility effects are investigated with high-speed models in high-speed tunnels. Sometimes additional section tests of the airfoils to be used are made in a two-dimensional tunnel, and if the design is entirely untested pressure distributions over the flap, flap vanes, etc., may be taken to determine design loads for the structural design.

Finally, when the first actual airplane is finished it can be tested in a full-scale tunnel for aerodynamic "clean-up" changes. Here also the manufacturing irregularities can be examined and improvements suggested. Military airplanes can be subjected to simulated battle damage so that studies can be made of possible catastrophic effects.

The cost of such a program is not small, of course. Yet, compared to the cost of building the actual airplane, testing it, and changing it, the model-testing cost becomes minor indeed. Rarely would a single concern have the entire facilities required by a complete testing program. The customary solution is for the complete model and the control surface panels to be tested in the company's own wind tunnel, leaving the spin, stability, flutter, and high Mach number work to tunnels especially designed for them.

5:1. General Testing Procedure. Since it is easy to invalidate a long and costly research program by insufficient preliminary thought or by a lax attitude during the tests, a set of general testing rules is in order. The rules represent experience gathered by engineers during many years of research and should be studied both before and during a testing program.

A. PRELIMINARY INVESTIGATION

1. Check over all data available that pertain to tests similar to those proposed. It is highly probable that some tests of a similar nature have already been made. It may be possible to profit from others' experience, even to the extent of uncovering the identical information sought. Use of the previously established symbols in presenting the results is advantageous.

2. Make sure that the set-up to be employed is basically sound. The various test set-ups each have their advantages and disadvantages up to and including the point where some arrangements cannot be expected to yield accurate results. Those must be

avoided. They include such obvious but occasionally attempted arrangements as trying to measure pressures without adequate tunnel velocity to assure reasonable fluid heads; trying to ascertain minimum drags when the tare and interference is several times the configuration drag; attempting to determine control surface hinge moments when the span loading is not properly simulated. It should always be remembered that enough difficulties are inherent in wind-tunnel testing without adding the unknowns of poor reproduction of the free-air flow about the full-scale airplane.

If the indications are that the measuring apparatus will not yield sufficient sensitivity, extra points may be taken "going up" and "coming down" and a curve faired through them. Statistical analysis may be employed.

3. Make sure that the model is right. There is obviously little to be gained by testing a model that is incorrectly made. The model's contours are of primary importance as well as being the indicators of control surface deflection.

B. Readying the Tunnel

The basic parameters of the tunnel that need direct attention before the wind is turned on include considerations of the average angle of flow, average q, and the balance loads.

The average angle of flow need not be considered before the full test of a three-dimensional wing. As shown in Sect. 4:11 it is accurately determined by the model normal and inverted tests of the alignment determination. A two-dimensional model should also be run normal and inverted. However, when inversion is not to be employed for any of a number of reasons, or when it is actually impossible as for a panel model, the procedure outlined in Sect. 3:3 may be followed for finding the average angle for a given model. A rough check may be made from the first run by comparing the expected and obtained angles of zero lift. Indeed, particularly for the panels, so much advantage accrues in the analysis of later data by assuming the models to be absolutely accurate and hence making expected and obtained angles of zero lift identical that that is the usual procedure.

As most tunnels expand somewhat with warmer weather, as well as experience varying Reynolds numbers at identical values of the dynamic pressure due to temperature changes, the mean flow angle in the tunnel may vary and should be checked at least several times a year.

The engineer who upon finding a change in the data for a second series test of a certain model proclaimed that $\alpha_{Z.L.}$ was "not where he left it" was not entirely without scientific backing.

The average dynamic pressure must be calculated for each model of different planform by a method like that for obtaining the average angle. That is, the product of local q (from the dynamic-pressure survey of the test section) and the model chord at the same station is plotted against the model span. If the area under the qc vs. span curve is then divided by the total wing area the resulting quotient is the average dynamic pressure. This average dynamic pressure is *not* used to find the various coefficients until it is increased by the blocking factor obtained from Sect. 6:2.

Last, but not least, an estimate of expected loads should be made in order to ascertain that ample provision is secured to run the entire program at one speed. Changing the tunnel speed during a program adds one more effect to the data.

If pressures are to be read, proper heavy liquids should be on hand for use to keep the manometers from overflowing.

C. PROCEDURE DURING TESTING

1. After the first run has been made, check it thoroughly against expected results. If possible, design a set-up so that the first run is simple enough for comparison with previous tests. Items to be checked include $\alpha_{Z.L.}$, $dC_L/d\alpha$, $C_{L\,max.}$, $C_{D0\,min.}$, and C_{m0}.

2. Determine the testing accuracy by:

(a) Running a test twice without any change in it at all. This tests the reproducible accuracy of the balance and the speed control.

(b) Resetting and repeating a run made previously after there have been several intervening runs. This determines the reproducible accuracy of setting the flaps, tabs, etc., as well as the accuracy of the balance and speed control.

(c) Repeating a run with another tunnel crew. This indicates the personnel error.

3. Keep a running plot of all data as they come out. Any uncertain points can be substantiated immediately by taking readings at small increments above and below the uncertain ones.

4. Occasionally repeat a basic run. This will indicate any gradual model warpage or other alterations occurring with time.

5. Repeat the first reading at the end of each run. This will indicate any control surface slippage, etc. Inspect the model frequently, checking all control settings, and wherever possible make angular measurements of controls, etc., with the inevitable slack taken out in the loaded direction.

6. Make every data sheet self-contained. Avoid using expressions such as "Same as Run 6," as this necessitates looking up Run 6. Every data sheet must contain the model designation, configuration, test speed, date, and tunnel temperature and pressure. Further data, such as effective Reynolds number and model dimensions, are valuable.

7. Keep an accurate log of everything that happens. When analyzing the data the exact point at which changes were made may be of paramount importance.

The size and design of the tunnel determine the size of the model that can be accommodated and, sometimes, other important criteria such as model weight or power arrangements. Occationally a gasoline motor can be operated in the tunnel (Ref. 5:1). The tunnel itself also determines the complexity of the model and hence its cost. The cost ranges from about $25 for the simplest small wing of 15-in. span to $165,000 for a complete four-engined bomber model using remotely operated ailerons, elevators, rudders, cowl flaps, landing gear, bomb-bay doors, and electrically driven propellers. The amount of remotely operated equipment is a function of the number of tests to be made and the type of tunnel.

5:2. Testing Three-Dimensional Wings. The first wind-tunnel tests ever made were concerned with the behavior of wings, and probably more tests are made today on this item than on any other. Much progress has been made on airfoil design, but wing design is still in its infancy. The variables of sweepback, twist, section, taper, and tips are too much for any short research program.

The foremost difficulties encountered in making wing-alone tests include the necessity of obtaining a moderately high Reynolds number (at least 2,500,000) if extrapolation to higher Reynolds numbers is to be attempted. Further, this Reynolds number should be obtained by a high-speed or large model, not by the introduction of turbulence into the airstream.

Tare and interference drag can be reduced by careful engineering of the supports and attachment points. (See Sect. 4:6.)

Wings that are part of a systematic airfoil research program should be made as simply as possible, preferably without taper and with simple tips. Their span should be held to less than 0.8 tunnel span to avoid excessive wall effects.

In wing-alone tests, care must be taken to find the complete tare and interference effects (Sect. 4:12) and the proper tunnel boundary corrections. For most such tests, buoyancy, constriction, and camber boundary corrections may be neglected, but span loading and downwash corrections will probably be needed. (See Chapter VI.)

The reduction of data is as follows:

A. LIFT, DRAG, AND ANGLE OF ATTACK

$$C_L = \frac{L}{(\rho/2)SV^2} = \text{lift coefficient} \tag{5:0}$$

$$C_D' = \frac{D'}{(\rho/2)SV^2} = \text{drag coefficient uncorrected for tunnel boundary effect} \tag{5:1}$$

$$\alpha = \alpha' + \delta \frac{S}{C} C_L 57.3 = \text{free air angle of attack} \tag{5:2}$$

$$C_D = C_D' + \delta \frac{S}{C} C_L^2 = \text{corrected drag coefficient} \tag{5:3}$$

where $\alpha' =$ angle of attack as measured in the tunnel, uncorrected.

$D' =$ drag as measured in the tunnel.

$S =$ wing area.

$C =$ tunnel jet cross-sectional area.

$\delta =$ from Chapter VI for proper wing span to jet width ratio, and jet shape and type.

B. SPAN EFFICIENCY FACTOR

The customary definition of the drag coefficient,

$$C_D = C_{D0\ \text{min.}} + \frac{C_L^2}{e^2 \pi R} \tag{5:4}$$

makes the determination of the span efficiency factor e of importance. This value may be determined most easily by making a plot of C_D vs. C_L^2 (Fig. 5:1). It will appear as a straight line along the major part of the plot, with a slight bending at both the lower and higher C_L's.* The significance of the divergence from the straight line at the low lift coefficients is that $C_{D0\ min.}$ does not occur at $C_L = 0$ for a cambered airfoil. The divergence

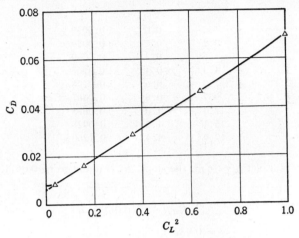

Fig. 5:1. C_D vs. C_L^2 for an NACA 23012 wing.

at the higher C_L's is due to flow separation. At any rate, the equation of the straight line (which is extended until it intersects the abscissa) is

$$C_D = C_{D0\ min.} + KC_L^2 \qquad (5:5)$$

and hence

$$K = \frac{1}{e^2 \pi R} \qquad (5:6)$$

and

$$e = \sqrt{\frac{1}{K \pi R}} \qquad (5:7)$$

It has been suggested that, as the low drag coefficient indicated by the intersection of the straight line and the C_D axis does not exist in a practical sense, it should be indicated not as $C_{D0\ min.}$ but as an effective parasite drag coefficient C_{DPe}. Hence we have

$$C_D = C_{DPe} + \frac{C_L^2}{e^2 \pi R} \qquad (5:8)$$

* Some of the newer airfoils may have to be broken down into two or three straight lines. When this occurs different values of e and $C_{D0\ min.}$ must be used for the appropriate range of C_r.

Example 5:1

Values of C_L and C_D are as given in Table 5:1. Find the span efficiency factor e if $AR = 6.0$.

TABLE 5:1

	C_L	C_D
−1.2	0.0	0.0079
0.2	0.1	0.0079
1.6	0.2	0.0090
4.3	0.4	0.0167
7.0	0.6	0.0298
9.7	0.8	0.0467
12.3	1.0	0.0673
15.1	1.2	0.0928
17.9	1.4	0.1260

From a plot of C_D vs. C_L^2, the slope, K, is found to be 0.0611. Hence

$$e = \sqrt{\frac{1}{K\pi R}} = \sqrt{\frac{1}{0.0611\pi \cdot 6}}$$

$$e = 0.932$$

It is also noted that $C_{DP_e} = 0.0061$.

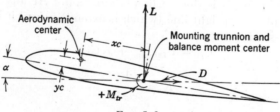

FIG. 5:2.

C. LOCATION OF THE AERODYNAMIC CENTER

Location of the aerodynamic center may be computed as follows.* Consider a wing mounted so that the axis of rotation is at some point behind and below the probable location of the aerodynamic center (Fig. 5:2). (The aerodynamic center is usually slightly ahead and above the quarter chord point.) Let the distance along the chord from the trunnion to the aerodynamic center be x_1, and let the distance above the chord be y_1. Both x_1 and y_1 are measured in fractions of the MAC.

* A second method of calculating the location of the aerodynamic center is given in the appendix of NACA TR 627.

It will be seen that

$$M_{ac} = M_{tr} - x_1 c(L \cos \alpha + D \sin \alpha)$$

$$- y_1 c(D \cos \alpha - L \sin \alpha) \quad (5{:}9)$$

where M_{tr} = the moment measured about the mounting trunnion. Hence

$$C_{mac} = C_{mtr} - x_1(C_L \cos \alpha + C_D \sin \alpha)$$

$$- y_1(C_D \cos \alpha - C_L \sin \alpha) \quad (5{:}10)$$

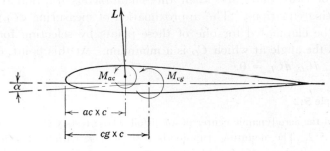

FIG. 5:3.

Applying the condition that C_{mac} does not vary with C_L we get

$$\frac{dC_{mac}}{dC_L} = 0 = \frac{dC_{mtr}}{dC_L} -$$

$$\left[\left(1 + C_D \frac{d\alpha}{dC_L} \right) \cos \alpha + \left(\frac{dC_D}{dC_L} - C_L \frac{d\alpha}{dC_L} \right) \sin \alpha \right] x_1 -$$

$$\left[\left(\frac{dC_D}{dC_L} - C_L \frac{d\alpha}{dC_L} \right) \cos \alpha - \left(1 + C_D \frac{d\alpha}{dC_L} \right) \sin \alpha \right] y_1 \quad (5{:}11)$$

The data may easily be used to find C_L, C_D, α, and also the slopes dC_{mtr}/dC_L and $d\alpha/dC_L$ since they are straight lines. The determination of dC_D/dC_L is difficult, for it is a curve.

If the wing efficiency factor has been determined, dC_D/dC_L may be found directly from

$$C_D = C_{D0\ min.} + \frac{C_L{}^2}{e^2 \pi R}$$

$$\frac{dC_D}{dC_L} = \frac{2C_L}{e^2 \pi R} \quad (5{:}12)$$

If information for the above equation is not available, the slope of the drag curve at the proper point may be obtained by the familiar mirror method. In this method a small hand mirror is set directly on the plotted curve and adjusted until the reflected curve appears as a smooth continuation of the original. Under these conditions the plane of the mirror will be perpendicular to the drag curve at the selected C_L, and the drag-curve slope may then be computed.

Equation 5:11, having two unknowns, requires the substitution of two points and then the simultaneous solution of the resulting equations. The approximation of measuring dC_D/dC_L may be eliminated for one of these points by selecting for the point the angle at which C_D is a minimum. At this point, obviously, $dC_D/dC_L = 0$.

Example 5:2

Find the aerodynamic center of an airfoil whose tests yield the data in Table 5:2. The mounting trunnion is at the 49 per cent chord point and 5.0 per cent above the chord line.

TABLE 5:2

	C_L	C_D	C_{mtr}
−2	−0.086	0.0120	−0.023
0	0.111	0.0095	0.024
2	0.326	0.0087	0.079
4	0.531	0.0096	0.131
6	0.737	0.0138	0.183
8	0.943	0.0195	0.231
10	1.118	0.0267	0.281
12	1.260	0.0369	0.317

Plots of the data yield $dC_{mtr}/dC_L = 0.254$.

$$\frac{dC_L}{d\alpha} = 0.1025 \text{ per degree}$$

$$= 5.87 \text{ per radian}$$

At $\alpha = 2.3°$, $C_L = 0.34$, $C_{D0 \text{ min.}} = 0.0084$, and $dC_D/dC_L = 0$.
At $\alpha = 8.8$, $C_L = 1.00$. $C_D = 0.0210$, and by the mirror method $dC_D/dC_L = 0.048$.

Substituting into eq. 5:11, we have:

$$\left[\left(1 + C_D \frac{d\alpha}{dC_L}\right) \cos \alpha + \left(\frac{dC_D}{dC_L} - C_L \frac{d\alpha}{dC_L}\right) \sin \alpha\right] x_1$$

$$+ \left[\left(\frac{dC_D}{dC_L} + C_L \frac{d\alpha}{dC_L}\right) \cos \alpha - \left(1 + C_D \frac{d\alpha}{dC_L}\right) \sin \alpha\right] y_1 = \frac{dC_{mtr}}{dC_L}$$

$$\left[\left(1 + \frac{0.0084}{5.87}\right)(0.999) + \left(0 - \frac{0.34}{5.87}\right)(0.0401)\right] x_1$$

$$+ \left[0 - \frac{0.34}{5.87}(0.999) - \left(1 + \frac{0.0084}{5.87}0.0401\right)\right] y_1 = 0.254$$

and

$$\left[\left(1 + \frac{0.0210}{5.87}\right)0.998 + \left(0.048 - \frac{1.0}{5.87}\right)(0.153)\right] x_1$$

$$+ \left[\left(0.048 - \frac{1.0}{5.87}\right)(0.998) - \left(1 + \frac{0.0210}{5.87}\right)(0.153)\right] y_1 = 0.254$$

These equations simplify to

$$1.0027x_1 - 0.0980y_1 = 0.254$$
$$0.9728x_1 - 0.2744y_1 = 0.254$$

and hence

$$x_1 = 0.249$$
$$y_1 = -0.0433$$

The aerodynamic center is $25 - (49.0 - 24.9) = 0.9$ per cent ahead of the quarter chord point, and $(5.0 - 4.33) = 0.67$ per cent above the chord.

In order to save time in locating the aerodynamic center, the assumption is sometimes made that the moment is due entirely to the lift and that the aerodynamic center is on the chord line. Since the lift and drag act through the aerodynamic center, the moment about the trunnion is

$$M_{tr} = M_{ac} + L(tr - ac)c \qquad (5:12a)$$

where M_{ac} = moment about the aerodynamic center, and tr = chordwise location of the balance trunnion.

Rewriting eq. 5:12a in coefficient form, we have

$$C_{mtr} = C_{mac} + C_L(tr - ac) \qquad (5:12b)$$

and differentiating and transposing $\left(\dfrac{dC_{mac}}{dC_L} = 0\right)$

$$ac = tr - \frac{dC_{mcg}}{dC_L} \qquad (5:12c)$$

Example 5:2a

Calculate the location of the aerodynamic center for the data of example 5:2, using eq. 5:12b.

1. From a plot of C_{mtr} vs. C_L,

$$\frac{dC_{mtr}}{dC_L} = 0.254$$

2. Substituting the trunnion location and dC_{mtr}/dC_L in eq. 5:12c we have $ac = 0.49 - 0.254 = 0.236$. This compares with 0.241 by the method of eq. 5:11.

Equation 5:12b indicates that, when $C_L = 0$, $C_{mac} = C_{mtr}$. In other words, the value of the moment coefficient at the point where the curve strikes the C_L axis is approximately the value of C_{mac}. Rather than call it that, the usual practice is to label the above intersection C_{m0}.

D. Moment Coefficients

After the location of the aerodynamic center has been obtained the moment coefficient about it may be found from:

$$C_{mac} = C_{mtr} - x_1(C_L \cos \alpha + C_D \sin \alpha)$$
$$- y_1(C_D \cos \alpha - C_L \sin \alpha) \quad (5:13)$$

Example 5:3

Calculate the C_{mac} for example 5:2.

Substituting each point into eq. 5:10 we have the data shown in Table 5:3.

TABLE 5:3

α	C_{mac}	α	C_{mac}
-2	-0.001	6	-0.000
0	-0.003	8	-0.001
2	-0.002	10	-0.000
4	-0.002	12	-0.000

It is not unusual to find some small spread in the values of C_{mac}, although strictly speaking the definition states that it must be constant.

It is a surprising fact that the location of the aerodynamic center is practically unchanged by flaps. The explanation lies in the manner in which the moment is generated:

$$C_{m \text{ total}} = C_{m \text{ due to changing } \alpha} + C_{m \text{ due to camber}}$$

As indicated by theory, the C_m due to changing α is constant about the quarter chord. The C_m due to camber is a constant. Hence adding camber in the form of flaps merely increases the value of C_{mac} without changing the location of the aerodynamic center as determined by changing α.

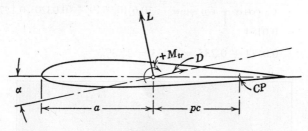

FIG. 5:4.

E. LOCATION OF THE CENTER OF PRESSURE

The center of pressure is defined as "that point on the chord of an airfoil through which the resultant force acts." Though its usefulness has declined with the introduction of the concept of the aerodynamic center, it must occasionally be determined from force tests. (See Sect. 4:15 for determining the center of pressure by the pressure-distribution method.) The procedure is as follows:

The forces measured appear as a lift force L, a drag force D, and a moment about the mounting trunnion M_{tr} (Fig. 5:4). At the point through which the resultant force acts, the moment vanishes. Hence

$$M_{CP} = 0 = M_{tr} + L(p \cos \alpha) + D(p \sin \alpha) \qquad (5:14)$$

where p is the distance from the trunnion to the center of pressure, positive to the rear of the trunnion.

We then have

$$- C_{mtr} = C_L \frac{p}{c} \cos \alpha + C_D \frac{p}{c} \sin \alpha = 0 \qquad (5:15)$$

and

$$\frac{p}{c} = \frac{-C_{mtr}}{C_L \cos \alpha + C_D \sin \alpha} \qquad (5:16)$$

The location of the center of pressure from the wing leading edge is then

$$CP = \frac{p}{c} + \frac{a}{c} \qquad (5:17)$$

Example 5:4

A wing is mounted with the trunnion at the 23.5 per cent chord point. At $\alpha = 7.3$, $C_L = 0.6$, $C_D = 0.0320$, $C_{mtr} = -0.011$. Find the center of pressure.

$$\frac{p}{c} = \frac{-C_{mtr}}{C_L \cos \alpha + C_D \sin \alpha} = \frac{0.011}{(0.6)(0.9919)+(0.0320)(0.127)}$$

$$= 0.0184$$

$$CP = 0.0184 + 0.235 = 0.253 = 25.3\%$$

Fig. 5:5. Model in a two-dimensional jet.

5:3. Testing Two-Dimensional Wings. Alterations to airfoil sections are frequently investigated in two-dimensional tunnels wherein a short constant chord section of a wing completely spans the jet width (Fig. 5:5), simulating infinite aspect ratio. The jet is usually 2½ to 4 times higher than it is wide. In most tunnels of this type the drag is read by the momentum survey method, and the lift by the pressure on the tunnel walls (Sect. 4:13). The pitching moment may also be read from the pressure on the tunnel walls, but in many cases the wing is mounted on trunnions and the moment is read with a simple beam balance.

The proportionately large drag of two endplates prohibits accurate drag measurements by the usual force tests and complicates the endplate seal.

As the models customarily used in two-dimensional tunnels are larger in proportion to jet size than others, corrections for constriction, buoyancy, and camber must be considered (Chapter VI). Frequently the models themselves are altered to take care of the camber effect, having slightly less camber than called for by the airfoil coordinates.

If the lift is to be measured from the tunnel-wall pressures, a correction factor is needed to account for lift not measured because of jet-length restrictions. This may be obtained by testing a common airfoil in the two-dimensional jet and comparing it with three-dimensional tests of the same airfoil at the same effective Reynolds number.

The information obtained from two-dimensional tests will be reducible to section coefficients c_l, c_{d0}, and $c_{m\frac{1}{4}}$. These coefficients (unlike wing coefficients C_L, C_D, and $C_{m\frac{1}{4}}$, which are an average of conditions including varying Reynolds number and effective angles of attack across the span) consider only a section under constant load and hence constant effective angle of attack. It is customary to consider the minimum profile drag coefficient C_{D0} as equivalent to c_{d0} when both are at the same Reynolds number. Likewise, it is assumed that $C_{mac} = c_{mac}$. The lift coefficients c_l and C_L may also be considered equal except at their maximum, where the spanwise lift distribution usually results in a diminution in lift of at least 5 to 10 per cent. Expressed symbolically,

$$C_{L \text{ max.}} = 0.90c_{l \text{ max.}} \text{ (approximately)} \qquad (5:18)$$

It has been found difficult to apply data made with a two-dimensional set-up to three-dimensional wings because spanwise pressure gradients frequently induce spanwise flow and invalidate the purely chordwise information. Yet the two-dimensional tunnel, by simplifying model construction and increasing the speed of testing and work-up of data, has an important place in the field of aeronautical research.

Reduction of section data is as follows:

(a) Lift, drag, and moment coefficients.

$$c_l = \frac{L}{(\rho/2)SV^2} \qquad (5:19)$$

$$c_{d0} = \frac{D}{(\rho/2)SV^2} \tag{5:20}$$

$$c_{m\frac{1}{4}} = \frac{M_{\frac{1}{4}}}{(\rho/2)SV^2c} \tag{5:21}$$

It will be noticed that, as there is no induced drag in a section test, the drag measured is therefore profile drag and

$$C_{D0} = c_{d0}$$

(b) The location of the aerodynamic center and the center of pressure may be calculated as discussed in Sects. 5:2C and 5:2E.

(c) There seems to be evidence that the slope of the lift curve $dc_l/d\alpha$ measured with a two-dimensional wing may exceed that obtained by reducing data from a finite wing to "infinite" aspect ratio. A reasonable explanation is that finite wing tests include edge losses. Lift curve slopes from section tests seem to be about 5 per cent above those obtained from wing tests.

5:4. Testing Component Parts of an Airplane. The testing of large-scale models of part of an airplane offers many advantages provided that the data can be properly applied to the airplane. Nacelles, tail surfaces, dive brakes, and ailerons are items belonging in this group.

To take a concrete example, models of 8-ft span are about the maximum usually tested in a 10-ft tunnel. If the original ship has a wing span of 80 ft the largest model that can be tested will be $\frac{1}{10}$ scale. This reduction in size makes it nearly impossible to reproduce small items accurately; their Reynolds number will be very small; and it will be virtually impossible to measure the hinge moments of control surfaces. A 30 per cent model of the vertical tail could be tested as well as a 30 per cent aileron model, but, if such large-scale panel models are to be employed, they must of course be tested under flow conditions that simulate those on the complete airplane. Mounting the panel like a complete wing (Fig. 4:13) permits an endflow about the inboard tip not actually existent on the real airplane. Such flow may easily invalidate the test results, and unfortunately even the addition of an endplate will not provide sufficient sealing to produce complete ship flow conditions.

Two alternate arrangements are satisfactory: mounting the panel on a turntable (Fig. 5:6), or with a small gap between its inboard end and the tunnel floor (Fig. 4:12). Either of these set-ups will seal the inboard end of the panel and subject it to

Courtesy the Glenn L. Martin Aircraft Co.

FIG. 5:6. Aileron panel in wind tunnel.

nearly the same flow conditions as would occur on the actual ship. Usually the effective aspect ratio then developed will be about $0.95(2b)^2/(2S_p)$, where b is the panel span and S_p the panel area.

An important and sometimes insoluble case may arise for aileron panels from sweptback wings. Here the flow over the aileron is affected very strongly by the remainder of the wing and cannot be simulated by any simple reflection plane. It is therefore suggested that a thorough study of spanwise loadings be made and adequate correlation assured before attempting panel tests of such ailerons.

A minor point in panel testing of the type shown in Figs. 4:12 and 5:6 is that, though the hinge moments should be reduced to coefficient form by using the tunnel dynamic pressure, the force coefficients should be based on tunnel dynamic pressure corrected to allow for the diminished velocity in the boundary layer. This corrected q is usually about 99 per cent of the centerline q. (See Sect. 5:1 for further discussion of the average dynamic pressure.)

Details of the calculations necessary for referring panel tests of ailerons, rudders, and elevators to the complete ship are in the following sections.

5:5. Testing Controls: Ailerons. The airplane designer is interested in three items concerning proposed ailerons. One, rolling moment, he is seeking. The other two, yawing moment and hinge moment, are the price that must be paid. The tunnel engineer in addition is concerned with referring the data to the complete airplane. The problem first apparent is that the panel model will not have the same lift curve slope as the complete wing. Actually, however, this is of small import as long as the roll due to a given aileron deflection is at a known wing lift coefficient. This, it will be shown, requires that the complete wing be previously tested and its lift curve known and available. The procedure for then referring the aileron panel angles of attack to the complete wing is as follows:

1. From the estimated performance of the airplane, note the speeds that correspond to various important flight conditions such as top and cruising speeds at various altitudes. Calculate the complete wing lift coefficients that correspond to these speeds.

2. Plot the span loading curve. (See Sect. 6:6, or Pearson's method, Ref. 6:7.) The total area under this curve, A_T, divided by the total wing area S_T is a measure of the wing lift coefficient. Likewise, the area of that part of span loading curve above the panel span A_p when divided by the area of the wing panel S_p is a measure of the panel lift coefficient. The ratio of these two ratios, then, is the ratio of the complete wing lift coefficient

C_{Lw} to the panel lift coefficient C_{Lp}. That is,

$$\frac{C_{Lw}}{C_{Lp}} = \frac{A_T/S_T}{A_p/S_p} \qquad (5:22)$$

Equation 5:22 may be used to find the panel lift coefficients that correspond to the selected wing lift coefficients.

3. Test the panel with aileron zero and obtain a plot of C_{Lp} vs. α_u, where α_u is the angle of attack uncorrected for tunnel-wall effect.

4. From item 3, read the uncorrected angles that should be set to read the desired panel lift coefficients. The tunnel operator may then set these uncorrected angles with arbitrary aileron deflections and maintain proper panel model to complete model correlation.

In testing one panel of a wing, it is seen that a yawing and rolling moment about the imaginary ship centerline is produced that in actuality would be canceled by the panel on the other side. Thus it is necessary to subtract the moments due to the panel with aileron zero from the moments with the aileron deflected. The subtraction also acts to remove the tare effects of the turntable, the net result being the yawing and rolling moments due to the deflection of the aileron only. The only proviso is that the test conditions must simulate the proper spanwise loading over the aileron.

In working up the data, the coefficients must be corrected to complete wing areas and spans so that the results will be usable. The definitions are as follows:

(The subscript p indicates "panel.")

$C_{Lp} = \dfrac{L_p}{qS_p}$ panel lift coefficient

$C_{D'p} = \dfrac{D'}{qS_p}$ panel drag coefficient including mounting plate drag

$C_{np} = \dfrac{YM_p}{qS_w b_w}$ panel yawing moment coefficient

$C_{lp} = \dfrac{RM_p}{qS_w b_w}$ panel rolling moment coefficient about balance rolling axis, based on wing area and span.

To get the rolling moment at the ship centerline we have (Fig. 5:7)

$$RM_{\text{ship}} = RM_p + La'$$

and

$$C_{l'\,\text{ship}} = C_{lp} + C_{Lp} \frac{S_p}{S_w} \frac{a'}{b_w} \qquad (5:23)$$

where a' is the distance from balance rolling moment axis to airplane centerline.

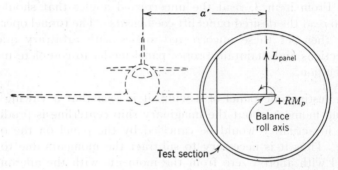

FIG. 5:7. Panel rolling moment and its relation to the rest of the airplane. (Front view.)

However, this represents the moment of one panel plus the aileron about the ship centerline; to find the part due to the aileron only, we subtract the rolling moment coefficient of the panel with aileron zero, C_{l0}. Hence the rolling moment coefficient of one aileron about the airplane centerline is

$$C_l = C_{lp} + C_{Lp} \frac{S_p}{S_w} \frac{a'}{b_w} - C_{l0} \qquad (5:24)$$

By a similar process, the yawing moment coefficient due to one aileron is

$$C_n = C_{np} + C_{D'p} \frac{S_p}{S_w} \frac{b'}{b_w} - C_{n0} \qquad (5:25)$$

where $C_{np} = \dfrac{YM_p}{qS_wb_w}$.

b' = distance of balance yaw axis to ship.

C_{n0} = yawing moment coefficient of one panel about ship centerline, aileron zero.

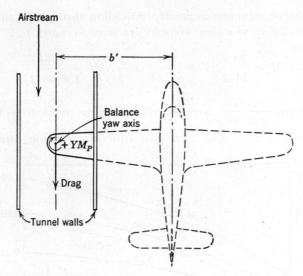

FIG. 5:8. Panel yawing moment and its relation to the rest of the airplane.
(Plan view.)

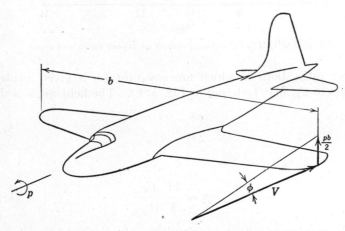

FIG. 5:9.

Although not directly apparent, the rolling moment coefficient also determines the helix angle (see Fig. 5:9) as follows:

At a given rate of steady roll the rolling moment is opposed
by an equal and opposite damping moment. In the usual symbols, the rolling moment

$$RM = \frac{\rho}{2}SV^2 C_l b = DM$$

where DM = damping moment. Dividing through by the helix angle, $pb/2V$ (p = rolling velocity, radians/second),

$$DM = \frac{pb}{2V}\frac{\rho}{2}SV^2b\frac{C_l}{pb/2V} = \frac{\rho}{2}SVp\frac{b^2}{2}\frac{dC_l}{d(pb/2V)}$$

The term $\dfrac{d(C_l)}{d(pb/2V)}$ is called the damping moment coefficient (frequently written C_{lp}) and is a function of wing taper and

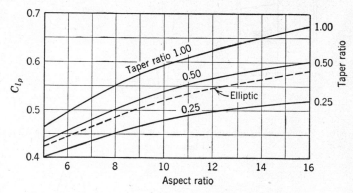

FIG. 5:10. C_{lp} for various values of aspect ratio and taper.

aspect ratio, both of which are constant for a given airplane. Values of C_{lp} may be found in Fig. 5:10. The helix angle is then

$$\frac{pb}{2V} = \frac{C_l}{C_{lp}} \tag{5:26}$$

and the rolling velocity is

$$p = \frac{2V}{b}\frac{C_l}{C_{lp}} \tag{5:27}$$

The maximum rolling velocity is usually limited by stick force considerations rather than by the airplane's actual ability to roll. Power-driven controls as well as aerodynamic balances to decrease the hinge moments are used to increase the rolling velocity.

Example 5:5

Data from a test run at $q = 25.6$ lb/ft^2 on a wing panel of 12 ft^2 yields $C_L = 0.789$, $C_D = 0.0599$ at $\alpha = 5.44°$, left aileron down 15°. (Data have been corrected for tunnel-wall effect.) $C_{lp} = -0.0102$, C_{np}

$= -0.0010$. Find the rolling and yawing moments about the ship centerline if the distance from the balance roll axis to the ship centerline is 8 ft. The rolling moment for aileron zero is $C_{l0} = 0.0191$, and yawing moment, $C_{n0} = -0.0028$. $S_w = 70$ ft^2, $b_w = 25$ ft.

$$C_l = C_{lp} + C_{Lp} \frac{S_p}{S_w} \frac{a'}{b_w} - C_{lp0}$$

$$= -0.0102 + 0.789 \frac{12}{70} \frac{8}{25} - 0.0191$$

$$= -0.0102 + 0.0433 - 0.0191 = 0.0140$$

$$C_n = C_{np} + C_{D'p} \frac{S_p}{S_w} \frac{b'}{b_w} - C_{np0}$$

$$= -0.0010 + 0.0599 \frac{12}{70} \frac{8}{25} - 0.0028$$

$$= -0.0015$$

Example 5:6

Assume that sufficient control force exists to develop the above C_l at 150 mph. Calculate the helix angle and rate of roll. The wing taper ratio is 2:1 ($\lambda = 0.50$), and the model is 40 per cent scale.

1. $AR = \dfrac{b^2}{S} = \dfrac{25^2}{70} = 8.93$ From Fig. 5:10 at $AR = 8.93$ and $\lambda = 0.50$,

$$C_{lp} = 0.520$$

$$\frac{pb}{2V} = \frac{C_l}{C_{lp}} = \frac{0.014}{0.520} = 0.0269 \text{ radian}$$

2. $p = \dfrac{pb}{2V} \dfrac{2V}{b} 57.3$

$$= 0.0269 \frac{(2)(150)(1.47)}{25/0.40} 57.3$$

$$= 10.9°/\text{sec.}$$

Typical data that might be expected from tests of a modern aileron are shown in Figs. 5:11, 5:12, and 5:13. The roll vs. yaw plot is particularly useful when figuring ratios for differential ailerons.

Perhaps at this point it would be fitting to discuss the lateral axis more fully in order to explain the reaction obtained before and during a roll. Consider the case when the ailerons are deflected, but no roll has yet had time to develop, or perhaps an asymmetrical span loading is being resisted. The down aileron creates more lift and induced drag and usually more profile drag, whereas the opposite effect is noticed for the up aileron. The net result is a yawing moment opposite in sign to the rolling moment: left yaw for right aileron. This condition is undesirable, of course; in many planes the pilot merely adds a slight

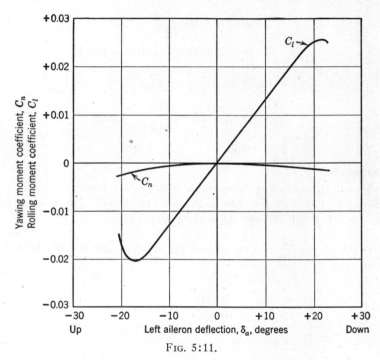

Fig. 5:11.

extra rudder deflection and never notices the aileron effect. In others, particularly where powered ailerons are employed to obtain the maximum deflections, the amount of rudder needed to balance the adverse yaw may be so large that little rudder is left to overcome additional asymmetrical drag caused by the inactivity of one engine. Many methods are suggested for balancing this adverse yaw, among them being an artificially increased profile drag of the raised aileron, which tends to pull the lowered wing into the turn. Such a profile-drag increase can be obtained either by a special aileron design or by gearing the aileron controls so that the raised aileron has a greater deflection than the depressed one. The latter system is referred to as "dif-

ferential ailerons." Differential ailerons reduce adverse yaw
but are usually accompanied by an overall reduction in maximum
rate of roll.

The designer, therefore, notes not only the maximum amount
of roll ($C_{l \, max.}$) from graphs such as Fig. 5:11 but also examines
data such as are shown in Fig. 5:12 to observe the amount of

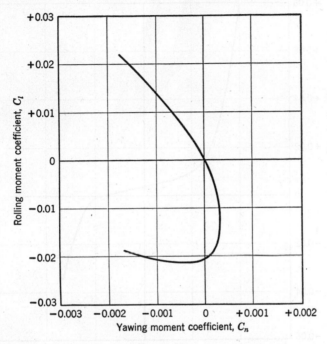

FIG. 5:12.

adverse yaw, a minimum being desirable. Since nose left yaw
is negative and right roll positive, the yaw is adverse when it
has an opposite sign to the roll.

Now we come to a point important to the tunnel engineer.
Referring to Fig. 5:12 again we note that, when the curve appears in the first and third quadrants, favorable yaw is indicated,
but it will actually exist only when the airplane does not roll.
When rolling occurs the direction of the relative wind over each
wing is so altered that a strong adverse yaw is developed, and
the results of the static tunnel test may be entirely erroneous.

Under most conditions, the air loads on the ailerons oppose
their deflection, producing a moment that must be supplied by

the pilot or by some outside means. Methods employed to help the pilots include powered "boosters" and mass and aerodynamic balance. The mass balances may only balance the weight of the surface or may be arranged to provide an inertia force while the ship is rotating. The aerodynamic balances include control

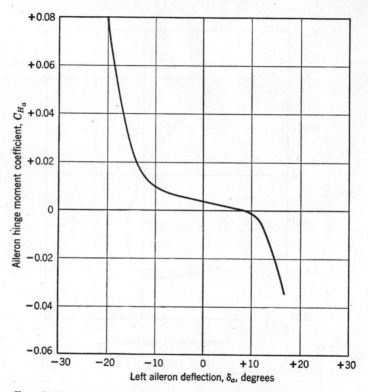

FIG. 5:13. Hinge moment coefficient C_{Ha} vs. aileron deflection δ_a.

surface area ahead of the hinge of various cross-sectional shapes and area disposition such as horns, shielded horns, and internal, medium nose, and sharp nose balances. They may also include variable area aft of the hinge line such as balance tabs and beveled trailing edges.

Aerodynamic balances are simpler and lighter than mass balances or power boost and hence are to be preferred as long as battle damage or icing need not be considered. Unfortunately, most aerodynamic balances are effective for only a portion of the aileron travel, as may be seen by the extent of the decreased slope in Fig. 5:13. A measure of balance superiority is then the range of decreased hinge moments as well as the slope of the balanced part of the curve. Complete aileron data must, of course, include the effect of the other aileron as well as the amount of the differential decided upon.

The aileron hinge moment coefficient C_{Ha} is frequently defined by

$$C_{Ha} = \frac{HM}{qS_a c_a} \qquad (5:28)$$

where HM = aileron hinge moment, positive when it aids control deflection.

S_a = area of aileron aft of hinge line.

c_a = average chord of aileron aft of hinge line.

Another definition of the hinge moment is based on using the root-mean-square chord aft of the hinge as follows:

$$C_{Ha} = \frac{HM}{q\bar{c}_f^2 b_f}$$

where $\bar{c}_f$ = root-mean-square chord of flap or aileron aft of the hinge.

b_f = flap or aileron span.

The quantity $\bar{c}_f^2 b_f$ is most easily obtained by integrating the area under the curve of local flap chord squared against flap span.

The variance of definitions again demonstrates the necessity of clear and complete statements on every item.

Complete consideration of hinge moments must include the lever ratio of the controls. Various limiting conditions may be imposed. One is that maximum aileron deflection must be obtained at the stall with a 50-lb stick or wheel force; another, that maximum wheel deflection should be limited to 100 degrees.* The second usually limits the use of gearing as a means of reducing wheel forces.

Sometimes ailerons and even airplanes are compared by the rolling velocity obtained at some particular altitude and airspeed with a 50-lb stick force. Plots of wheel movement vs.

---

* Owing to aileron cable stretch, the calculated aileron deflection for a given wheel deflection may not be attained. The engineer must consider this in his design.

rolling velocity at various airspeeds may be made. (For methods of measuring hinge moments see Sect. 8:6.)

Example 5:7

An airplane has the following specifications:

$W = 40,000$ lb.
$S = 755$ sq ft.
$S_{ail.} = 17.43$ ft.
Wheel radius = 0.625 ft.
Aileron differential = 1:1.
At $+10°$ aileron, $C_{Ha} = -0.0089$.
At $-10°$ aileron, $C_{Ha} = 0.0188$.
$b = 71.5$ ft.
Aileron chord aft of hinge = 1.426 ft.
$\dfrac{\text{Wheel throw}}{\text{Aileron deflection}} = 3.33.$

Calculate the wheel force (one hand) necessary to deflect the ailerons $10°$ at 262 mph.

(1) The total hinge moment coefficient due to both ailerons

$$C_{Ha} = 0.0188 - (-0.0089) = 0.0277$$

$$M_{ail.} = qS_aC_aC_{Ha} = (175.2)(17.43)(1.426)(0.0277)$$

$$= 120.5 \text{ lb-ft}$$

$$\text{Wheel moment} = \frac{120.5}{3.33} = 36.2 \text{ lb-ft}$$

$$\text{Wheel force} = \frac{36.2}{0.625} = 58.0 \text{ lb}$$

5:6. Testing Controls: Rudders. The rudder is supposed to produce a side force that in turn produces a yawing moment about the center of gravity of the airplane. This may or may not produce yaw, for the lateral loading may be asymmetrical and the rudder employed only to maintain a straight course. Some drag, a small moment about the quarter-chord line of the tail itself, and a rudder hinge moment will also be created. The fact that the drag moment is stabilizing is no argument in favor of a large vertical tail drag since, in maintaining a straight course with asymmetrical loading, drag is decidedly harmful.

The designer of a vertical tail seeks:

1. A large side force with minimum drag.

2. The steepest slope to the side force curve so that small yaw produces large stabilizing forces.

3. The smallest hinge moment consistent with positive control feel. On a full-scale military ship 180 lb pedal force is considered a maximum.

4. Proper rudder balance so that under no conditions will the pilot be unable to return the rudder to neutral, and preferably it should not even tend to overbalance.

Courtesy the Glenn L. Martin Aircraft Co.

FIG. 5:14. Rudder panel in wind tunnel.

5. A zero trail angle * so that control-free stability is the same as control-fixed stability. It will be seen that the zero trail angle

---

* For zero trail angle the rudder is so balanced that it remains at a zero deflection even when the airplane is yawed.

permits smaller pedal forces and rudder movements to return a
yawed ship to zero.

6. The largest yawing moments about the airplane's center
of gravity. This moment is almost entirely due to the side force.
The proportions due to the yawing moment of the vertical tail
about its own quarter-chord and the yawing moment of the
vertical tail surface due to its drag are quite small but not always
insignificant.

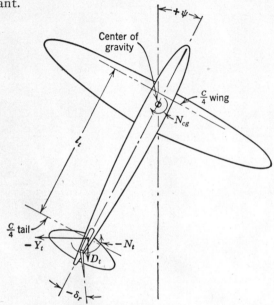

FIG. 5:15.   Plan view of yawed airplane.

The rudder calculations, unlike the aileron panel tests, will
require the absolute value of the drag coefficient. (See eq. 5:29.)
This is not easily obtained with the rudder set-up shown in Fig.
5:14, but, in view of the small contribution of the drag effect,
an approximation may be made by reading the section drags
with a wake survey rake at stations along the vertical tail with
the rudder angle zero, and by summing them to get the total
drag coefficient. This may be subtracted from the minimum
drag as read by the balance to get the drag of the endplate. The
method as outlined makes the very questionable assumption
that the tare drag is unaffected by rudder angle, which is justified only by the peculiar conditions of this set-up in which tare
accuracy is not vital.

The signs of the rudder angles are confusing and hence are stated below. They follow the rule for right aileron, elevator, and rudder that positive control angle produces negative airplane movement. Negative movement embraces left roll, nose left yaw, and dive. Another definition for control deflections is that they are positive if the air load on them has a positive direction, that is, if the force increment due to the control deflection is directed up or towards the right wingtip. This rule also holds for tabs as well as complete surfaces.

The rudder set-up to find N (and hence C_n) is shown in Fig. 5:15. The contributing parts are: (1) the moment due to the vertical tail side forces, (2) the moment due to the vertical tail drag, (3) the moment due to the vertical tail moment about its own quarter-chord.

In symbols these factors become:

$$N_{cg} = (N_t)_t - Y_t l_t \cos \psi - D_t l_t \sin \psi$$

$$= q S_t (MAC)_t C_{n\frac{1}{4}t} - q S_t C_{Yt} \cos \psi \cdot l_t - q S_t C_{Dt} \sin \psi \cdot l_t$$

$$C_{ncg} = \frac{S_t (MAC)_t}{S_w b_w} C_{n\frac{1}{4}t} - \frac{S_t}{S_w} \frac{l_t}{b_w} C_{Yt} \cos \psi - \frac{S_t}{S_w} \frac{l_t}{b_w} C_{Dt} \sin \psi$$

$$(5:29)$$

where N_{cg} = moment of vertical tail about center of gravity.

S_t = vertical tail area.

$C_{n\frac{1}{4}t}$ = vertical tail moment coefficient about its own quarter-chord.

$(MAC)_t$ = mean chord of vertical tail.

S_w = wing area.

b_w = wing span.

l_t = distance from tail quarter-chord to ship center of gravity.

$C_{Yt} = \dfrac{Y_t}{q S_t}$.

ψ = yaw angle.

Y_t = side force due to tail.

$(N_t)_t$ = moment of vertical tail about its own quarter-chord.

D_t = drag of vertical tail.

It was mentioned in Sect. 5:5 that span loading must be considered in order to properly apply data from an aileron panel test to the complete airplane. In Sect. 5:7 attention is drawn to the proper method of applying the data from an isolated horizontal tail by evaluating the downwash. The vertical tail is less affected by the remainder of the airplane, but some side-wash does exist when the airplane is yawed. Hence 15 degrees of yaw by no means results in the vertical tail angle of attack being 15 degrees. Proper evaluation of the sidewash can be made by equipping the complete model with a vertical tail whose incidence is variable, and by going through the procedure out-lined for the horizontal tail in Sect. 5:7. However, general prac-tice is to neglect the sidewash.

Example 5:8

A vertical tail model whose area is 12 ft^2 is tested at 100 mph. The model $MAC = 3.0$ ft. The actual airplane, of which the model is 40 per cent scale, has a wing area of 750 ft^2 and a span of 78 ft. The tail length is 30 ft. Find the tail yawing moment coefficient about the center of gravity if $C_{Yt} = 0.794$, $C_{Dt} = 0.0991$, $C_{n\frac{1}{4}t} = -0.1067$ for $\psi = 6°$. The rudder is deflected 10 degrees.

$$C_{ncg} = \frac{S_t}{S_w}\frac{(MAC)_t}{b_w} C_{n\frac{1}{4}t} - \frac{S_t}{S_w}\frac{l_t}{b_w} C_{Yt} \cos\psi - \frac{S_t}{S_w}\frac{l_t}{b_w} C_{Dt}\sin\psi$$

$$= \frac{12}{(0.40)^2(750)}\frac{3}{(0.4)78}(-0.1067) - \frac{12(0.4)(30)}{(0.40)^2(750)(0.4)(78)}0.794(0.9945)$$

$$- \frac{12}{(0.40)^2(750)}\frac{0.4(30)}{0.4(78)}(0.991)(0.1045)$$

$$= -0.001025 - 0.0304 - 0.000399$$

$$= -0.0318$$

5:7. Testing Controls: Elevators. The elevators may be also tested by the panel mounting method. With this arrangement, one-half the horizontal tail is usually mounted as shown in Fig. 5:14, and the results are doubled to get the data for the entire tail.

It will be noted that, for airplanes of conventional dimensions, the pitching moment of the horizontal tail about its own quarter-chord and the pitching moment about the airplane center of gravity produced by the horizontal tail drag are negligible when compared to the moment produced by the tail lifting force. Hence it will probably be necessary only to measure the lift of the panel model along with the elevator hinge moments in order to evaluate the desired qualities. Occasionally it will be desirable to compare two different methods of trimming to determine which has the lesser drag for a given lift. Then, of course, drag measurements will be necessary.

The tail lift curve slope as determined from the panel model may require adjustment in order to apply the test results. In

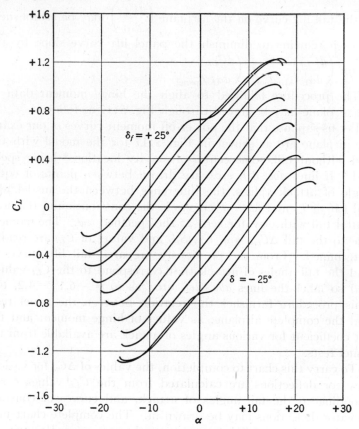

Fig. 5:16. Typical panel lift curves. The breaks in the curves for large flap deflections occur when the flap stalls.

determining this factor, cognizance must be taken of the difference in Reynolds number of the two tests. See Sect. 7:2.

For example, suppose that the complete model has been tested at a constant angle of attack with varying settings of the stabilizer. The pitching moment about the airplane center of gravity due to the horizontal tail

$$M_t = l_t q_t S_t C_{Lt} \qquad (5:30)$$

may be measured, and with the known tail area S_t and tail length l_t the value of C_{Lt} may be determined. In these calculations it is probably better to use $q_t = q_{\text{freestream}}$ than the very questionable $q_t = 0.8 q_{\text{freestream}}$ sometimes arbitrarily employed. From the calculated C_{Lt} and known stabilizer angles the slope of the tail lift curve on the airplane $\left(\dfrac{dC_{Lt}}{d\alpha_t}\right)$ may be established. It then remains to diminish the panel lift curve slope by the factor $\left(\dfrac{dC_{Lt}}{d\alpha_t}\right)_{\text{airplane}} \div \left(\dfrac{dC_{Lt}}{d\alpha_t}\right)_{\text{panel}}$.

The procedure followed to align the hinge moment data to the airplane may be traced through Fig. 5:17 as follows:

Let us suppose that the power-off moment curves of our example airplane are as shown in Fig. 5:17 for the model with tail and without tail, some center-of-gravity location * being specified. If lines abc, def, etc., are drawn between points of equal angle of attack values, the difference between the model plus tail $(M + T)$ and $M - T$ curves is the contribution of the horizontal tail with elevator zero at the specified α_W. The moment due to the tail $\Delta C_{mt} = q_t(C_{Lt})S_t l_t$ and values of C_{Lt} are readily determined. From the previously prepared tail lift curve we find the tail angles of attack that correspond to the C_{Lt} values, and so label the lines abc, def, etc., as $\alpha_t = -6.1$, -4.2, etc. This procedure furnishes the relation between the panel tests and the complete airplane, as values of hinge moment and tail lift coefficient for various angles of attack are available from the panel tests.

To carry this chart to completion, the values of ΔC_m for various elevator deflections are calculated from the C_{Lt} values corresponding to the tail angles of attack, and curves of constant elevator deflections may be drawn in. The complete chart may then be used to read the amount of elevator needed to trim at any C_L or the amount of moment available for maneuvering with a specified stick load. The maneuvering investigation requires the hinge moment data and the mechanical advantage, as follows:

1. Assume the chart to indicate that an elevator deflection of

---

* If another location is desired for the center of gravity the curves may be rotated about zero lift by the relation

$$\Delta \frac{dC_m}{dC_L} = \frac{\% \ MAC \ \text{change}}{100}$$

$-15°$ is required to trim at $C_L = 1.9$ and $\alpha_{\text{tail}} = +12$. From the airplane geometry and $C_L = 1.9$, the value of q may be found from $q = W/SC_L$.

2. From the chart of hinge moment vs. α_{tail} we read (say) for $\alpha = +12$ and $\delta_e = -15°$ a $C_{He} = 0.0640$.

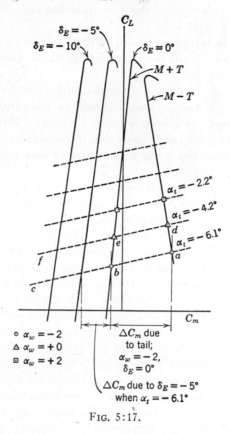

FIG. 5:17.

3. From the airplane geometry and q (step 1) the elevator hinge moment is calculated from $HM_e = qS_eC_e \cdot C_{He}$.

4. From the curve of mechanical advantage vs. δ_e, and the known linkage lengths, the stick force may then be found.

In this manner the various flight conditions may be investigated and desirable balance changes evaluated. It should be noted that the ability of an elevator to stall the ship may well be a function of the elevator size, for, if the elevator is not large enough to do the job, additional deflection through trim tabs or power boost will be of no avail.

5:8. Testing Complete Models. The six-component test of a complete model is the most difficult of all wind-tunnel tests. More variables are under consideration than in other tests, for one thing, and the individual tests are more complicated, for another. For instance, each drag run requires *three* additional runs in order to evaluate the tare, interference, and alignment. (See Sects. 4:11 and 4:12.)

The complete testing of an entire model includes the investigation of the effect of all major variables (flaps, gear, etc.) on all forces and moments.

For most tests of complete models the boundary corrections large enough to matter are confined to buoyancy, wake displacement, downwash, and pitching moment. But it is a good policy to investigate corrections due to constraint, asymmetrical loading, and propeller wake effects just in case any of them are in the range of accuracy.

A list of the runs usually employed for an unpowered model is provided in Table 5:4. The numerical values in this table are, of course, only approximate, exact values being dictated by the particular design in question. Additional runs would be needed to check fillets, alternate tail surfaces, or ground effect.

Attention is drawn to items in Table 5:4 marked "correlation." In many instances correlation runs are added to evaluate separate effects of configurations that would never be flown. For example, a two-motored model usually has a run made without nacelles. The data from this run compared with those from the run with them in place aid in identifying the effect of the nacelles on the airplane's efficiency, drag, and lift. After several models have been tested the usual effects of a "good" nacelle become known, and, when a "poor" one turns up, it is so identified and attention is directed towards improving it. A standard procedure is to list the important performance parameters in tabular form, noting the change in each as each component is added to the wing. Studies made of such tables can be informative indeed.

Comments on the customary curves and information desired follow:

A. THE LIFT CURVE, FLAPS UP

Items of interest on the flap-up lift curve include the value of $C_{L\ max.}$ for determining flap-up stalling speed and minimum

TABLE 5:4. TEST PROGRAM OF UNPOWERED MODEL

W = wing.
B = fuselage.
H = horizontal tail.
"Tare" = dummies in.
"Correlation" refers to
    data accumulated to
    assist in laying out
    new designs.

V = vertical tail.
G = gear.
F = flaps.
Polar plot = C_L vs. α,
    C_D, and C_m from $\alpha_{Z.L.}$
    through stall.
Polar run = L, D, M,
    from $\alpha_{Z.L.}$ through
    stall.

Runs	Model Configuration	Data Sought	Run Consists of
1–4	W	Tare, interference, and alignment; final polar plot.	Polars, model normal and inverted, dummies in, dummies out.
5–6	W	Wing lateral stability for future correlation.	Yaw ±30°, at C_L = 0.3 and 1.0.
7–10	WB	Tare, interference, and alignment, final polar plot.	Polars, model normal and inverted, dummies in, dummies out.
11–12	WB	Wing and body lateral stability for future correlation.	Yaw ±30° at C_L = 0.3 and 1.0.
13	WBH	Polar plot, effect of horizontal tail.	Polar.
14–15	WBH	Lateral stability for evaluating vertical tail and correlation.	Yaw ±30° at C_L = 0.3 and 1.0.
16	$WBHV$	Polar plot; effect of vertical tail.	Polar.
17–18	$WBHV$	Directional stability.	Yaw ±30° at C_L = 0.3 and 1.0.
19–23	$WBHV$	Tailsetting and downwash.	Polar with tail incidence -4, -3, -2, -1, 1.
24–25	$WBHV$	Effect of yaw on static longitudinal stability.	Polar with ψ = 5°, 10°.
26–44	$WBHV$	Rudder equilibrium and power.	Yaw ±30° at C_L = 0.3 and 1.0; rudder, 2, 5, 10, -2, -5, -10, -15, -20, -25 degrees.
45–63	$WBHV$	Aileron power.	Yaw ±30° at C_L = 0.3 and 1.0 with aileron -25, -20, -15, -10, -5, 5, 10, 15, 20 degrees.
64–72	$WBHV$	Elevator power.	Polars with elevators from $-25°$ to 15°, ψ = 0.
73–89	$WBHVF$	Effect of flaps on elevator and trim.	Polars with elevators from $-25°$ to 15°, ψ = 0, flaps 30°, 55°.
90–95	$WBHVF$	Effect of flaps on lateral stability.	Yaw ±30° at α = 3.0 and 10°, flaps 20, 35, and 55.
96–104	$WBHVF$	Effect of flaps on lateral control.	Polars with flaps 55°, ψ = 0, ailerons at -25 to 20.
105	$WBHFG$	Effect of gear down.	Polars with flaps 55°, ψ = 0. Model inverted to reduce interference between supports and gear, and vertical tail removed to avoid physical interference with tail strut.
106	$WBHFG$	Effect of gear down on lateral stability.	Yaw ±30° with α = 3° and 10°, flaps 55°. Model inverted.

radius of turn; the shape of the curve at the stall (it should be moderately smooth, but rarely is); the angle of zero lift; the slope of the lift curve $dC_L/d\alpha$; and the value of negative $C_{L\,max.}$. At the Reynolds numbers usually encountered in the wind tunnel, $C_{L\,max.}$ will be from 1.1 to 1.5, and $dC_L/d\alpha$ for modern wings will be slightly greater than $0.1R/(R + 2)$ per degree where R = aspect ratio. The complete ship values for $C_{L \, max.}$ and $dC_L/d\alpha$ will be about 10 per cent greater than the wing alone. The angle of zero lift will vary from zero for symmetrical wings to $-5°$ for those with heavy camber, being approximately equal in degrees to the camber in per cent. Negative $C_{L \, max.}$ is of interest for the wing stress analysis.

B. The Lift Curve, Flaps down

This curve will have very nearly the same slope as the flap-up curve and the same location of the aerodynamic center. The value of flap-down $C_{L \, max.}$ is important for determining the increment due to the flap $\Delta C_{L \, max.}$, for this apparently does not change with Reynolds number and may be used to determine full-scale $C_{L \, max.}$, flaps down (see Sect. 7:2), which is needed for landing and take-off runs. $C_{L \, max.}$, flaps down, will vary from 1.6 to 2.9, with the higher value much sought after but rarely attained.

The angle of $C_{L \, max.}$ is of interest for landing-gear-length considerations. It will probably be from ½ degree to 3 degrees less for flaps down than for flaps up if the flaps cover the inboard wing area, and 5 to 8 degrees less if they cover the entire span.

Again the sharpness of the stall is of interest as large lift coefficients that are perilously close to a violent stall cannot be safely utilized to their full value. There is usually little need to take the flap-down lift curve as low as the angle of zero lift. The stall should be read in very small steps so that its shape is accurately determined.   •

C. The Drag Curves, Flaps up and down

The designer is particularly interested in $C_{D \, min.}$ for top-speed calculations. In order to insure accuracy in this range the readings should be made every degree. Ship $C_{D \, min.}$ will vary widely with the type of airplane and wing loading, a value of 0.0175 being not unreasonable for a clean fighter.

The airplane drag coefficient, C_D, at $C_{L \, max.}$ is needed for take-off and landing-run calculations. Varying widely, depending on type of airplane and amount of flap, this coefficient may range from 0.1000 to 0.5000.

The shape of the drag curve is important for climb and cruising, a minimum change with C_L being desirable.

D. The Pitching Moment Curve

The slope of the pitching moment curve must be negative for stability, of course, although definite values for the desired slope have not yet been agreed upon. The usual practice is to test the model mounted at its most rearward center of gravity location and to increase the tail area until the slope of the pitching moment curve dC_m/dC_L is between -0.1 and -0.15 for power off,

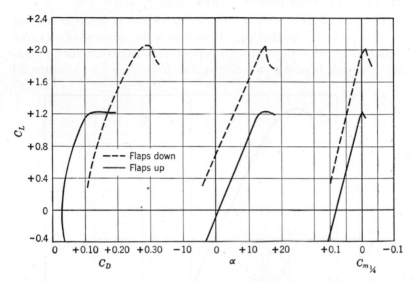

Fig. 5:18. Typical curves of lift, drag, and pitching moment; flaps up and down.

controls fixed. Assuming a loss of 0.08 due to power and 0.02 for free controls it is seen that the value of $dC_m/dC_L = -0.1$ will be just sufficient to achieve neutral stability ($dC_m/dC_L = 0$) under the most critical condition. Many of the high-powered airplanes lose more than 0.08, so that dC_m/dC_L power off may occasionally need to be as low as -0.50.

Sometimes the stability is stated in terms of the added rearward travel possible without instability. This might be 0.1c, meaning that the ship will still be stable if the center of gravity is moved one-tenth chord aft of the normal rearward location. It should further be stated whether this is for control-free or control-fixed condition.

Actually, the amount of maximum stability is also a function of center-of-gravity travel. If a large travel (say 15 per cent

MAC) must be tolerated, excessive stability may be required in the most forward position.

The lift, drag, and moment data are usually presented on one sheet (see Fig. 5:18). The reversal of the moment plus and minus values makes the moment curve appear "normal" when viewed with the page on end.

E. The Elevator Power Curve

The plot of ΔC_m against elevator deflection is made at several values of the lift coefficient. It indicates the amount of elevator deflection needed to produce a certain moment coefficient. Usually the plot is nearly a straight line from plus 15 to minus 20

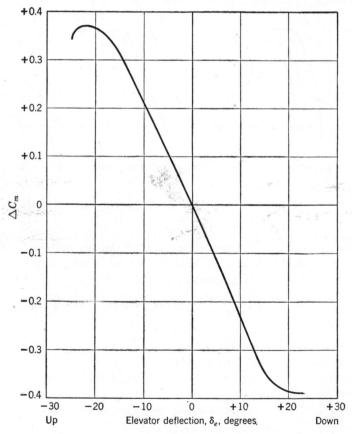

FIG. 5:19. Typical plot of change in moment coefficient with elevator deflection.

degrees deflection with a slope of about -0.02. The elevator stalls on one side above that, and further deflection is useless. Some of the newer designs seem to hold good for a slightly greater range.

A further study of the elevator may be made from a plot of C_{mcg} vs. C_L for several elevator angles. The intersections of the curves with the axis indicate trim condition. This plot may also be made against α.

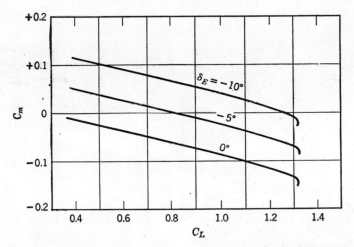

FIG. 5:20. Typical plot of C_{mcg} vs. C_L for several elevator deflections.

The elevator should have plenty of power to stall the airplane, flaps down, with the most forward location of the center of gravity. (See Sect. 8:7 for the effect of the ground on the elevators.)

F. THE AILERON POWER CURVES

The aileron criteria are usually determined at zero yaw and may be considered from the plots of C_l vs. C_n (Fig. 5:12), C_l and C_n vs. δ_a (Fig. 5:11), and C_{Ha} vs. δ_a (Fig. 5:13). The important qualities of good ailerons are high rolling moment and low hinge moments—the latter usually not obtainable from tests of a complete model. (See Sect. 5:4.) The maximum rate of roll and the maximum helix angle are determined from $C_{l\,max.}$ (see Sect. 5:5), a $C_{l\,max.}$ of 0.03 being satisfactory for one aileron. The maximum rate of roll (taking due account of the stick forces) will vary from 50 degrees per second for a medium bomber to 150 degrees per second for a very maneuverable fighter.

Sometimes the criteria may be stated in terms of the helix angle (Sect. 5:5), typical needs being (for military aircraft): (1) a helix angle of at least 0.07 at $0.7\,V_{max}$ with rudder zero, flaps and gear up, normal rated power; and (2) a helix angle of at least 0.07, rudder zero, power off, flaps and gear down, at $1.2\,V_{stall}$.

Courtesy Northrop Aircraft Corp.

FIG. 5:21. Measuring the stalling speed of the Black Widow.

Requirements for commercial airplanes are usually satisfied with less than the above amounts.

Tests required to determine the above information embrace runs at the proper angles of attack, $\psi = 0$. The rolling moments are measured for various aileron deflections and the helix angles computed as per Sect. 5:5. (See runs 45–63 of Table 5:4.) A discussion of aileron hinge moments is also presented in Sect. 5:5.

G. RUDDER POWER AND EQUILIBRIUM CURVES

In most single-engined aircraft the rudder is not a critical component. It must furnish adequate control on the ground and in the air, but no criteria similar to "rate of roll" or "pounds of stick force per g" have been established. The problem of the high-powered single-engine aircraft becomes difficult under the high-power low-airspeed (wave-off) condition. Here it is not unusual to require full rudder to overcome torque to maintain straight flight. The criteria become more those of hinge moments (Sects. 5:5 and 5:6) than those usually obtainable from

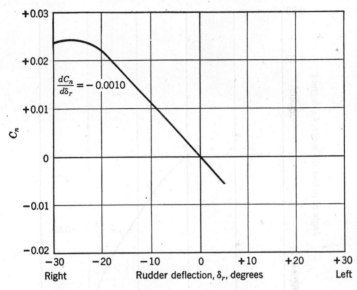

Fig. 5:22. Rudder equilibrium.

the complete model. Particular attention must be paid to avoiding overbalance at high rudder deflections.

The modern high-performance multiengined airplane must possess sufficient directional stability to prevent it from reaching excessive angles of yaw or developing rudder forces that tend to keep the plane yawing. Further, it must also be able to be balanced directionally at the best climb speed with asymmetric power (one engine out, other at full power for a two-engined airplane), rudder free and trim tab neutral, without exceeding a 15-degree angle of bank.

The most critical condition for the criterion of decreasing pedal force occurs at high thrust coefficient, flaps and gear down, at large angles of right sideslip, and test runs must be made accordingly.

The asymmetric power condition requires yaw runs with asymmetric power, possibly with flaps at take-off setting, corresponding to $1.2 V_{\text{stall}}$ with one motor inoperative and the other using take-off power. Again the test runs must be made with asymmetric power.

Usually the rudder information is grouped into two curves. The first, rudder equilibrium, is a plot of rudder deflection against

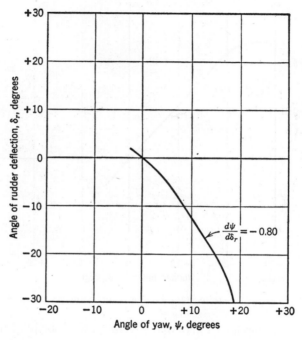

FIG. 5:23.   Rudder power.

angle of yaw, or in other words δ_r for $C_n = 0$. This need be taken for yaw in only one direction, for it will be similar in the other owing to symmetry. The slope $d\psi/d\delta_r$ can be around 1.2 for maneuverable airplanes on down to 0.5 for the more stable types.

The second curve, rudder power, is a plot of C_n vs. δ_r. A slope of $dC_n/d\delta_r = -0.001$ is reasonable, varying widely with airplane specifications. Again the curve need be plotted only for either plus or minus rudder.

The effect of yaw on the characteristics of the airplane is shown in Fig. 5:24.

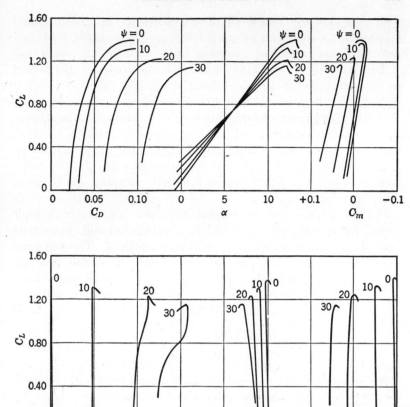

Fig. 5:24. Effect of model yaw on basic characteristics.

H. THE AMOUNT OF LATERAL STABILITY AS COMPARED WITH THE AMOUNT OF DIRECTIONAL STABILITY

Information about the roll axis is needed to determine whether sufficient dihedral is incorporated in the design to provide lateral stability at the most critical condition. This will be, for most airplanes, the approach with flaps down and power on where power and flaps combine to reduce the dihedral effect. The ailerons should be free if possible.

The tests for lateral stability embrace yaw runs at the approach attitude, flaps and gear down, and 50 per cent normal power. (See runs 90–95 in Table 5:4 for gear-up data; add runs with gear down.)   The angle of attack for the approach should be chosen on the basis of tunnel $C_{L\,max.}$ (used to get $1.2V_{stall}$), but the thrust coefficient should be based on full-scale conditions.

Too much lateral stability for a given amount of directional stability results in an objectionable motion called a "Dutch roll." Too little lateral stability for a given amount of directional stability results in spiral instability. However, the advantages in general control and handling characteristics are so great with a relatively large vertical tail that some spiral instability is acceptable. Hence dihedral investigations are usually more concerned with avoiding Dutch roll than escaping spiral instability.

For most airplanes the critical condition will occur at high speed, where dihedral effect will be a maximum and directional stability a minimum owing to small power effects. The test runs therefore embrace yaw runs at high speed, flaps and gear up with propeller windmilling or at high-speed thrust coefficient.

Recent tests indicate that a value of roll to yaw that will give what pilots call satisfactory stability is

$$\frac{dC_l/d\psi}{dC_n/d\psi} \cong -0.8 \qquad (5:31)$$

A value of $dC_n/d\psi = -0.0010$ for controls fixed and -0.0007 for controls free is reasonable for a large transport.

A very rough idea of the proper distribution of dihedral and fin area may be obtained from Fig. 5:25, which is an adaptation from Fig. 4 of Ref. 5:3. This figure is for a lightly loaded high-wing monoplane; for low-wing airplanes, γ should be replaced by γ_L, where

$$\gamma_L = \gamma + 3° \qquad (5:32)$$

The airplane should have enough vertical tail to be near or within the boundary of spiral instability.

It is convenient at this point to draw attention to an alteration that may have to be made to the ordinary wind-tunnel data when the model is yawed.

The majority of the wind-tunnel balances read pitching moment about a horizontal axis perpendicular to the wind-tunnel jet axis and passing through the balance resolving center. The rolling moment is read about the centerline of the wind tunnel test section, and the yawing moment perpendicular to roll and

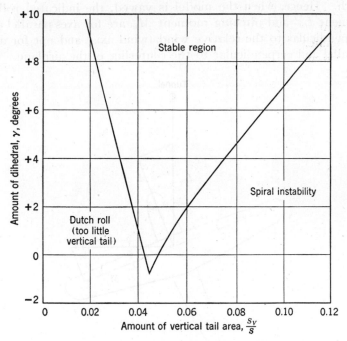

FIG. 5:25. Proper dihedral for various amounts of fin area.

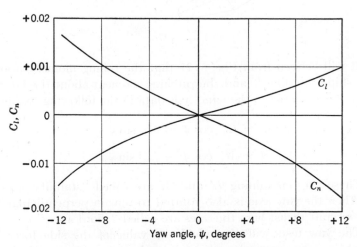

FIG. 5:26. Typical yaw characteristics.

pitch.   Hence, when the model is yawed, the indicated rolling moment L_w' and pitching moment M_w are for axes parallel and perpendicular to the relative wind (wind axis) and not for axes parallel and perpendicular to the centerline of the airplane.

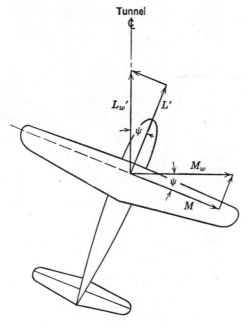

FIG. 5:27.

It will be seen from Fig. 5:27 that the rolling moment about the ship centerline L' and the pitching moment about the lateral axis M are related to the wind axis data in the following manner:

$$L' = L_w' \cos \psi + M_w \sin \psi$$

$$M = M_w \cos \psi - L_w' \sin \psi. \qquad (5{:}32a)$$

These axes containing L' and M are called "stability axes."

When the yaw axis is also rotated to remain perpendicular to the aircraft thrust line, the axes are called "chord axes."

The yaw tests will also yield the value of the side force $Y = qSC_Y$.   No particular slope or values to C_Y are required. The only use of C_Y is to calculate the side force for asymmetrical flight and hence the necessary angle of bank to counteract said side force with a tangent component of lift. The side force needed to overcome the torque reaction at low speed while maintaining straight flight may also be evaluated.

I. Tailsetting and Average Downwash Angle

In order to avoid the drag of cruising with elevators deflected, and the loss of maximum ΔC_m due to elevator if partial elevator is needed for trim, it is usually desirable to set the stabilizer incidence so that the ship is trimmed at cruising with $\delta_e = 0$. For stability considerations as well as correlation

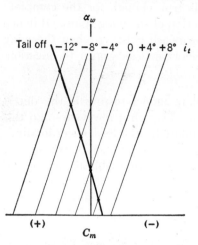

FIG. 5:28.

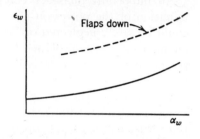

FIG. 5:29.

for future designs, it is necessary to know the angle of downwash at the tail for each wing angle of attack. The procedure is as follows:

1. Run the model with the horizontal tail removed, probably obtaining a tail-off stability curve as shown in Fig. 5:28. The corrections of Sect. 6:15 must be applied.

2. Next run the model with the horizontal tail on, using tail incidence, i_t, angles of, say, −8, −4, 0, 4, 8°. Curves as indicated in Fig. 5:28 will be obtained.

Now the intersections of the horizontal tail-on curve with the tail-off curve are points where, for a given wing angle of attack, α_w, the tail-on pitching stability equals the tail-off pitching stability; i.e., the tail is at zero lift, and hence

$$\alpha_T = \alpha_w + i_t - \epsilon_w = 0 \qquad (5:32b)$$

where α_w = downwash angle at the tail.

α_T = tail angle of attack.

Since ϵ_w and i_t are known for the points of intersection, ϵ_w may be determined from eq. 5:32b, and a plot of ϵ_w against α_w or C_L may be made. This plot and the usual effect of flaps on downwash are shown in Fig. 5:29. Not infrequently the curve of ϵ_w vs. α_w is a straight line.

Methods shortcutting the above lengthy procedure have been devised based on the assumption that the wing downwash is zero at zero lift. Though this is true enough for the complete wing, the tail occupies only a fraction of the wing span and hence quite often shows a value of downwash existing when the wing is at zero lift. This makes the short methods open to question.

J. POWER EFFECTS

An important phase of complete model testing is the determination of the power-on effects. Though a few years ago this could be safely neglected or "estimated," the low power loadings on many modern airplanes lead to differences in power-on and power-off flight characteristics that are impossible to ignore and very difficult to predict.

The effects of the power are divided into two classes:

(a) The effects due primarily to the power. These include the thrust moment and torque reaction.

(b) The effects due to the resulting slipstream. These effects depend very largely on when and how completely the tail is immersed in the slipstream and on the flight condition, which in turn determines the ratio of the dynamic pressure in the slipstream q_s to the freestream dynamic pressure q.* Also important are the rotation of the slipstream and the change of downwash at the tail.

In a conventional single-engine aircraft, the application of power is accompanied by a rolling moment due to torque and slipstream over the wings. When ailerons are applied to correct this effect, a nose left yawing moment is incurred. The twist of the slipstream striking the vertical fin produces a large side force and more left yaw. The yawed propeller adds still a further small amount of nose left yaw. At the same time, depending on the location of the horizontal tail, changes in longitudinal trim occur, due to both thrust moment and slipstream. All these changes keep the pilot very busy, and it becomes important that the loss of stability about any of the axes should not be added to his troubles.

* q_s/q varies from about 1.05 at top speed to 1.8 at take-off.

Fortunately, the above effects may be evaluated in the wind tunnel, and the aircraft may be revised or the pilot forewarned.

The model engine-propeller combination should be chosen to duplicate the full-scale conditions as nearly as possible. In order to preserve the proper ratio of q_s/q, it is important that the thrust of the model propeller be proportionately the same as in the full-scale ship. To preserve the same twist, the torque should also be the same. These conditions lead at once to the necessity of having the model propeller similar to the full-scale propeller. The blade setting that most nearly aligns the model and full-scale thrust is that of equal V/nd ratios. For convenience this may be put in coefficient form as follows:

Define

$$T_C = \frac{T}{\rho V^2 d^2}$$

and

$$Q_C = \frac{Q}{\rho V^2 d^3}$$

where T and Q are thrust and torque respectively, and d the propeller diameter. Then letting subscript S = full-scale airplane and subscript M = model, we have for similarity

$$\frac{V_S}{n_S d_S} = \frac{V_M}{n_M d_M} \qquad (5:33)$$

also

$$T_{CM} = \frac{T_M}{\rho V_M^2 d_M^2} \quad \text{and} \quad T_{CS} = \frac{T_S}{\rho V_S^2 d_S^2}$$

Dividing,

$$\frac{T_{CM}}{T_{CS}} = \frac{T_M}{\rho V_M^2 d_M^2} \frac{\rho V_S^2 d_S^2}{T_S}$$

Substituting from eq. 5:33 and clearing

$$\frac{T_{CM}}{T_{CS}} = \frac{T_M}{T_S} \frac{n_S^2 d_S^4}{n_M^2 d_M^4}$$

Now it can also be shown that the thrust

$$T_S = \rho n_S^2 d_S^4 C_{TS}$$

and

$$T_M = \rho n_M^2 d_M^4 C_{TM}$$

and that, for a given V/nd, if the two propellers are geometrically similar, $C_{TS} = C_{TM}$ (this omits scale effect). Hence

$$\frac{T_M}{T_S} = \frac{n_M{}^2 d_M{}^4}{n_S{}^2 d_S{}^4}$$

and

$$\frac{T_{CM}}{T_{CS}} = 1$$

or, if the model is tested at $T_{CM} = T_{CS}$, similarity of thrust will be preserved. In a similar manner, Q_{CM} should equal Q_{CS}.

Obtaining equal model and full-scale values of T_C and Q_C, however, is a little more complicated than duplicating equal lift and drag coefficients, and a proper procedure must be followed. This includes calibrating the model motor-propeller combination and arranging some suitable procedure for duplicating desired values of T_C and Q_C while the tests are being run.

1. *Calibration of the motor and propeller.* Since it usually takes every last fraction of allowable space to house the motor in the model, there is rarely sufficient room left for the installation of devices for reading the torque as the tests are proceeding. Hence it is necessary to calibrate the motor and obtain various thrusts and torques in the tunnel by regulating the power supplied at various blade angles.

The motor-propeller calibration is as follows:

(a) Set the motor in a dynamometer and obtain curves of bhp for various values of kw input and rpm. The plot will appear as Fig. 5:30.

(b) With thrust line at zero angle of attack, install the model with motor and propeller in the tunnel. For various rpm and 'motor outputs, read the thrust for various blade angles. Plot this as T_C vs. Q_C for constant blade angle. See dotted curves in Fig. 5:31.

(c) From the actual airplane-performance calculations, read the thrust and torque for a given power condition. It will be observed that constant power does not result in constant thrust because the propeller efficiency varies. Plot the thrust and torque as T_C vs. Q_C on the same plot as the model T_C and Q_C. See solid line, Fig. 5:31. From this combined plot select the model blade angle which most nearly matches the required T_C vs. Q_C curve.

As the airplane curve includes many blade angles due to the

constant-speed propeller, no one fixed blade angle on the model will be suitable throughout the range. Usually one angle can be picked for low speeds and another for high speeds.

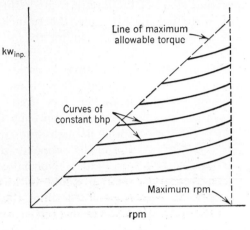

Fig. 5:30.

2. *Running the tests.* Now, although the calibration has defined various values of thrust and torque, the tunnel operators are not yet in a position to know what thrust to apply. The thrust output of the airplanes motor varies with C_L (forward

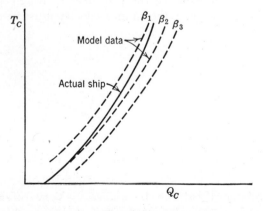

Fig. 5:31.

speed). To isolate this variation, a plot of T_C vs. C_L is made for the airplane (Fig. 5:32). From Fig. 5:31 the corresponding Q_C for the model is read, and from a plot of T_C vs. rpm (not shown) the rpm is read. After the rpm and torque are known, the bhp is calculated, and the kw input is found from Fig. 5:30. The airplane C_L is used to calculate the corresponding model lift, and an operating chart of kw input vs. model lift in pounds is prepared. By watching his lift scale, the tunnel operator is able to set the kw input to the model motor that will yield the proper T_C and Q_C.

The necessity of approximating full scale V/nd leads to unusually high rpm for the model propeller. This condition follows

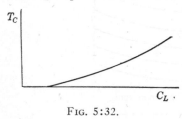

FIG. 5:32.

from the fact that the tunnel speed may approach the airplane speed though the diameter of the model propeller may well be $\frac{1}{10}$ scale. Normally this scale relation would indicate a model rpm of ten times the actual airplane rpm, but a second effect tends to diminish the exceedingly high rpm on many models, particularly those of low power loading. It is shown in Chapter VI that to a large degree the size of the wind tunnel limits the size of the model to be tested. In turn the size of the model dictates the maximum size of the electric motor to be installed for driving the propeller. If no motor can be found that supplies enough power to drive the propeller at design V/nd when the tunnel is at full speed, the tunnel velocity must be diminished

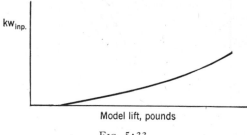

Model lift, pounds

FIG. 5:33.

until the proper V/nd can be realized. Very often the final tunnel speed is of the order of one-half of the speed used for the power-off runs.

The need for meeting the requirements of wind-tunnel model motors has brought about the introduction of special electric motors combining small frontal area and high rpm and requiring in turn water cooling and a current source of variable frequency. Some of the motors available are listed in Table 5:5. In many set-ups both the power and cooling water enter the tail of the model through the rear support.

TABLE 5:5. DIMENSIONS OF SOME WIND-TUNNEL-MODEL MOTORS

Hp	Diameter, inches	Length, inches	Rpm
35	4	10	18,000
130	8	16	5,400
200	10	33	5,000
1,000	28	38	2,100

TABLE 5:6. SOME WIND-TUNNEL-MODEL PROPELLER SIZES AND WEIGHTS

Propeller Diameter, inches	Weight per Blade, pounds	Centrifugal Load under Operating Conditions, pounds
7	0.02	600
14	0.10	...
22	1.00	...

The effect of power is, as has been mentioned, hard to predict. The results of some tests are given in Fig. 5:34 to show one method of presentation.

5:9. Testing Fuselages and Nacelles. Tests of fuselages alone are rarely made, for the interference effect of the wing on the fuselage is of such prime importance and magnitude that fuselage tests without the presence of the wing are of very questionable value. For most set-ups the tare drag is greater than the drag of the fuselage alone, tending to reduce the accuracy of the results. Buoyancy effects (see Sect. 6:1) are important, especially if the fuselage is large. Constraint corrections usually are small but not negligible.

The value of nacelle tests is much greater than that of fuselage tests because usually entirely different items are being investigated. Generally * the nacelle tests are concerned only with cooling pressure drops and cooling drags and not with the total nacelle drag, which would be largely dependent on the wing-nacelle interference.

* Sometimes a solid ductless nacelle is tested on a short-span wing for drag only. In this manner the larger-scale nacelle achieves a higher Reynolds number and fillets are more accurately laid. This procedure is also more accurate than attempting to duplicate fairings on several nacelles at once.

The effect of the rigid tunnel boundary on a nacelle is composed of three parts: (1) horizontal buoyancy, (2) constraint, and (3) wake variation. These items are considered in Chapter VI. The horizontal buoyancy can cause 30 per cent of the indicated drag, depending, of course, on the longitudinal static-

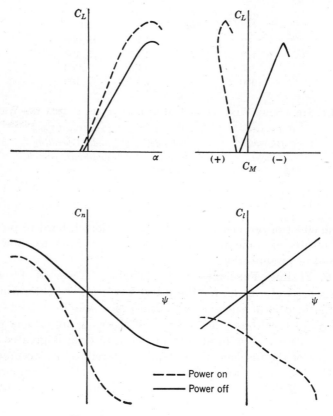

FIG. 5:34. Possible effects of power.

pressure gradient of the tunnel and the size of the model. The flow constraint will probably increase the effective velocity about 2 per cent. The wake variation is usually insignificant.

If a power-driven propeller is to be utilized in the set-up, extreme consideration should be given to the control and measurement of the rpm. For nacelles simulating modern high-powered units, the loss of a single revolution per minute can represent a large thrust decrement and, in turn, invalidate any

drag measurements that may be made. It is usually advantageous to fix the rpm by means of a synchronous driving motor
and to vary the tunnel speed and propeller blade angle to get
various flight conditions. Such an arrangement corresponds to
the customary constant-speed set-up of most airplanes.

Two methods of mounting nacelles in the wind tunnel are
shown in Figs. 5:35 and 5:36.

Fig. 5:35. Nacelle model on three-point support.

The usual nacelle is of such dimensions that buoyancy, constriction, and propeller corrections are important. For clarity,
let us assume that a model is to be tested at 100 mph. The constriction effect of the closed jet increases the velocity over the
model so that the results are similar to those encountered in free
air at a slightly higher speed, say 102 mph. The effect on the
propeller is opposite, however, yielding the results expected in
free air at 96 mph. It is therefore necessary to increase the
tunnel speed to approximately 104 mph, at which time the pro-

peller slipstream is the same as in free air at 100 mph. The propeller coefficients are then based on 100 mph.

The buoyancy effect is assumed to be the same as expected at 100 mph without the propeller.

Courtesy the Glenn L. Martin Aircraft Co.

FIG. 5:36.   Nacelle model on single support.

The pressure distributions must be corrected both for buoyancy and constriction.   (See Sects. 6:1 and 6:2.)

Drag coefficients for a nacelle may be based either on nacelle frontal area or on engine disk area.   The choice should be clearly stated.   The quantity of cooling air per second Q is usually defined by

$$Q = KS \sqrt{\frac{2\Delta p}{\rho}}$$

where K = engine conductivity.
$\quad\ S$ = nacelle or engine frontal area, ft².
$\quad \Delta p$ = baffle pressure drop, lb/ft².
$\quad\ \rho$ = air density, slugs/ft³.

5:10. Testing Propellers. Propellers are frequently investigated in wind tunnels either alone or in conjunction with a fuselage or nacelle. If an entire model is tested, the propeller diameter will be small compared to the tunnel jet diameter, and the

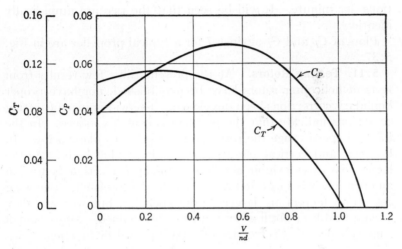

Fig. 5:37.

corrections to be described will become small also. For tests wherein propeller characteristics are to be determined, the propeller diameter may well be 60 per cent of the jet diameter, and the corrections are not only large but unfortunately not as accurate as those for wings. An approach to the problem has been made by Glauert; boundary corrections for propellers may be found in Sect. 6:17.

Numerous coefficients have been advanced for presenting propeller data, each type perhaps being advantageous for particular applications. One of the more popular forms is

$$C_P = \frac{P}{\rho n^3 d^5} = \text{power coefficient} \qquad (5{:}34)$$

$$C_T = \frac{T}{\rho n^2 d^4} = \text{thrust coefficient} \qquad (5{:}35)$$

where P = power input, ft-lb/sec.

n = rps.

d = propeller diameter, ft.

T = thrust, lb.

The "variable" of propeller testing is usually the advance ratio, $J = V/nd$, where V is in feet per second and n in revolutions per second. A form using more conventional quantities is $J = 88V/Nd$, where V is in miles per hour and N in revolutions per minute. It will be seen that the two are numerically identical.

Plots of C_P and C_T against J for a typical propeller are in Fig. 5:37.

5:11. Testing Rotors. At the present time, few results from tests of helicopter rotors have been published, nor have proper boundary corrections been developed. The wide range of testing conditions indicate that the problem is complex indeed. In the forward speed range the rotor possibly behaves like a wing. In hovering and vertical ascent, it resembles a bluff body. As the latter two cases exhibit smaller boundary correction factors in an open jet, it is suggested that the rotor be so tested. The wing correction factors are larger in the open jet, but whether they are applicable or not has not yet been determined. Many tunnel engineers use wing corrections for the forward flight range.

Rotor variables include the rotor solidity $\left(= \dfrac{\text{blade area}}{\text{disk area}} \right)$, disk angle of attack α, blade angle θ, blade azimuth angle ψ (ψ is measured from downstream), blade flapping angle β, number of blades B. The forward speed is usually referred to the rotor tip speed by the tip-speed parameter $\mu = \dfrac{V \cos \alpha}{V_t}$, where V = tunnel speed and V_t = rotor tip speed. High values of μ correspond to diving the helicopter. Under this condition the freestream velocity tends to unload the retreating blade, and severe vibrations ensue. The testing procedure should be to bring the tunnel speed up very gradually and to shut it down instantly when vibrations appear. The rotor should usually be left running until the tunnel speed has vanished. Spare rotors should be available.

Helicopter progress is still in such a state of flux that no standard procedure in presenting the test results can be outlined.

Plots of lift, drag, and torque against rotor disk angle for constant blade angle can be made, or any other arrangement, depending on the points under scrutiny. Many engineers prefer to have the data directly in pounds, etc., instead of coefficient form. In general, lift and drag increase with μ for a constant blade angle, and torque decreases.

The interference of the rotor support and support shield can be large and in any event should be evaluated and separated out, as should be the tare drag of the exposed portion of the rotor drive mechanism. The latter may be approximated by removing

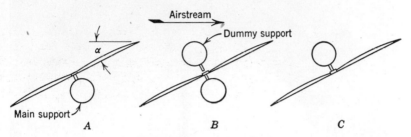

Fig. 5:38. Rotor and image system.

the rotor and measuring the lift and drag of the driving mechanism for the various speeds and angles. This procedure does not include the effect due to the rotor slipstream, but in most cases this should be small and the great increase of set-up complexity to measure it is not worth while.

The support interference can be evaluated by a dummy support as follows:

(a) Measure the lift, drag, and torque with the rotor at an angle of attack α, and the regular support as shown in A. The measurements M_A include the effect of a support *behind* the rotor.

(b) Place a dummy ahead of the rotor. The measurements M_B now include the effect of a support ahead and behind the rotor. $(M_B - M_A)$ is the effect of a support ahead of the rotor when there is a support behind the rotor.

(c) Rotate the support through 180 degrees and change the blade angles through 180 degrees also. The rotor is now at the same angle of attack and lifts in the same direction as before. The measurements M_C include the effect of a support *ahead* of the rotor. $(M_B - M_C)$ is the effect of a support behind the rotor when there is a support ahead of the rotor. The true forces on the rotor are then

$$M_{\text{true}} = M_B - (M_B - M_A) - (M_B - M_C) \qquad (5{:}36)$$

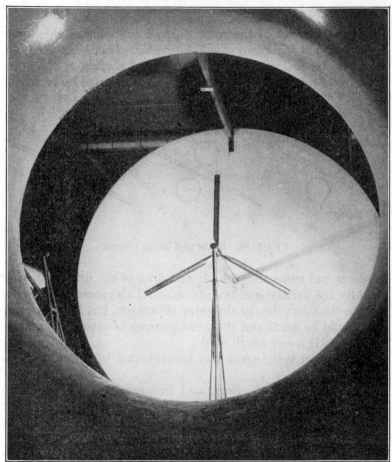

Courtesy Georgia School of Technology.

FIG. 5:39. Testing a rotor for ground effect.

To nullify the effects of gravity on the model rotor, it is useful to operate the rotor so that its axis is vertical, at least for starting and stopping and in the forward flight range. A system that will accomplish this is shown in Fig. 5:40. Here the drive shaft is horizontal, and a right-angle gear box is provided in the model.

A vertical support to a rotor whose axis is also vertical does not permit large angles of pitch. Both ±90 degrees are usually required.

It will be noted that the horizontal shaft design also has the rotor disk vertical for vertical ascent and descent, but it does fulfill most of the conditions outlined in the paragraph above.

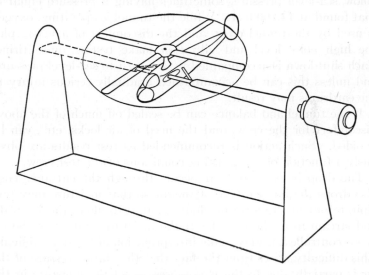

FIG. 5:40. A helicopter test set-up.

With the rotor tests arranged as in Fig. 5:40, the tare and interference evaluation becomes:

1. Measure the forces and moments with, say, clockwise rotation of the rotor.

2. Measure the forces and moments with counterclockwise rotation.

3. Add an image strut (shown dotted) symmetrically opposing the support strut. All parts of the support exposed to the airstream should be duplicated in the image system and attached to the model so that their effect is measured. A small clearance should be provided within the image windshield as in Fig. 4:24. It will be seen that

Item 3 − Item 2 = tare and interference of support

5:12. Testing at High Mach Numbers. Testing at high speed offers more difficulties than testing at low speeds, and a great deal more weight on the tunnel personnel as well. A large number of the high-speed tunnels utilize an air exchanger for cooling. This arrangement, by opening a "high"-pressure section of the tunnel to atmospheric pressure, drops the low-pressure section (the jet) below atmospheric. Frequently the tunnel balance room is directly surrounding the test section, and hence it too is below sea-level pressure, sometimes having a pressure equal to that found at 14,000 feet. While the tunnel is operating, oxygen is used by the tunnel crew, and the discomfort of a mask, plus the high noise level and vibration make testing quite tiring. Each shutdown is accompanied by a return to sea-level pressure, and unless this can be accomplished gradually serious injury to the eardrums may result.

If the tunnel and balance can be sealed off much of the above discomfort for the crew, and the need of air locks, etc., can be avoided. Such action is recommended as test results are obviously a function of the working conditions of the test crew.

The drop in pressure that occurs through the entrance cone also drops the temperature of the air so that moisture may precipitate out in the form of clouds that rush along the jet walls and stream from the model. If the moisture content of the air is not controlled, it may make interpretation of the data difficult. This difficulty arises from the fact that the static pressure of the air is partially due to the vapor pressure of the moisture in the air. When this moisture precipitates out, the pressure due to the moisture is also removed, and a local drop of total head is thereby incurred. This precipitation does not necessarily occur in a plane perpendicular to the tunnel centerline, further confusing the test results.

The proper procedure for testing above the speed of sound, correcting the results, and presenting the data is at present in a state of flux as additional knowledge is being gained. (See Sect. 6:19.)

Models for high-speed tests must be extremely strong and rigid, usually needing a margin of safety of 4.0. Even so, the deflections of the model under the great loads is awe-inspiring to see. The cutting effect of dust particles at high speeds necessitates repeated cleaning of the tunnel. Usually a simple device to help in this respect is the coating of the corner vanes with grease so that the dust will adhere to them. At frequent intervals they may be washed off and recoated.

As will be gathered from the section on Mach number effects (Sect. 7:5), the proper procedure for testing and correcting the results of high-speed tests has not been completely established. One source of difficulty arises from the great difference in the flow pattern that obtains when the critical Mach number is reached. It will be seen that, if the tunnel is run at a speed that would be just below the critical Mach number in free air, blocking may raise the effective speed enough to reach the critical. This small speed change could completely alter the flow pattern in a manner that would be most difficult to evaluate. It appears that the accentuated blocking and the shock-wave reflection off the tunnel walls contribute to the uncertainty of high-speed testing.

At the present time the blocking effect is being diminished by the utilization of small models and special designs to reduce the frontal area of the mounting struts. Some engineers prefer to keep model wing spans below 0.3 jet diameter, which makes the model quite small by ordinary standards. As the wall corrections are questionable, flight tests are used for correlation. An approach to the blocking effect may be made by testing a wing spanning the longer dimension of the jet and by comparing it with the same wing tested spanning the shorter jet length. It will be seen that this procedure varies the amount of blocking but unfortunately also varies the distance from the wing to the tunnel walls as well.

Coefficients from tests at high speed should be based on true rather than indicated dynamic pressure. The relation can be determined from

$$q_{\text{true}} = \frac{q_{\text{indicated}}}{1 + \dfrac{M^2}{4} + \dfrac{M^4}{40} + \dfrac{M^6}{1600} \cdots} \qquad (5:37)$$

5:13. Testing Jet-Engined Models. The purpose of designing a model of a jet-engined airplane so that the flow from the jet tailpipe may be simulated is to determine the effect that flow may have on the downwash. The effect of thrust moment is easily calculable, and there is no slipstream of high rotation to change the power-off stability seriously.

Two items in the full-scale design will probably be impossible to duplicate in the model: the high temperature of the actual jet, and the fact that the jet uses the freestream air while the model must have outside air provided. The difference in temperature is of little account, producing no measurable effect as long as the proper mass flow is maintained. That the freestream air is not employed produces more serious effects: the drag of the engine nacelle will be in error because some of the air on the full-scale ship goes through it instead of around it, and, if the same thrust coefficient is maintained for model and full-scale ship, the change of mass flow at the model's tail due to the addition of outside air will not reproduce true conditions. A solution to this problem is to adjust the flow from the model jet so that the same thrust coefficient is maintained for both model and full-scale ship, defining the coefficient:

$$T_c' = \frac{\text{Thrust}}{(\rho/2)SV_0{}^2} \qquad (5{:}38)$$

but subtracting from the model thrust the momentum mV_0 due to the freestream air. This will make the flow at the tail of the model simulate that developed by the actual airplane. Definitions used above include:

m = mass flow per second from model jet.
V_0 = freestream velocity.
S = wing area.

Possibly the nearest approach to measuring the drag of the engine nacelles is accomplished by adding a smoothly faired nose piece to produce the streamline flow that will actually occur. The simulated jet will tend towards producing the proper flow conditions near the tail of the nacelle.

Not infrequently the entrance loss is under scrutiny and the wind-tunnel engineer need consider duplication of the entering flow only. This greatly simplifies the problem: in many cases no air need be added nor is a pump or source of high-pressure air required. If the ratio of intake air velocity to freestream is below 1.0, simple variations of the exit passage may suffice. If inlet velocity ratios above 1.0 are required an enlarged exit passage will act as a pump and draw in the added air.

5:14. Testing for Dynamic Stability. Though few tunnel tests are made to ascertain the dynamic stability of a conventional aircraft, an occasional radical design may appear on the borderline and indications of its dynamic stability be needed.

The data sought usually embrace (1) the time to complete a single oscillation (i.e., the "period," T); (2) the time to damp to one-half amplitude, $t_{\frac{1}{2}}$; (3) the number of oscillations to damp to one-half amplitude, $n_{\frac{1}{2}}$; and (4) the damping factor, D.F. The derivation of the theory for dynamic stability is beyond the scope of this book, and the reader is referred to Ref. 5:4 for the basic dynamic stability theory.

In greatly condensed form it may be stated that the theory for dynamic stability requires more than the usual tunnel param-

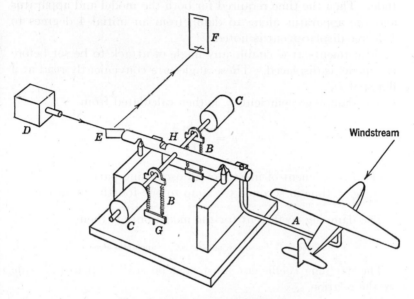

FIG. 5:41.   Dynamic stability rig.

eters for fixed models such as C_L, C_D, C_m, $dC_L/d\alpha$, $dC_D/d\alpha$. The additional information needed includes moments of inertia and damping coefficients that are unattainable with a fixed model. As for longitudinal stability it may be said that the uncertain time lag between flow changes at the wing and their corresponding effect at the tail is one of the problems not soluble from model fixed tests.

An apparatus that may be used to make dynamic stability studies is shown in Fig. 5:41. Basically it consists of a mounting arm (A) arranged on knife-edges in such a manner that the model mounted on the arm rotates about its center of gravity. Springs (B) and weights (C) are adjusted to insure that the motion persists long enough for accurate measurements. A light source (D) projects a beam on a mirror (E) mounted on the mounting arm, and the image then is reflected to a convenient marked wall (F). These marks may be calibrated for given model deflections, if desired.

One procedure is to note on the wall the position for the light when the model is displaced, say, 4 degrees, and also mark one-fourth of the displacement so that a reference will be provided to define when a displacement has damped to one-fourth amplitude. Then the time required for both the model and apparatus and the apparatus alone to damp from an initial 4 degrees to 1 degree displacement is noted.

Adjustments at G enable any angle of attack to be set before the model is displaced. These angles are conveniently read at a flat spot H.

The damping coefficient, c, is then calculated from

$$c = \frac{2I \ln 4}{t_{1/4}}$$

where I = moment of inertia of all oscillating parts.

$t_{1/4}$ = time in seconds to damp to one-fourth amplitude.

The damping coefficient for the model only is then

$$c_{\text{model}} = c_{\text{model + apparatus}} - c_{\text{apparatus alone}}$$

The damping coefficient must next be scaled up to full scale by the relation

$$c_{\text{full scale}} = c_{\text{model}} \times (\text{scale ratio})^4 \times \frac{V_{\text{full scale}}}{V_{\text{model}}}$$

where scale ratio $= \dfrac{\text{airplane span}}{\text{model span}}$

$V_{\text{full scale}}$ = velocity for the airplane with due reference for the angle of attack tested.

V_{model} = velocity of test.

The apparatus as described always has the model angle of attack coinciding with the deflection phase angle and hence fails to simulate the true free airplane oscillatory motion. However, for investigating the short-period longitudinal oscillation, and oscillations about the vertical and roll axes, it is quite useful.

PROBLEMS

5:1. Outline five procedures that should be followed in any research program.

5:2. The results from a wind-tunnel test of a wing of aspect ratio = 5.5 are in the following table. Find e.

C_L	C_D	C_L	C_D
0.1	0.0068	0.5	0.0224
0.2	0.0073	0.6	0.0294
0.3	0.0104	0.7	0.0375
0.4	0.0160	0.8	0.0470

5:3. For the wing of problem 2 find $\dfrac{dC_D}{dC_L}$ at $C_L = 0.7$ by eq. 5:12, and check by the mirror method.

5:4. Locate the center of pressure for a wing whose moment center is at the 25 per cent chord point. $C_{mtr} = -0.300$, $C_L = 1.375$, $C_D = 0.0969$, and $\alpha = 0.0°$.

5:5. Explain why wings of finite aspect ratio show a smaller $C_{L\ max}$. than wings of "infinite" aspect ratio.

5:6. A wing has a constant chord center-section of 2-ft chord and 3-ft semi-span. The panel is then tapered 2:1 and has a 4-ft span. The tip which is outside the panel is a semicircle. Find the ratio between panel and complete wing lift coefficients, assuming no twist. Use Schrenk's method.

REFERENCES

5:1. B. LOCKSPEISER, Ventilation of 24 ft Wind Tunnel, *R&M* 1372, 1930.

5:2. C. C. CLYMEN, Power Requirements for Wind Tunnel Motors, *Aero Digest*, December, 1941.

5:3. GOTTHOLD MATHIAS, Supplemental Data and Calculations of the Lateral Stability of Airplanes, *TM* 742, 1934.

5:4. C. H. ZIMMERMAN, An Analysis of Longitudinal Stability in Power-off Flight with Charts for Use in Design, *TR* 521, 1935.

CHAPTER VI

WIND-TUNNEL-BOUNDARY CORRECTIONS

The conditions under which a model is tested in a wind tunnel are not the same as in free air. There is absolutely no difference traceable to having the model still and the air moving instead of vice versa, but the longitudinal static pressure gradient usually present in the test section as well as the open or closed jet boundaries in most cases produce extraneous forces that must be subtracted out. These may be summarized as follows:

The variation of static pressure along the jet produces a drag force known as "horizontal buoyancy."

The presence of the lateral boundaries produces:

1. A lateral constraint to the flow pattern known as "blocking." This alters all forces and moments as well as the pressure distribution.

2. An alteration to the local angle of attack along the span. This changes the spanwise load distribution and hence the start of the stall and its spread.

3. An alteration to the normal curvature of the flow about a wing so that the wing moment coefficient is changed.

4. An alteration to the normal downwash so that the measured drag and angle of attack are in error.

5. An alteration to the normal downwash behind the wing so that the measured tailsetting and static stability must be corrected. The location of the wake at the tail is also in error.

6. A flow alteration so that measured control surface hinge moments are in error.

7. An alteration to the normal flow about an asymmetrically loaded wing such that the boundary effects become asymmetric and the observed rolling and yawing moments are in error.

8. An alteration to the normal flow behind a propeller so that the measured thrust is in error.

The additional effects due to the customary failings of actual wind tunnels—angularity, velocity variations, and turbulence—have been discussed in Chapter III. The magnitude of the corrections necessitated by the above effects is discussed in the following paragraphs; suggestions regarding their use are in Chapter V.

6:1. Horizontal Buoyancy. Almost all wind tunnels with closed throats have a variation in static pressure along the axis of the test section due to the thickening of the boundary layer as it progresses toward the exit cone and to the resultant effective diminution of the jet area. It follows that the pressure is

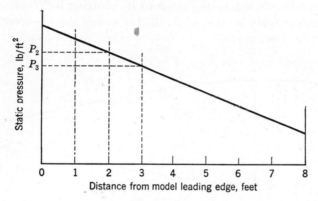

FIG. 6:1. Static-pressure gradient.

usually progressively more negative as the exit cone is approached, and there is hence a tendency for the model to be "drawn" downstream.

Glauert finds that the magnitude of the gradient may be expressed as a non-dimensional factor k defined by

$$\frac{dp}{dl} = -k \frac{(\rho/2) V^2}{h} \tag{6:0}$$

where l = jet length, ft.
    p = pressure, lb/ft^2.
    h = jet width, ft.

The factor k is from 0.016 to 0.040 for a closed square jet of width h.

The amount of this "horizontal bouyancy" is usually insignificant for wings, but for fuselages and nacelles it is larger and becomes important. Corrections may be calculated as follows:

Suppose that the static-pressure variation along a jet is as shown in Fig. 6:1 and that the model to be tested has the cross-section areas S as shown in Fig. 6:2. It will be seen that the variation of static pressure from, say, station 2 to station 3 is $p_2 - p_3$ and that this pressure differential acts on the average area $(S_2 + S_3)/2$. The resulting force for that segment of the fuselage is therefore

$$D_B = (p_2 - p_3)\frac{S_2 + S_3}{2} \tag{6:1}$$

This equation is most simply solved by plotting local static pressure against body section area, the buoyancy then becoming the area under the curve.

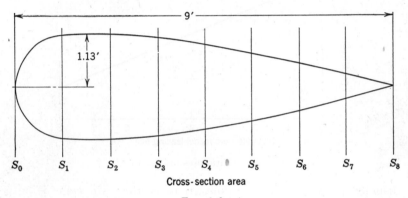

FIG. 6:2.

For the case where the longitudinal static pressure gradient is a straight line the equation becomes:

$$D_B = -\Sigma S_x \frac{dp}{dl} dl \tag{6:2}$$

where S_x = fuselage cross-section area at station x.

l = distance from fuselage nose.

$\dfrac{dp}{dl}$ = slope of longitudinal static-pressure curve.

Since $\Sigma S_x\, dl$ = fuselage volume, we have

$$D_B = -\left(\frac{dp}{dl}\right)(\text{fuselage volume}) \tag{6:3}$$

As the existence of a static-pressure gradient implies a varying velocity over the model, it will be seen that, relative to the fluid, the model is accelerating. Hence the concept of virtual mass is applicable, and the "volume" of eq. 6:2 should have added to it a small increment. This has been discussed by Glauert (Refs. 6:1 and 6:5), who indicates that an acceptable effective fuselage volume may be found from

$$\text{E.F.V.} = \frac{\pi}{4} \lambda_3 t^3$$

and the drag due to buoyancy becomes

$$D_B = -\frac{\pi}{4} \lambda_3 t^3 \frac{dp}{dl} \quad \text{for a three-dimensional body} \quad (6:4)$$

where λ_3 = body-shape factor for three-dimensional bodies, from Fig. 6:6.
$\quad\quad t$ = body maximum thickness.

For a two-dimensional body,

$$D_B = -\frac{\pi}{2} \lambda_2 \cdot t^2 \frac{dp}{dl} \quad\quad\quad (6:5)$$

where λ_2 = body-shape factor from Fig. 6:4.

Example 6:1

Calculate the drag due to buoyancy for the model of Fig. 6:2 when tested in a closed round tunnel of 9-ft diameter at 100 mph. The static-pressure gradient is -0.026 lb per sq ft per ft.

1. The volume of the body is 16.62 ft³. Neglecting the virtual mass

$$D_B = -\frac{dp}{dl}(\text{volume}) = (0.026)(16.62) = 0.43 \text{ lb}$$

2. From Fig. 6:6 for an $l/t = 3.98$, $\lambda_3 = 2.2$ (estimated), $t = 2.26$ ft.

$$D_B = -\frac{\pi}{4} \lambda_3 t^3 \frac{dp}{dl}$$

$$= -\frac{\pi}{4}(2.2)(2.26)^3(-0.026)$$

$$= 0.519$$

As seen from Ex. 6:1, neglecting the virtual mass may change the buoyancy drag as much as 70 per cent, but this in turn would be only about 1 per cent of the total model drag for models of ordinary dimensions.

6:2. Flow Constraint (Blocking). The presence of a model in the wind-tunnel jet reduces the area through which the air must pass and hence increases the velocity of the air that flows over the model. This effect is called "flow constraint" or "blocking." Since the amount of area reduction varies as the model maximum cross-section area, the change of velocity does also. The total effect on a body is usually expressed as an *average* change in velocity u_1, which is a function of body shape and length, jet area, and maximum body frontal area.

Lock and Johansen (Refs. 6:2, 6:19) and Glauert (Refs. 6:5, 6:20) have considered this change in velocity, reaching the conclusion that the constraint effect must be considered not only for the body but also for the wake behind it. The problem is sufficiently different for the two-dimensional and three-dimensional cases to warrant examining them separately.

Considering first the effect of constraint on a two-dimensional body, we find that limiting the normal flow expansion results in closed-tunnel data at velocity V and actually compares with free air data at velocity V_1, which is u_1 greater than V. The speed increase is a function of body shape and size, and tunnel jet shape and size and may be found from

$$\frac{u_1}{V} = \tau\lambda_2 \left(\frac{t}{h}\right)^2 \tag{6:6}$$

where τ = coefficient of jet shape.

$\quad\quad$ = 0.822 for rigid walls and = -0.411 for a free jet.

$\quad \lambda_2$ = coefficient of body shape (Fig. 6:4).

$\quad\quad t$ = maximum thickness of body.

$\quad\quad h$ = tunnel jet height.

Although eq. 6:6 has been used for a considerable time, a simplification presented by Young and Squire (Ref. 6:27) leads to a more direct form. Basically the approach to the problem considered that, as plots of λ_2 are nearly linear against fineness ratio, the blocking could be taken as being based on the volume. Equation 6:6 then reduces to

$$\frac{u_1}{V} = 0.62 \frac{\text{Vol.}}{h^2 b} \tag{6:6a}$$

where Vol. = model volume $\cong$ 0.7 chord $\times$ thickness $\times$ span.

$\quad\quad b$ = length of side of tunnel parallel to wing span.

$\quad\quad h$ = length of other side of tunnel.

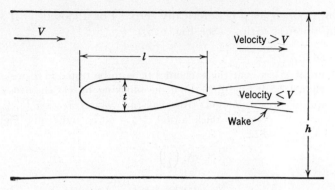

FIG. 6:3.

The walls of the two-dimensional tunnel also produce an effect on the wake, as follows:

The existence of a wake of reduced velocity behind the body implies, according to the law of continuity, that the velocity outside the wake must be *higher* than freestream in order that a constant volume of fluid may pass through the test section (Fig. 6:3). This higher velocity has, by Bernoulli's equation, lowered pressure. In turn, this lowered pressure appears in the wake and results in a lowered pressure at the rear of the body and an apparent increase of drag. The tunnel drag is then

$$D = D_0 \left(1 - \mu \frac{t}{h} \right)^{-2} \quad (6:7)$$

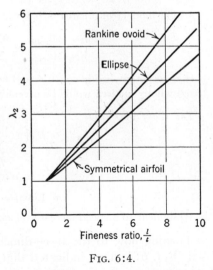

FIG. 6:4.

where D_0 = free air drag.

μt = the effective width of the wake as regards this special effect.

For a closed jet, the ratio of observed drag to free air drag is:

$$\frac{D}{D_0} = \left[1 + \tau \lambda_2 \left(\frac{t}{h} \right)^2 \right]^2 \left(1 - \mu \frac{t}{h} \right)^{-2} \quad (6:8)$$

For an open jet μ is practically zero. For a closed jet it varies as the fineness ratio. (See Fig. 6:5.)

Example 6:2

An airfoil 15 per cent thick, chord 2 ft, is to be tested in a two-dimensional tunnel 2.5 ft by 10 ft. Find the blocking by (1) eq. 6:6, (2) eq. 6:6a, and (3) area reduction. Also find the wake correction.

1. For a 15 per cent thick airfoil, $l/t = 6.67$, and, from Fig. 6:4, $\lambda_2 = 3.3$. $\tau = 0.822$

$$\frac{u_1}{V} = \tau\lambda_2 \left(\frac{t}{h}\right)^2$$

$$\frac{u_1}{V} = (0.822)(3.3) \left(\frac{0.3}{10}\right)^2$$

$$= 0.00244$$

2. The model Vol. $= 0.7$ span $\times$ chord $\times$ thickness $= 1.05$ ft^3.

$$\frac{u_1}{V} = 0.62 \frac{\text{Vol.}}{h^2 b} = (0.62) \frac{1.05}{(10)^2(2.5)} = 0.0026$$

3. The model frontal area $= 0.3 \times 2.5 = 0.75$ ft^2.

$$\frac{u_1}{V} = \frac{A_{\text{model}}}{A_{\text{tunnel}}} = \frac{0.75}{25} = 0.0300$$

It is seen that, while eqs. 6:6 and 6:6a are in agreement, a correction based wholly on area would be excessive.

The Wake Correction

$$D = D_0 \left(1 - \mu \frac{t}{h}\right)^{-2}$$

$$= \frac{D_0}{[1 - (0.07)(0.3/10)]^2}$$

$$= 1.003 D_0$$

or equivalent to a speed increase (blocking) of $u_1/V = 0.0015$.

Turning now to the three-dimensional case, Lock and Johansen (Ref. 6:2) have indicated that the velocity increase is

$$\frac{u_1}{V} = \tau\lambda_3 \left(\frac{S}{C}\right)^{\frac{3}{2}} \tag{6:9}$$

where $\tau =$ tunnel jet shape factor (Table 6:1).
$\qquad \lambda_3 =$ body-shape factor (Fig. 6:6).
$\qquad S =$ body maximum cross-section area.
$\qquad C =$ tunnel jet cross-section area.

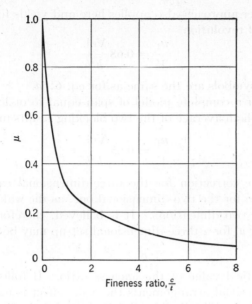

FIG. 6:5. Values of μ for various fineness ratios.

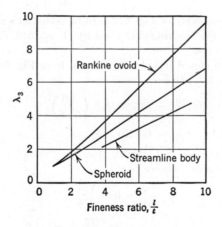

FIG. 6:6. Values of λ_3.

TABLE 6:1.   VALUES OF τ FOR THREE-DIMENSIONAL BODIES

Jet Shape	Closed Jet	Open Jet
Circular	0.797	−0.206
Square	0.809	−0.238
Duplex	1.030	....

The newer approach also applies here and yields for a streamline body of revolution

$$\frac{u_1}{V} = 0.68 \frac{\text{Vol.}}{h^2 b} \qquad (6:9a)$$

where the symbols are the same as for eq. 6:6a.

Hence for a complete model of span equal to or less than the tunnel width an average of the two blocking results may be used:

$$\frac{u_1}{V} = 0.65 \frac{\text{Vol.}}{h^2 b} \qquad (6:9b)$$

The wake correction for the three-dimensional case is much smaller than for the two-dimensional one, as the wake may then contract in two dimensions. It is believed, therefore, that the wake factor μ' for a three-dimensional set-up may be found from

$$\mu' = \mu^2 \qquad (6:10)$$

for an identical value of the fineness ratio. It follows that for three-dimensional arrangements the wake effect is usually negligible, except for bluff bodies, dive brakes, and the like.

Example 6:3

The symmetrical body of Fig. 6:2 is to be tested in a round jet of 9-ft diameter. Find the blocking correction by (1) eq. 6:9, (2) eq. 6:9a, and (3) the area reduction.

1. For a round closed jet $\tau = 0.797$, and, from Fig. 6:6, $l/t = 9/2.26 = 3.98$ and $\lambda_3 = 2.2$. Hence

$$\frac{u_1}{V} = (0.797)(2.2) \left(\frac{4.0}{63.8}\right)^{3/2}$$

$$= 0.0276$$

2. The model volume $= 17.00$ ft^3. For the "sides" of the tunnel use a square of equal area. Hence

$$\frac{u_1}{V} = 0.68 \frac{\text{Vol.}}{h^2 b}$$

$$= 0.68 \frac{17}{8^3}$$

$$= 0.0233$$

3. On an area reduction basis

$$\frac{u_1}{V} = \frac{(1.13)^2}{(4.5)^2} = 0.0631$$

Once again the area reduction is shown to be excessive.

For both two- and three-dimensional cases the forces should be reduced to coefficient form by using a corrected dynamic pressure

$$q_b = \frac{\rho}{2}(V + u_1)^2 \qquad (6:11)$$

where ρ = tunnel air density, slugs/ft^3.

V = clear jet velocity, ft/sec.

u_1 = blocking increment from eq. 6:6 or 6:8.

q_b = free jet q corrected for blocking.

Wings spanning the jet should use the two-dimensional blocking correction, and conventional tests the three-dimensional data; the special case of panel testing remains doubtful as being in neither category. It is believed that the three-dimensional correction as per eq. 6:9 is most acceptable if the value of τ for a duplex tunnel is used. The model frontal area S should then include the image area as well, and the jet area should include the image jet.

A second effect of the flow constraint is the alteration of the free air static-pressure distribution over the model. Some authors make the assumption that the pressure distribution around the body in a closed wind tunnel at velocity $(V + u_1)$ is the same as in a freestream at velocity $V' = (V + u_1)$.

Then the freestream static pressure at a point on the body is

$$p_f = H - \tfrac{1}{2}\rho V^2$$

where H = freestream total head and V = freestream velocity. The tunnel static pressure at the same point on the model is

$$p_t = H - \tfrac{1}{2}\rho(V + u_1)^2$$

This approach using the average u_1 may yield the average overall pressure distribution effect, but it makes no distinction for blocking variation over the model. A tunnel velocity set to include the effect of u_1 will be low at the entry points (leading edges, etc.) where blocking has not yet commenced, and excessively high at the body midpoints where blocking is maximum. Although to increase the speed further would seem to augment the blocking at the body midpoint, the truth is that if the pressures are being read for later extrapolation to high Mach number (see Sect. 7:5) it is of advantage to do so. First the critical pressure points will probably be near the leading edges where less than average blocking has occurred, and it is important to have full dynamic pressure there. Second, unless a higher q than indicated by eq. 6:11a is used, no full stagnation points $\left(\dfrac{\Delta p}{q} = +1.0\right)$ will appear.

Considering the rather complex problem in a numerical form, suppose that the model is to be tested at an IAS = 100 mph. From the model dimensions, the blocking is found to be equal to 3.0 mph; that is, if a jet speed of 97 mph is set the forces should be based on the dynamic pressure of 100 mph. Obviously the dynamic pressure at the model leading edges before blocking has occurred will be that of 97 mph ($q = 24.09$ lb per ft^2). A peak negative pressure of -48.18 lb per ft^2 is really a $\Delta p/q = -2.0$, but assuming the flow the same as in free air at $(V + u_1)$ yields $\Delta p/q = -48.18/25.58 = -1.88$. This last value when extrapolated to high Mach number would yield an unconservative critical force speed (Sect. 7:5). It is therefore suggested that when reading pressures on a large model the tunnel speed be raised until a search reveals that full stagnation pressures are developed. Then the forward and most critical portions of the airplane will yield proper pressure coefficients, and the rearward less critical portions will be conservative.

In closing the discussion on blocking it will be noted that, although the constraint raises the effective velocity by u_1, the total head is unaltered.

6:3. Lift Distribution Interference (Round Jets). The variation of spanwise distribution due to the walls of a closed-throat wind tunnel is small unless the wing has large span. If this condition exists, the data become pessimistic, tip stall starting earlier and being more severe than it actually would be in free air.

Lift distribution interference in a round closed tunnel is discussed by Stewart (Ref. 6:3), who finds that span tunnel width ratios greater than 0.8 will indicate early tip stall. An interesting numerical example shows that for a wing of $AR = 7$, span/tunnel width = 0.9, and $C_L = 1.2$, an effective washin amounting to 1.44 degrees is caused by the tunnel walls.

The designer of wind-tunnel models cannot correct for this in the model design since the effect of the walls varies with C_L. The amount of twist induced by a round closed tunnel on wings of elliptic planform is shown by Stewart to be

$$\frac{\Delta\alpha_i}{\alpha_i} = \frac{4R^2}{b^2}\left[\left(1 - \frac{b^4}{16R^4}\right)^{-\frac{1}{2}} - 1 - \frac{b^4}{32R^4}\right] \qquad (6:12)$$

where $\Delta\alpha_i$ = induced washin of wing due to wind-tunnel-wall interference.

α_i = induced angle of attack = $C_L/\pi AR$.

R = wind-tunnel radius.

b = wing span.

A plot of eq. 6:12 is shown in Fig. 6:7.

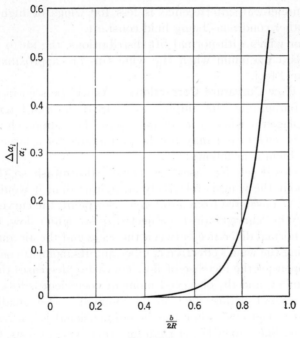

FIG. 6:7.

6:4. Lift Distribution Interference (Elliptic Jets). Gavin and Hensel (Ref. 6:4) have discussed the effect of the tunnel walls on the spanwise distribution of lift for closed elliptic jets with wings of aspect ratio = 8.0. Though the example discussed is very limited, further calculations using their method are possible. Their calculations may be summarized as follows:

1. At high lift coefficients when the wing tips lie outside the focal points of the elliptic jet the variation of the induced angle

of attack along the span is no longer negligible. This amounts to apparent washin which becomes severe as the wing tip approaches the stall. As a result, when the wing span approaches the tunnel major diameter, determination of stall characteristics in the tunnel are conservative; i.e., the wing tips will stall at higher angles in free air.

2. Other things being constant, tunnel-wall interference is less for lift distributions in which the lift is concentrated toward the center line. That is, for untwisted wings, those with high taper ratio have tunnel-induced upwash of smaller magnitude than wings with low taper ratios.

3. Tunnel-wall interference is less for wings of high aspect ratio, other conditions being held constant.

4. For wings with normal lift distributions, the mean upwash factor is a minimum when the wing tips are approximately at the tunnel foci.

6:5. Flow Curvature Corrections. As will be seen in the following paragraphs, the simple way to treat the wall interference is to replace the wing by a "lifting line." This approach neglects chordwise effects and may not be permissible for a large model. The problem is as follows:

The closed jet decreases the normal downwash so that the flow about the wing is relatively straighter than it would be in free air. Considered from a different viewpoint, the curved wing, normally in "curved" air, is subjected to straighter flow, increasing the normal difference between the wing and the air and hence increasing the wing's effective camber and its moment coefficient. In an open jet the increase of flow curvature decreases the effective camber, and the observed moment coefficient is less.

The amount of this effect on the moment is very small and is frequently neglected. For the two-dimensional jet, where wing chords are likely to be larger than for other types of tests, Glauert (Ref. 6:5) shows the magnitude of the moment change to be:

$$\Delta k_m = \frac{1}{32}\left(\frac{c}{h}\right)^2 k_L$$

which in conventional symbols is

$$\Delta C_m = \frac{1}{32}\left(\frac{c}{h}\right)^2 C_L \qquad (6:13)$$

where c = wing chord.
h = tunnel height.

The above correction is still very small.   (See Sect. 6:14 for more complete treatment.)

6:6. General Downwash Corrections.   At the beginning of this chapter it was stated that the tunnel boundaries affected the downwash.   This is shown in Fig. 6:8 where the effect of an open jet is seen to augment the normal downwash and to tilt the true lift and drag.   As the balance is mounted perpendicular and parallel to the relative wind, a component of the lift ($L_{\text{true}} \cdot \sin \Delta\alpha$) appears in the drag.   Further, the lift that occurs at a particular geometric angle of attack in the tunnel is too small and actually

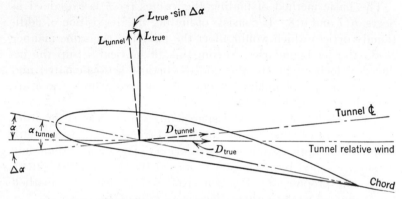

Fig. 6:8.   Effect of tunnel boundary on lift and drag, open jet.

would appear at a smaller angle in free air.   It is customary to hold the lift constant as measured and to correct the tunnel geometric angle of attack and the measured drag.

The closed jet does not permit the free air downwash to develop, and the results are therefore optimistic, showing too small a drag for a given lift.

Since the angle induced by the jet boundaries is proportional to the downwash and hence to the lift, the correction to the angle of attack may be expressed as

$$\Delta\alpha = \delta \frac{S}{C} C_L \quad \text{radians} \tag{6:14}$$

where S = wing area.

C = tunnel jet cross-section area.

Similarly, since the induced drag coefficient is proportional to the square of the downwash, its correction may be written

$$\Delta C_D = \delta \frac{S}{C} C_L{}^2 \tag{6:15}$$

The values of δ in eqs. 6:14 and 6:15 are functions of wing span to tunnel-width ratio, span load distribution, model location, and jet shape and type. In other words, wall corrections should be worked out for each wing tested. Practically, no such accuracy is attempted, wind-tunnel engineers usually being content with approximate correction factors based on either uniform loading or elliptic loading, as the case may be. If the model span exceeds eight-tenths of the jet width, special corrections are needed,* and calculations in the direction described above are sometimes employed.

The basic method of finding the values for δ is explained in Sects. 6:7 and 6:8. It consists of finding the disposition of additional vortices which would affect the model in the same manner as do the jet boundaries. From this theoretical set-up the induced velocities due to the added vortices are calculated and become the jet boundary effects. Numerical values for δ are given in Sects. 6:9 to 6:14.

A knowledge of the model span loading is necessary in order to determine whether to use the wall corrections for wings with uniform or elliptic span load distribution. The span loading may be simply found by a method proposed by Schrenk (Ref. 6:6), or by one proposed by Pearson (Ref. 6:7). Schrenk's method for untwisted wings without flaps is as follows:

(1). Plot the wing chord against the span.

(2). On the same graph, plot a quarter ellipse whose area is equal to half the wing area, and whose span equals the wing span.

(3). The span loading will be represented by a line midway between 1 and 2. (See Fig. 6:9.)

Attention is drawn to a short cut that may be employed in determining the downwash correction factor for a wing. As pointed out by Glauert (Ref. 6:5), the correction factor based on the span loading usually evolves down to that of an elliptic wing, for even rectangular wings tend toward that distribution. Hence the determination of the span loading may usually be omitted, and an elliptic distribution may be assumed. However, Silverstein (Ref. 6:17) points out that the correction factor based on the assumption of uniform loading over an *effective* span is essentially equal to that of the elliptic distribution based on the geometric span and has the added advantage of being mathematically simpler to derive.

* See Sects. 6:3 and 6:4.

The effective "vortex" span may be approximated by 0.8 wing span for tapered wings and by 0.85 wing span for rectangular wings. Additional values are given in Table 6:2.

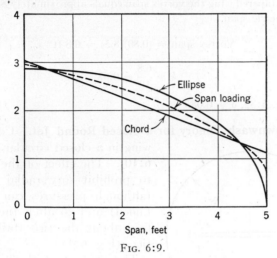

FIG. 6:9.

The wind-tunnel engineer has, then, the choice of two methods for determining δ. They are demonstrated in Example 6:4.

TABLE 6:2

Planform	s'/s
Elliptic	0.785
Rectangular $A/m_0 = 0.50$	0.844
$A/m_0 = 0.75$	0.862
$A/m_0 = 1.00$	0.875
$A/m_0 = 1.25$	0.887
$A/m_0 = 1.50$	0.896
$A/m_0 = 1.75$	0.903

A = aspect ratio.

$m_0 = \dfrac{dC_L}{d\alpha}$ for infinite aspect ratio, per radian. (The table has been corrected from k_L to C_L units.)

$2s'$ = vortex span.

$2s$ = wing span.

Example 6:4

A wing of 8.5-ft span, 2 to 1 taper, is to be tested in a closed elliptic tunnel, 2 to 1 breadth ratio. Compare the downwash correction factors obtained (a) by using an elliptic loading based on the geometric span and (*b*) by using a uniform loading based on the effective span. The tunnel jet width is 10 ft.

(*a*) $k = 8.5/10 = 0.85$. From Fig. 6:38, $\delta = 0.084$.

(*b*) For a tapered wing the vortex span equals approximately 80 per cent of the geometric span.

$$\text{Vortex span} = (0.80)(8.5) = 6.8 \text{ ft}$$

$$k = \frac{6.8}{10} = 0.68$$

From Fig. 6:32, $\delta = 0.085$

6:7. Downwash Theory for a Closed Round Jet.

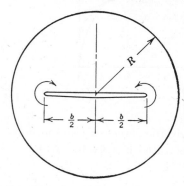

FIG. 6:10.   Wing in closed circular tunnel.

Consider a wing in a closed circular jet (Fig. 6:10). The effect of the walls is to prohibit any radial velocity (although pressures can be sustained) and to alter the normal field about the two trailing vortices (Fig. 6:11).

The amount of this alteration can be found if a series of sources, sinks, and vortices is discovered which make the zero streamline ($\psi = 0$) coincide with the tunnel wall. When this occurs, the induced velocities introduced by the tunnel wall (which are the same as for the added flows) can be calculated.

Such a condition exists when two vortices of opposite sense to the trailing vortices, but of equal strength, are places on the x axis at $x = +\dfrac{R^2}{b/2}$ and $-\dfrac{R^2}{b/2}$. (See Fig. 6:14.)   The normal field of these vortices (Fig. 6:12) so reacts with that of the bound wing vortices (Fig. 6:11) that the resultant duplicates the tunnel wall (Fig. 6:13).

The wing vortices as well as the added vortices are singly infinite as they start at the lifting line of the wing. Hence the velocity (positive up) at the tunnel centerline due to the two added vortices is

$$w = 2 \, \frac{\Gamma}{4\pi r}$$

where r is the distance from the vortex to the point in question. Substituting $r = \dfrac{R^2}{b/2}$ we have

$$w = \frac{\Gamma b}{4\pi R^2}$$

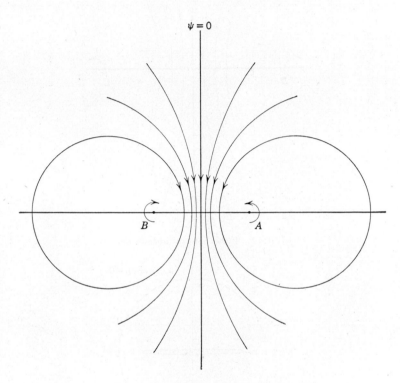

$\psi = 0$

B A

FIG. 6:11.   Field of bound vortices.

The strength of the bound vortices may be found from the lift of the wing as follows:

$$L = \frac{\rho}{2}SV^2C_L = \rho V\Gamma b$$

or

$$\Gamma = \frac{C_LSV}{2b}$$

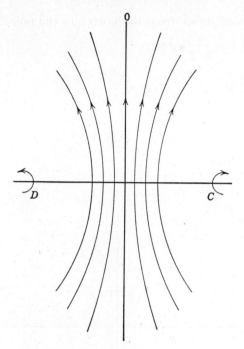

Fig. 6:12. Flow field of added vortices.

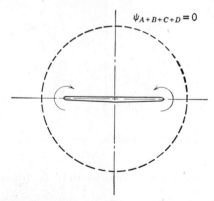

Fig. 6:13. Total flow field of both bound and added vortices; $\psi = 0$.

Since the added vortices are equal in strength to the bound vortices, the induced velocity becomes by substitution

$$w = \frac{1}{8} \frac{SV}{\pi R^2} C_L$$

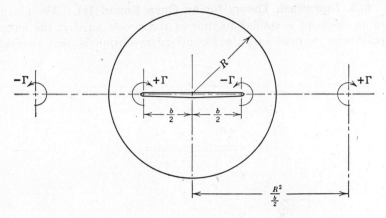

FIG. 6:14. Location of added vortices, closed round jet.

and the induced angle due to the boundaries is

$$\Delta\alpha_i = \frac{w}{V} = \frac{1}{8}\frac{S}{\pi R^2}C_L$$

Letting the tunnel area $= C$, we have

$$\Delta\alpha_i = \frac{1}{8}\frac{S}{C}C_L \qquad (6:16)$$

or the effect of the jet walls is to *decrease* the angle of attack necessary for a given C_L, making the wing appear to have a larger aspect ratio than it actually has.

Since $C_{Di} = C_L w/V$, we have

$$\Delta C_{Di} = \frac{1}{8}\frac{S}{C}C_L{}^2 \qquad (6:17)$$

The actual coefficients become

$$\alpha = \alpha_{\text{tunnel}} + \delta\frac{S}{C}C_L(57.3) \qquad (6:18)$$

$$C_D = C_{D\,\text{tunnel}} + \delta\frac{S}{C}C_L{}^2 \qquad (6:19)$$

where $\delta = 0.125$ for a closed round tunnel when the model is very small compared to the jet size.

6:8. Downwash Theory for an Open Round Jet. The effect of an open jet is similar to that of the closed jet, but the basic parameter is reversed; the boundary condition is that normal

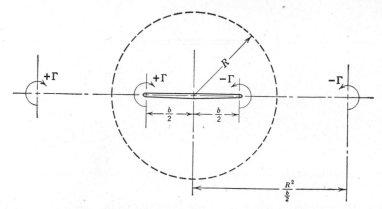

FIG. 6:15. Bound and added vortices, open round jet.

pressure must equal zero although radial velocities are possible. This condition is also met when vortices are placed at $x = -\dfrac{R^2}{b/2}$ and $+\dfrac{R^2}{b/2}$, but they must have the same sense as the nearest bound vortex (Fig. 6:15). The normal pressure zero condition

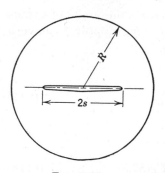

FIG. 6:16.

occurs when the potential function $\phi = 0$. An analysis similar to that of the closed jet shows that the induced angle and drag are affected the same amount as before but in the opposite direction; that is, δ is negative for an open jet.

6:9. Downwash Corrections for Circular Jets. The corrections for uniform loading in a circular jet have been completed by Kondo (Ref. 6:8), and those for elliptic loading by Glauert (Ref. 6:9) following a method proposed by Rosenhead (Ref. 6:10). They are both based on the ratio of span to tunnel diameter $k = 2s/2R$, actual values being presented in Fig. 6:17. Glauert's data have been corrected to more modern units.

Owing to model length or mounting, it is sometimes necessary to place the model with its wing not on the jet centerline. This places the trailing vortices closer to one wall than to the other,

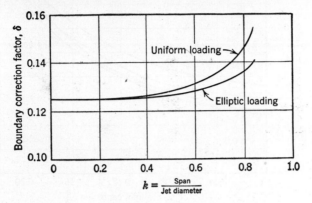

FIG. 6:17. Values of δ for a wing with elliptic loading and for one with uniform loading in a closed round jet. For an open round jet the sign of δ is negative.

altering the flow pattern and hence the proper value of δ. This condition has been examined by Silverstein (Ref. 6:17), who finds the values of δ with a displaced wing of uniform loading in a round jet to be as shown in Fig. 6:19. The nomenclature is described in Fig. 6:18.

6:10. Downwash Corrections for Rectangular Jets. Van Schliestett (Ref. 6:11) has discussed basic rectangular jet corrections for very small wings, correcting a mathematical error that appears in *TR* 461 (Ref. 6:12). His results are given in Fig. 6:20).

The boundary corrections for wings of moderate span

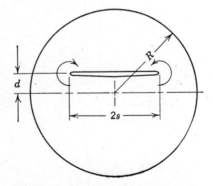

FIG. 6:18. Nomenclature for a wing displaced from the centerline of a round jet.

compared to the tunnel width have been worked out for uniform loading by Terazawa (Ref. 6:13) and for elliptic loading by Glauert (Ref. 6:14). Figures 6:21, 6:22, and 6:23 give the values for δ.

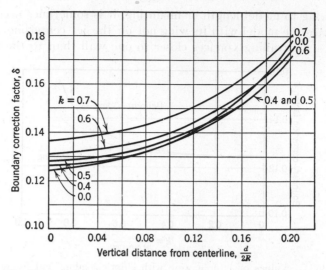

FIG. 6:19. Values of δ when a wing with uniform loading is displaced above or below the centerline of a closed round jet. δ is negative for the open jet.

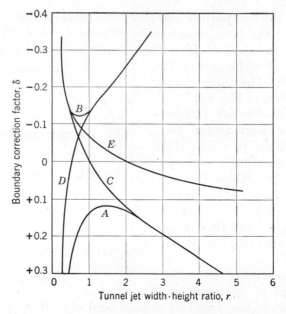

FIG. 6:20. Values of δ for open and closed rectangular jets, very small wings only. *A*. Closed tunnel. *B*. Free jet. *C*. Jet with horizontal boundaries only. *D*. Jet with vertical boundaries only. *E*. Jet with one horizontal boundary.

Values of δ for the square and duplex tunnel when the wing of uniform span loading is above or below the centerline are found in Figs. 6:24–6:27.

6:11. Downwash Correction for Circular-Arc Jets. The testing of panels as discussed in Sects. 5:4 to 5:7 requires special corrections that mathematically simulate the tunnel boundaries

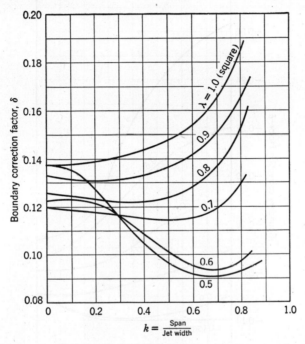

FIG. 6:21. Values of δ for a wing with uniform loading in a closed rectangular jet.

and the image wing which theoretically exists on the other side on the mounting plate. This condition has been considered by Kondo (Ref. 6:8) for a test section whose original shape was round before the addition of the mounting plate. No information has yet been released on corrections for panels tested in other types of jets.

The variables are the wing area S, the area of the *original circle before the plate was added* S_0, the ratio of tunnel radius to tunnel height

$$\sigma = \frac{a}{b} \tag{6:20}$$

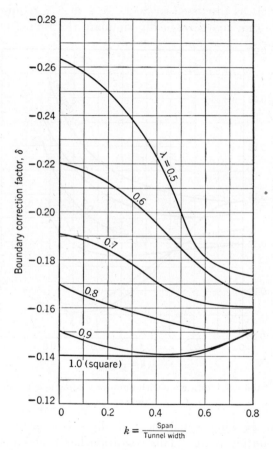

FIG. 6:22. Values of δ for a wing with uniform loading in an open rectangular jet.

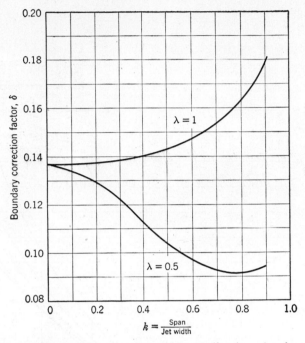

FIG. 6:23. Values of δ for a wing with elliptic loading in a closed rectangular jet.

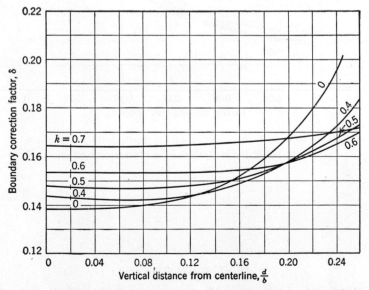

FIG. 6:24. Values of δ when a wing with uniform loading is displaced above or below the centerline of a closed square jet.

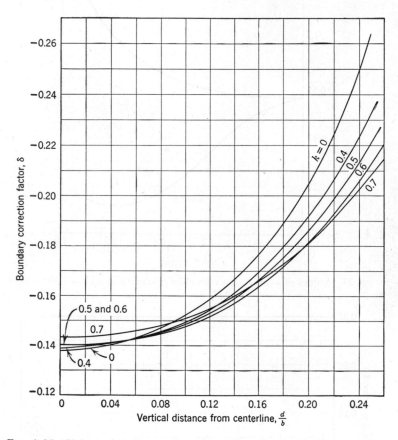

Fig. 6:25. Values of δ when a wing with uniform loading is displaced above or below the centerline of an open square jet.

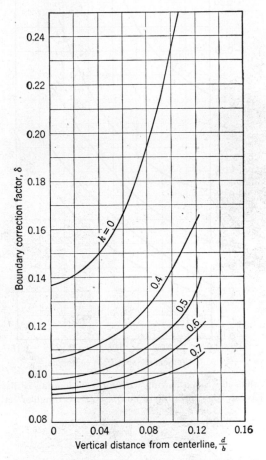

FIG. 6:26. Values of δ when a wing with uniform loading is displaced above or below the centerline of a closed 2:1 rectangular jet.

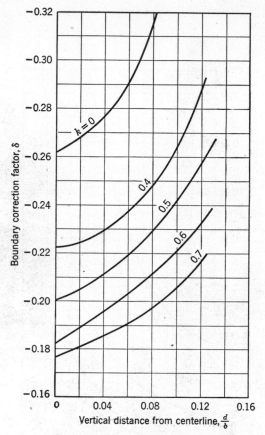

FIG. 6:27. Values of δ when a wing with uniform loading is displaced above or below the centerline of an open 2:1 rectangular jet.

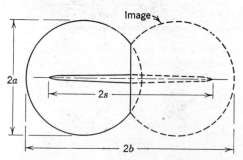

FIG. 6:28. A model in a tunnel whose boundaries are circular arcs.

and the ratio of span to tunnel height

$$k = \frac{s}{b} \qquad (6:21)$$

The additive corrections as usual take the form

$$\Delta\alpha = \delta \frac{S}{C} C_L(57.3)$$

$$\Delta C_D = \delta \frac{S}{C} C_L{}^2$$

but a word of caution is necessary. In Ref. 6:8 some confusion exists in the definition of "wing area" and "tunnel area." The

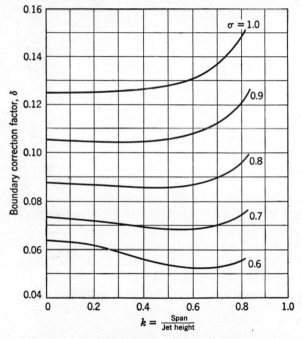

Fig. 6:29. Values of δ for a wing with uniform loading in a closed circular-arc jet.

wing area to be used is the *actual wing area including the image area,* and the tunnel area is the area of the original circle *not including the image circle.*

Values of δ for variations of k and σ may be found in Fig. 6:29 for closed circular-arc jets and in Fig. 6:30 for open circular-arc jets.

It will be noted that these corrections are not strictly applicable to aileron tests as in practice the "image" wing would have the control surface deflected oppositely. Until proper corrections are released, the above values should serve as a first approximation.

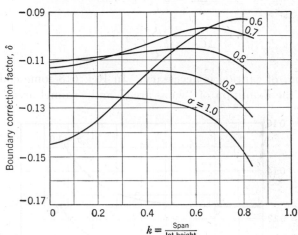

Fig. 6:30. Values of δ for a wing with uniform loading in an open circular-arc jet.

6:12. Downwash Corrections for Elliptic Jets. The corrections for wings with uniform loading in an elliptic jet have been completed by Sanuki (Ref. 6:15) and those for elliptic loading by Rosenhead (Ref. 6:16).

Sanuki bases his values for δ (uniform loading) on the ratio of the minor to the major axis of the jet λ, and the ratio of the span to the major axis k (Fig. 6:31).

$$\lambda = \frac{2a}{2b} \qquad (6:22)$$

$$k = \frac{2s}{2a} \qquad (6:23)$$

Values of δ are shown in Figs. 6:32 and 6:33.

The values for the wing not on the tunnel centerline (uniform loading) may be found in Figs. 6:35 and 6:36.

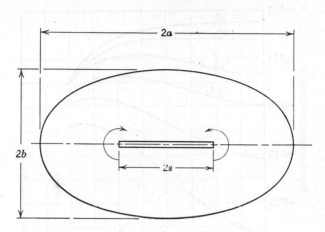

FIG. 6:31. Wing in an elliptic jet.

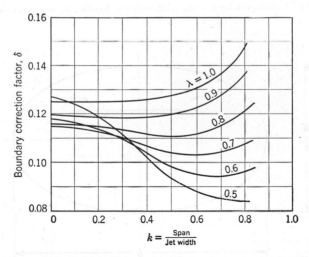

FIG. 6:32. Values of δ for a wing with uniform loading in a closed elliptic jet.

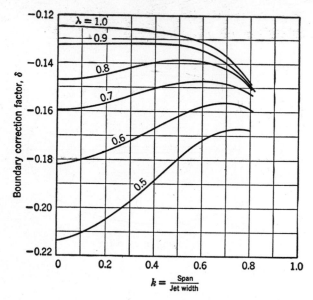

Fɪɢ. 6:33. Values of δ for a wing with uniform loading in an open elliptic jet.

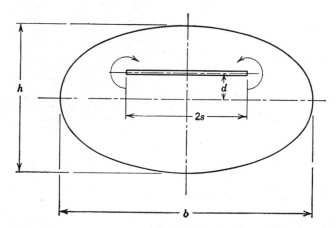

Fɪɢ. 6:34. Nomenclature for a wing displaced from the centerline of an elliptic jet.

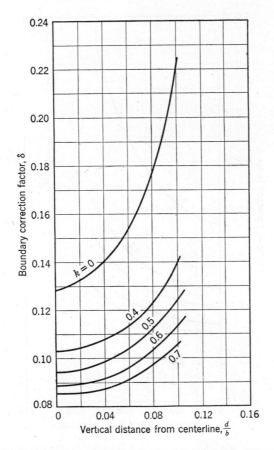

FIG. 6:35. Values of δ when a wing with uniform loading is displaced from
the centerline of a closed 2:1 elliptic jet.

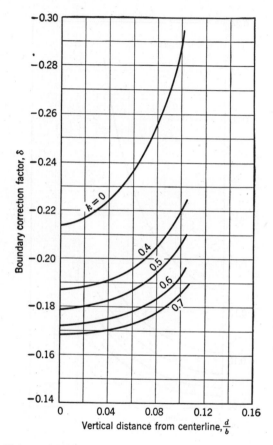

FIG. 6:36. Values of δ when a wing with uniform loading is displaced above or below the centerline of an open 2:1 elliptic jet.

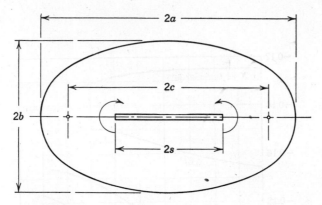

FIG. 6:37.

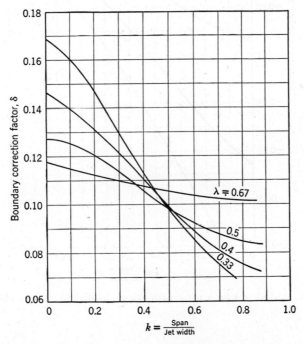

FIG. 6:38. Values of δ for a wing with elliptic loading in a closed elliptic jet

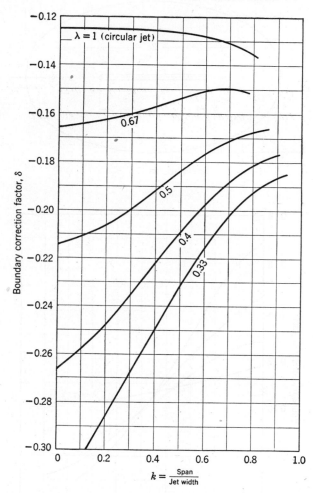

F<small>IG</small>. 6:39. Values of δ for a wing with elliptic loading in an open elliptic jet.

Rosenhead bases his values for δ (elliptic loading) on the ratio of the axis containing the wing to the other axis of the jet λ and on the ratio of the span to the focal length $2s/c$. For presentation here, however, the latter has been reconverted to the ratio of span to tunnel width $k = 2s/2a$. The values of δ are shown in Figs. 6:38 and 6:39.

Example 6:5

Compare the wall correction factors for testing an 8-ft tapered wing in the following closed jets: (a) round, 10-ft diameter; (b) rectangular 2:1, 10-ft width; (c) square, 10-ft width; (d) elliptic, 2:1, 10-ft width.

(a) vortex span = $0.80 \times 8.0 = 6.4$ ft.

$$k = \frac{\text{vortex span}}{\text{tunnel width}} = \frac{6.4}{10} = 0.64$$

From Fig. 6:17, uniform loading, $k = 0.64$ $\delta = 0.133$.
(b) From Fig. 6:21, $k = 0.64$, $\lambda = 0.5$, $\delta = 0.091$.
(c) From Fig. 6:21, $k = 0.64$, $\lambda = 1.0$, $\delta = 0.1575$.
(d) From Fig. 6:32, $k = 0.64$, $\lambda = 0.5$, $\delta = 0.0865$.
It will be noted that the 2:1 tunnels have much smaller correction factors.

6:13. Downwash Correction for Closed Octagonal Jets.

Wings with elliptic loading in octagonal test sections have been considered by Batchelor (Ref. 6:25) and Gent (Ref. 6:26). The

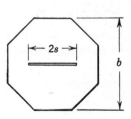

FIG. 6:40. Wing in an octagonal jet.

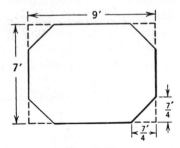

FIG. 6:41.

conclusion is that, for regular octagonal test sections (Fig. 6:40), the corrections for circular sections may be used, the maximum error being 1.5 per cent in δ or well under 0.2 per cent in C_D for the most critical case.

The octagonal test section formed by tempering the corners of a rectangular jet has been discussed only for the case where a 7 ft by 9 ft rectangular jet is reduced by 45-degree flat fillets whose vertical height reduce the amount of side wall exposed by one-half (Fig. 6:41). The effect of these fillets is to make the basic rectangular jet more nearly approach the elliptic jet. The wind-tunnel boundary factor is hence reduced.

The correction factors for both the 7 by 9 rectangular and octagonal test sections are shown in Fig. 6:42. As may be surmised, the corrections of the octagonal jet are essentially those of an elliptic jet of the same height-width ratio.

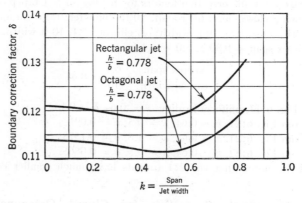

FIG. 6:42.

6:14. Downwash Corrections for Two-Dimensional Jets.

Glauert (Ref. 6:5) has examined the corrections for models that completely span the test section. The conclusion is reached that the usual downwash corrections will not be needed owing to the absence of the trailing vortices, but, since larger models are usually tested in a two-dimensional jet, corrections for flow curvature must be considered.

For the closed test section Glauert's corrections (after changing to more modern units) are

$$c_{m\frac{1}{2}} = c_{m\frac{1}{2}}'$$
$$c_{d0} = c_{d0}'$$
$$c_l = c_l' \left[1 - \frac{\pi^2}{48} \left(\frac{c}{h}\right)^2 \right] \tag{6:23a}$$

and

$$\Delta\alpha = \frac{1}{2\pi} \frac{\pi^2}{48} \left(\frac{c}{h}\right)^2 (c_l' + 4c_{m\frac{1}{4}}')57.3$$

where c = airfoil chord, ft.
       h = tunnel height, ft.

The prime indicates uncorrected tunnel data.

The moment correction of Sect. 6:5 is usually neglected as small.

The case of the free two-dimensional jet (floor and ceiling off, but wingtip walls in place) requires an additional factor that

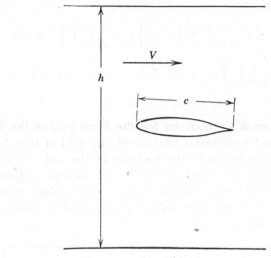

FIG. 6:43.

accounts for the downward deflection of the airstream as follows (both flow curvature and downwash deflection are included):

$$\Delta\alpha = -\left[\frac{1}{4}\left(\frac{c}{h}\right)c_l + \frac{\pi}{24}\left(\frac{c}{h}\right)^2(c_l)\right] \quad (57.3)$$

$$\Delta c_{d0} = -\frac{1}{4}\left(\frac{c}{h}\right)c_l^2 \quad (6:23b)$$

$$\Delta c_{m\frac{1}{4}} = -\frac{\pi^2}{96}\left(\frac{c}{h}\right)^2 c_l$$

These values should be added to the observed data.

It is noted that a drag correction is present here, and further that these corrections are extremely large.

The case where a wing completely spans a free jet without lateral restraining walls is not of much usefulness in practice. Such a set-up is rarely used except in small tunnels for preliminary tests. The spillage around the wingtip makes the wing area less effective so that the coefficients as obtained should be increased. One test (unpublished) indicates that, for $c/h = 0.2$, the measured lift was 18 per cent low. This amount should be applied over and above the free jet correction with lateral walls.

Example 6:6

Find the corrections for a 24-in chord wing tested in a 9-ft closed two-dimensional tunnel.

$$c_l = c_l' \left[1 - \frac{\pi^2}{48}\left(\frac{c}{h}\right)^2 \right] = c_l' \left[1 - \frac{\pi^2}{48}\left(\frac{2}{9}\right)^2 \right] \doteq 0.990 c_l'$$

$$\Delta\alpha = \frac{1}{2\pi}\frac{\pi^2}{48}\left(\frac{c}{h}\right)^2 [c_l' + 4c_{m\frac{1}{4}}'] \, 57.3 = 0.0927\,[c_l' + 4c_{m\frac{1}{4}}']$$

$$c_{m\frac{1}{4}} = c_{m\frac{1}{4}}' \qquad c_{d0} = c_{d0}'$$

6:15. Downwash Corrections for the Flow behind the Wing. The wind-tunnel boundaries also affect the field of flow behind the wing, altering not only the location of the wake at the tail but also the angle of attack of the horizontal tail surfaces. A closed tunnel indicates a higher wake location than would be encountered in free air and greater static stability than would actually be attained.

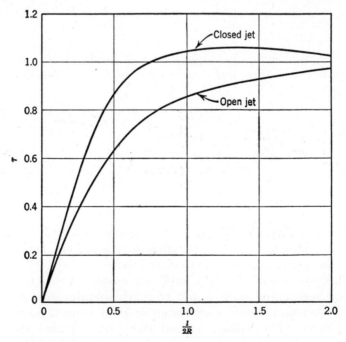

FIG. 6:44. Values of τ for open and closed circular jets.

This problem has been discussed by Lotz (Ref. 6:23), and the downwash effects at a distance behind the quarter-chord line have been presented as an induced velocity w_k which may be found from

$$w_k = \delta \frac{S}{C} C_L (1 + \tau) V \quad \text{for open jets} \qquad (6:24)$$

$$w_k^* = -\delta \frac{S}{C} C_L (1 + \tau^*) V \quad \text{for closed jets} \qquad (6:25)$$

where w_k = downwash velocity positive when directed down in the plane of symmetry at distance l behind the quarter-chord. (w_k does not vary greatly along the span.)

C = jet cross-section area.

V = tunnel velocity.

τ = downwash correction factor.

Values of δ for the proper span, span loading, and jet shape may be found in Sects. 6:9 through 6:13. The values of τ for circular and elliptic jets may be found from Figs. 6:44 and 6:45.

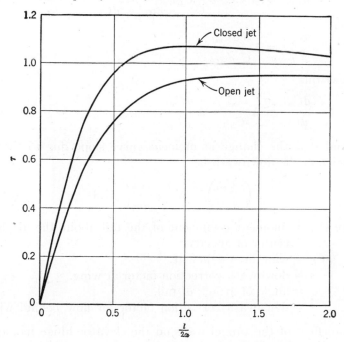

FIG. 6:45. Values of τ for open and closed elliptic jets.

The change in the horizontal tail angle of attack is

$$\Delta\alpha_t = \frac{w_k}{V} \quad \text{radians} \tag{6:26}$$

The effect of this altered angle on the static-stability curve may be derived as follows:

The tail moment coefficient $C_{mt} = \dfrac{q_t}{q}\dfrac{S_t}{S}\dfrac{l_t}{C}C_{Lt}$ where the subscript t means "horizontal tail" and other symbols are conventional.

Expressing $\dfrac{q_t}{q}\dfrac{S_t}{S}\dfrac{l_t}{C} = $ tail volume coefficient (t.v.c.), we have $dC_{mt}/dC_{lt} = $ t.v.c. Obviously

$$dC_{Lt} = \frac{dC_{Lt}}{d\alpha_t}d\alpha_t = \frac{dC_{Lt}}{d\alpha_t}\frac{w_k}{V} = \delta\frac{S}{C}C_{L\tau}\frac{dC_{Lt}}{d\alpha_t}$$

and also

$$dC_{mt} = (\text{t.v.c.})\,\delta\frac{S}{C}C_{L\tau}\frac{dC_{Lt}}{d\alpha_t} = \frac{dC_{mt}}{dC_{Lt}}\delta\frac{S}{C}\frac{dC_{Lt}}{d\alpha_t}$$

so that

$$\frac{dC_{mt}}{C_L} = \delta\frac{S}{C}\frac{dC_{mt}}{d\alpha_t}$$

Rewriting

$$\frac{dC_{mt}}{dC_L} = \Delta\frac{C_{mt}}{C_L} = \Delta\frac{dC_{mt}}{dC_L}$$

we find that the change in moment curve slope due to the inclination of the downwash is

$$\Delta\left(\frac{dC_{mt}}{dC_L}\right) = \delta\frac{S}{C}\tau\frac{dC_{mt}}{d\alpha_t}\,(57.3) \tag{6:27}$$

where $C_{mt} = $ moment coefficient of the tail about the airplane center of gravity.

$C_L = $ wing lift coefficient.

$\delta = $ downwash correction factor at wing.

$\alpha_t = $ angle of attack of tail.

$\tau = $ downwash correction factor for flow behind wing.

The effect of the tunnel walls on the elevator hinge moments caused by tail-angle corrections is usually negligible.

The amount that the wake is displaced by the tunnel boundaries may be found by calculating the induced velocities at several stations back of the wing and by making a step-by-step integration, solving for the time for each increment by dividing the distance between stations by the tunnel velocity.

The wake location is of great importance when considering tail buffeting due to wing flaps and dive brakes.

Example 6:7

A rectangular wing of 6-ft span and 1-ft chord is tested in a closed round jet (9-ft diameter) at 100 mph. Find the approximate wake displacement caused by the tunnel walls 2 ft behind the wing quarter-chord at $C_L = 1.0$.

1. For this wing and tunnel

$$k = \frac{(0.85)(6)}{9} = 0.566$$

From Fig. 6:17, $\delta = 0.130$.
From Fig. 6:44, $\tau = 0.475$ for $l/2R = 0.222$.

2. $w_k{}^* = -\delta \frac{S}{C} C_L (1 + \tau^*) V$

$$= -(0.130) \frac{6}{63.8} (1.0)(1 + 0.475)(147)$$

$$= -0.265 \text{ ft/sec}$$

That is, the wall effect 2 ft behind the quarter-chord is an upward velocity of 0.265 ft/sec.

3. The time required for a particle of air to travel from the quarter-chord to the station 2 ft farther back is

$$\Delta t = \tfrac{2}{147} = 0.0136 \text{ sec}$$

The average upwards velocity during this period is $\dfrac{0 + 0.265}{2} = 0.1325$ ft/sec. Hence the displacement is

$$h = \overline{V} \, \Delta t$$

$$= (-0.1325)(0.0136)$$

$$= -0.0018 \text{ ft}$$

This amount is obviously negligible. For larger models, however, the wake correction must be considered. Greater accuracy in making this correction may be obtained by considering the process in a series of short steps, summing up to get the total correction.

6:16. Jet Arrangements with Zero Corrections. Figure 6:20 indicates that rectangular jets may have several arrangements that yield zero boundary effects. Such arrangements include jets with one horizontal boundary and a width-height ratio of 2.0, with two horizontal boundaries and a width-height ratio of 1.0, and with two vertical boundaries and a width-height ratio of 0.5. But it must be remembered that Fig. 6:20 applies to very small wings only.

In practice, nearly every wing requires its own specific downwash correction factor δ, and it is obvious that each wing would require its own specific jet configuration in order to have zero boundary effect. Therefore the zero boundary-correction jet is impracticable although it is an interesting theoretical problem.

It so happens that the downwash correction *may* be neglected for one type of test—that of wings or complete models when they are tested in the tunnel for ground effect. This type of test utilizes a ground board (see Sect. 8:7) close to the model to simulate the ground. The effect of the board is opposite in sign to the boundary effect of a closed jet and practically cancels it out. Data from tests of this type made with the wing within one chord of the ground plane may be used directly without downwash corrections (Ref. 6:24).

The set-up is similar to that of a wing far off the tunnel centerline. However, when considering the wall effect of the three remote walls (in a rectangular tunnel) by subtracting out the interference of the fourth wall which represents the ground and hence should have its "interference" in, it develops that the effect of the remote walls is quite small and may be neglected as far as pitch stability is concerned.

6:17. Boundary Correction for Propeller Tests. Glauert (Ref. 6:5) has examined the problem of testing propellers in a wind tunnel and suggests that the propeller diameter be kept small relative to the jet diameter and that an open-throat tunnel be employed. Under these conditions no boundary corrections are needed.

Unfortunately, for various practical reasons it is not always possible to adhere to the above stipulations. An approach to the wall corrections for propeller tests in a closed-throat tunnel may be made as follows:

In a closed jet the propeller slipstream under conditions of positive thrust will have a velocity u greater than the velocity in the jet without the propeller V. Since the same volume of air that passes section x ahead of the propeller must pass section y behind it, it follows that the velocity w outside the slipstream will be less than V. In free air, w would, of course, equal V. The lower-velocity outside air has a higher static pressure, and it follows that the slipstream also has too high a static pressure. This reacts back to the propeller so that it develops the thrust

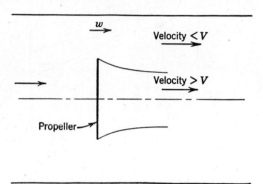

Fig. 6:46.   Propeller in a closed-throat wind tunnel.

that might be expected at a lower speed V'. The test should therefore be run at a speed above V in order to develop the proper forces for V.

The amount of correction for this "continuity" effect may be found from

$$\frac{V'}{V} = 1 - \frac{\tau - \alpha_1}{2\sqrt{1 + 2\tau}} \qquad (6:28)$$

where $\tau = \dfrac{T}{\rho A V^2}$.

$\alpha_1 = \dfrac{A}{C}$.

A = propeller disk area.
C = jet cross-section area.
T = thrust.

One approach is to place a pitot-static tube in the plane of the propeller and to operate the tunnel at constant w, basing the coefficients on w, also. The difficulty of finding the average w, however, makes this seem less valuable than reading the thrust and correcting V by eq. 6:28.

Values of V'/V may be obtained from Fig. 6:47.

If the tunnel utilized has an open jet, the airstream surrounding the propeller slipstream is free to contract; hence no correction is necessary.

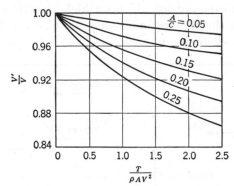

FIG. 6:47.

6:18. Asymmetrical Loading Corrections. When the ailerons of a model are deflected, the downwash is no longer symmetrical, and the effect of the jet boundaries becomes asymmetrical also. The effect on the rolling moment is small and is frequently neglected. Biot (Ref. 6:21) shows that for full-span ailerons of customary model size it amounts to about 3 per cent. Stewart (Ref. 6:22) has considered the correction to the yawing moment coefficient necessary for round jets. He reaches the conclusion that the total yawing moment correction may be found from

$$\Delta C_n = \Delta C_{n1} + \Delta C_{n2} + \Delta C_{n3} \qquad (6:29)$$

where

$$\Delta C_{n1} = C_l C_L \frac{SR^2}{b^2(a_2{}^2 - a_1{}^2)}\left[F_1\left(\frac{ba_2}{2R^2}\right) - F_1\left(\frac{ba_1}{2R^2}\right)\right] \qquad (6:30)$$

$$F_1(x) = -\frac{2}{\pi}\ln\left(1 + \sqrt{1 - x^2}\right) \qquad (6:31)$$

and may be found from Fig. 6:48 wherein

$$x = \frac{ba_1}{2R^2} \quad \text{or} \quad \frac{ba_2}{2R^2} \qquad (6:32)$$

$$\Delta C_{n2} = C_l C_L \frac{S}{a_2{}^2 - a_1{}^2}\left[F_2\left(\frac{a_2}{2R^2}\right) - F_2\left(\frac{ba_1}{2R^2}\right)\right] \qquad (6:33)$$

where

$$F_2(x) = \frac{1 - \sqrt{1 - x^2}}{2\pi x^2} \qquad (6:34)$$

and may be found from Fig. 6:49.

$$\Delta C_{n3} = -C_l^2 \frac{Sbr}{2\pi(a_2^2 - a_1^2)} F_3\left(\frac{a_2}{R}, \frac{a_1}{a_2}\right) \qquad (6:35)$$

where $F_3(a_2/R, a_1/a_2)$ may be found from Fig. 6:50.

The symbols not readily apparent are

a_1 = distance from wing centerline to inner tip of aileron.
a_2 = distance from wing centerline to outer tip of aileron.
b = wing span.
R = tunnel radius.

The correction Δc_n should be subtracted for a closed wind tunnel and added for an open one. Further, Δc_{n3} should be omitted when both ailerons are deflected. Though it may seem

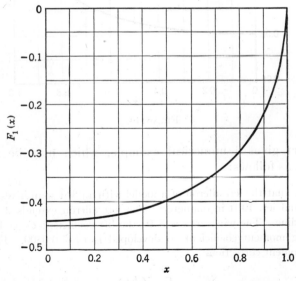

FIG. 6:48.

surprising that correction of one aileron only is even mentioned, this is not an unusual case. When two aileron designs are under consideration it is customary to build one into the right aileron and one into the left aileron, testing each separately.

The sign conventions for ailerons are such that down aileron is "plus," regardless of whether the right or left aileron is under consideration. It should therefore be mentioned, with the signs employed, which aileron is being tested.

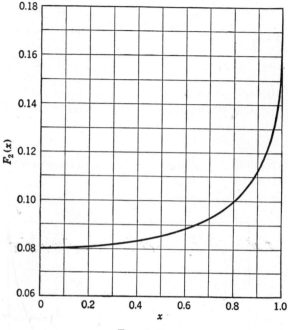

FIG. 6:49.

Stewart gives a numerical example, which may be readily checked, as follows:

Suppose that the left aileron of a model with an 8-ft span is tested in a closed round jet, 10 ft in diameter. The left aileron extends 2 ft from the centerline. The wing area is 8 ft; the lift coefficient $C_L = 1.5$; and the rolling moment coefficient so developed is $C_l = 0.0300$. Find the yawing moment correction.

$$\Delta C_{n1} = C_l C_L \frac{SR^2}{b^2(a_2{}^2 - a_1{}^2)} \left[F_1\left(\frac{ba_2}{2R^2}\right) - F_1\left(\frac{ba_1}{2R^2}\right) \right]$$

$$= (0.0300)(1.5) \frac{(8)5^2}{8^2(3.5^2 - 2^2)} \left[F_1\frac{(8)(3.5)}{(2)(5^2)} - F_1\frac{(2)(8)}{(2)(5^2)} \right]$$

$$= 0.00069$$

$$\Delta C_{n2} = C_l C_L \frac{S}{a_2{}^2 - a_1{}^2}\left[F_2\left(\frac{a_2}{2R^2}\right) - F_2\left(\frac{ba_1}{2R^2}\right)\right]$$

$$= (0.0300)(1.5)\frac{8}{(3.5^2 - 2^2)}\left[F_2\frac{(3.5)}{(2)(5^2)} - F_2\frac{(8)(2)}{(2)(5^2)}\right]$$

$$= 0.00024$$

$$\Delta C_{n3} = -C_l{}^2 \frac{SbR}{2\pi(a_2{}^2 - a_1{}^2)}F_3\left(\frac{a_2}{R}, \frac{a_1}{a_2}\right)$$

$$= -(0.0300)^2 \frac{(8)(8)(5)}{2\pi(3.5)^2 - 2^2}F_3\left(\frac{3.5}{5}, \frac{2}{3.5}\right)$$

$$= 0.00008$$

$$\Delta C_n = 0.00069 + 0.00024 + 0.00008 = 0.00101$$

ΔC_n should be subtracted from the observed yawing moment.

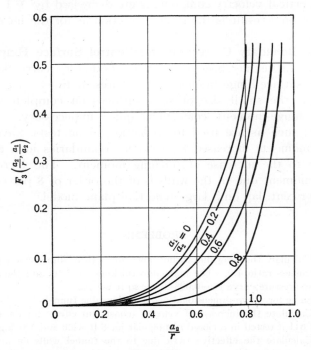

Fɪɢ. 6:50.

6:19. Corrections at High Subsonic Speeds. For a first approximation to be used with small models at speeds below Mach number = 0.9, the following corrections are suggested.

(a) Blocking: Use the blocking from Sect. 6:2 increased by $1/(\sqrt{1 - M^2})^3$ or

$$\left(\frac{u_1}{V}\right)_{\text{compressible}} = \left(\frac{u_1}{V}\right)_{\text{low speed}} \left(\frac{1}{(\sqrt{1 - M^2})^3}\right) \quad (6:36)$$

(b) Wall interference. Use the same wall corrections as for the incompressible case.

Both these corrections arise from considering the compressible flow to be similar to that of an incompressible flow for a thicker body in a smaller tunnel. The wall interference correction considers that the span of the model is decreased by $\sqrt{1 - M^2}$, and consequently so is the wing area. The tunnel area is decreased by $(1 - M^2)$, leaving an increase of $\Delta\alpha$ of $1/\sqrt{1 - M^2}$. However, vertical velocity components are decreased by $\sqrt{1 - M^2}$, and the final result is the same correction as for the incompressible case.

6:20. Boundary Corrections for Control Surface Hinge Moments. Little has been released on boundary corrections for control surface hinge moments at the present time. It is apparent that the small size of such surfaces on complete models makes hinge-moment corrections quite unnecessary. Larger models, such as are used for reflection plane tests, have their hinge moments increased by solid jet boundaries in a manner similar to the increase of pitching moment. The increase of hinge moment due to the walls is of the order of 8 per cent for a 30 per cent flap on a large reflection plane model.

PROBLEMS

6:1. Calculate the drag due to buoyancy for a three-dimensional Rankine ovoid, fineness ratio 4.0. The maximum thickness is 2 ft, and the slope of the static-pressure curve is -0.008 lb per sq ft per ft.

6:2. Same for a two-dimensional ovoid in the same tunnel.

6:3. Calculate the increase of velocity (constraint effect) for the ovoid of problem 6:1 if tested in a closed rectangular jet 8 ft wide and 4 ft high.

6:4. Calculate the effective twist due to the tunnel walls on a tapered wing of span 8 ft, $AR = 8$, tested in a round closed jet of 9-ft diameter at $C_L = 1.0$.

6:5. A wing has a 10-ft span. The root chord is 3 ft, and the tip chord is 1.5 ft. Using Schrenk's method, find the span load distribution.

6:6. The wing of problem 6:5 is to be tested in the following tunnels; find the value of δ for each.

(a) 12 ft round, open jet.
(b) 12 ft round, closed jet.
(c) 12 ft elliptical closed jet, 2 to 1 breadth ratio.
(d) 12 ft square closed jet.
(e) 12 ft by 8 ft rectangular, closed jet.

6:7. A propeller of 4-ft diameter is to be tested in a round closed tunnel of 9-ft diameter. What tunnel speed is needed to simulate a free air speed of 100 mph, if a thrust of 200 lb is developed at 1000 rpm.

REFERENCES

6:1. H. GLAUERT, The Effect of a Static Pressure Gradient on the Drag of a Body Tested in a Wind Tunnel, R&M 1158, 1928.

6:2. C. N. H. LOCK and F. C. JOHANSEN, Wind Tunnel Interference on Streamline Bodies, R&M 1451, 1931.

6:3. H. J. STEWART, The Effect of Wind Tunnel Wall Interference on the Stalling Characteristics of Wings, JAS, September, 1941.

6:4. J. R. GAVIN and R. W. HENSEL, Elliptic Tunnel Wall Corrections, JAS, December, 1942.

6:5. H. GLAUERT, Wind Tunnel Interference on Wings, Bodies, and Airscrews, R&M 1566, 1933.

6:6. O. SCHRENK, A Simple Approximation Method for Obtaining the Spanwise Lift Distribution, TM 948, 1940.

6:7. H. A. PEARSON, Span Load Distribution for Tapered Wings with Partial Span Flaps, TR 585, 1937.

6:8. K. KONDO, The Wall Interference of Wind Tunnels with Boundaries of Circular Arcs, ARI, TIU 126, 1935.

6:9. H. GLAUERT, The Interference of the Characteristics of an Airfoil in a Wind Tunnel of Circular Section, R&M 1453, 1931.

6:10. L. ROSENHEAD, Uniform and Elliptic Loading in Circular and Rectangular Tunnels, PRS, Series A, Vol. 129, 1930, p. 135.

6:11. G. VAN SCHLIESTETT, Experimental Verification of Theodorsen's Theoretical Jet-Boundary Correction Factors, TN 506, 1934.

6:12. T. THEODORSEN, Interference on an Airfoil of Finite Span in an Open Rectangular Wind Tunnel, TR 461, 1931.

6:13. TERAZAWA, On the Interference of Wind Tunnel Walls on the Aerodynamic Characteristics of a Wing, ARI, TIU 44, 1932.

6:14. H. GLAUERT, The Interference on the Characteristics of an Airfoil in a Wind Tunnel of Rectangular Section, R&M 1459, 1932.

6:15. M. SANUKI and I. TANI, The Wall Interference of a Wind Tunnel of Elliptic Cross-Section, Proc. Physical Mathematical Soc. Japan, Vol. 14, 1932, p. 592.

6:16. L. ROSENHEAD, The Airfoil in a Wind Tunnel of Elliptic Cross-Section, PRS, Series A, Vol. 140, 1933, p. 579.

6:17. A. SILVERSTEIN, Wind Tunnel Interference with Particular Reference to Off-Center Positions of the Wing and to the Downwash at the Tail, TR 547, 1935.

6:18. H. GLAUERT, Elements of Airfoil and Airscrew Theory, Cambridge University Press, 1926, p. 168.

6:19. C. N. H. Lock, The Interference of a Wind Tunnel on a Symmetrical Body, *R&M* 1275, 1929.

6:20. H. Glauert, The Interference of a Wind Tunnel on a Symmetrical Body, *R&M* 1544, 1933.

6:21. M. Biot, Correction for the Measured Rolling Moment of a Wing in a Circular Wind Tunnel, *ZFM*, August, 1933.

6:22. H. J. Stewart, A Correction to the Yawing Moment Due to Ailerons for Circular Wind Tunnels, *JAS*, June, 1939.

6:23. I. Lotz, Correction of Downwash in Wind Tunnels of Circular and Elliptic Sections, *TM* 801, 1936.

6:24. I. G. Recant, Wind Tunnel Investigation of Ground Effect, *TN* 705, 1939.

6:25. G. K. Batchelor, Interference in a Wind Tunnel of Octagonal Section, *ACA* 1, January, 1944.

6:26. Betty L. Gent, Interference in a Wind Tunnel of Regular Octagonal Section, *ACA* 2, January, 1944.

6:27. A. D. Young and H. B. Squire, Blockage Corrections in a Closed Rectangular Tunnel, *R&M* 1984, 1944.

CHAPTER VII

EXTRAPOLATION TO FULL SCALE

The very subject of extrapolating wind-tunnel data to full scale will probably bring many a grim smile to aeronautical engineers who see this page. The aerodynamicist disparages the wind-tunnel engineer; the wind-tunnel engineer thinks the aerodynamicist wants too much; and if any poor soul is assigned the combination of jobs, well, one is reminded of the classic experiment of crossing a hound dog and a rabbit wherein the offspring ran itself to death.

Probably the nearest approach to the truth lies in the fact that wind tunnels are very rarely called upon to test exact models of items that may be flown. Though this offers a magnificent "out" to the wind-tunnel engineer, it is not meant that way. Reynolds number effects on small items are too great even if they could be accurately constructed; hence the small excrescences are left off the models. In many cases the aerodynamicist who plans on adding these items selects the lowest possible drag values with the net result that he underestimates their interference and overestimates the performance of the airplane. The cure for this situation is to consolidate these items and minimize their effect. Room for improvement can surely exist when examples can be cited of airplanes that have no less than twenty-two separate air intakes and over thirty removable inspection panels. Of course, the effects of small excrescences can be tested in the full-scale tunnel on the actual airplane itself, provided the wingspan is not too great.

The fact that flight tests have been made on a certain airplane helps only partially in aligning flight tests and wind-tunnel data. Two unknowns still remain—the actual horsepower that the engine puts out, and the propeller efficiency. About 1938 the torque nose appeared and made available data as to actual horsepowers being developed in flight. Few data from tests of a thrust mounting have been made generally available, and hence actual propeller efficiencies developed in flight are not precisely known. (See Ref. 7:6.)

Excluding, then, the effects not measurable in the usual wind tunnel, let us examine the effects of scale (Reynolds number) and of compressibility (Mach number) as far as practicable.

7:1. Scale Effect on Wing Drag. The basic effects on the wing drag of increasing Reynolds number are:

1. If the region is at a constant static pressure, the transition from laminar to turbulent boundary-layer flow is moved towards the leading edge. In a region of varying pressure such as over a wing the transition moves forward until it reaches the minimum pressure point.

2. The drag coefficient of both laminar and turbulent boundary layers decreases.

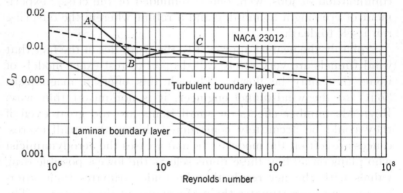

FIG. 7:1.   Plot of $C_{D0min.}$ vs. log RN (from TR 586).

The effects of these phenomena can be examined in the light of what happens to the minimum drag coefficient of a wing as the Reynolds number varies widely. Tests in the Variable-Density tunnel indicate the variation of the minimum drag coefficient of the NACA 23012 airfoil to be as shown in Fig. 7:1. An explanation can be advanced as follows: It is well known that a laminar boundary layer will separate from the surface of an object much more readily than will a turbulent boundary layer. Hence at a Reynolds number of 150,000 the downstream position of the transition point permits a large amount of separation and hence large form drag. This condition corresponds to A of Figs. 7:1 and 7:2.

With increasing Reynolds number the transition region moves forward until it occurs at a point beyond which the turbulent flow remains on the wing. This flow, with the lower drag laminar flow extending a maximum along the chord, results in a low drag coefficient as shown by B in Figs. 7:1 and 7:2.

From then on, increasing the Reynolds number moves the transition region forward until it reaches the minimum pressure point. As the percentage of laminar flow decreases, the drag coefficient increases as shown from B to C in Fig. 7:1.

For still greater Reynolds numbers, no change in the flow pattern is supposed, the drag coefficient following the downward

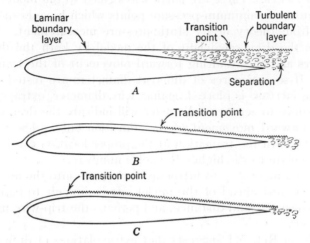

FIG. 7:2. Effect of increasing Reynolds number on boundary-layer flow.

trend of laminar and turbulent boundary-layer flows as stated by the theory, i.e.,

$$C_{D \text{ laminar}} = \frac{2.656}{\sqrt{RN}} \qquad (7:0)$$

$$C_{D \text{ turbulent}} = \frac{0.910}{(\log_{10} RN)^{2.58}} \qquad (7:1)$$

That laminar flow exists over the forward 15 to 25 per cent of the 23012 is indicated by the pressure distribution and borne out in practice. Hence the fact that the drag coefficient of this wing is greater than that for pure turbulent flow completely over the surface indicates that a moderate amount of form or pressure drag actually exists. Further, from Fig. 7:1 it may be inferred that tests below the Reynolds number of point C can hardly be used for extrapolation to full-scale conditions since no regularity exists. It is believed that, though comparison tests between objects may be made with fair accuracy, a test Reynolds number of 1,500,000 to 2,500,000 would be needed if extrapolation is intended. This necessitates a 1½- or 2½-ft chord at 100 mph or equivalent.

Two artifices are employed to simulate the proper boundary-layer disposition when for various reasons sufficient Reynolds number cannot be attained in the wind tunnel. One is the use of "trip" wires. These are small wires glued to the model along the contour of minimum-pressure points which have been determined from theory or by static-pressure measurement. These increase the drag coefficient of the model by both the drag of the wires and the resulting forward movement of the transition point. If several wires of different diameters are tested and if the drag increase is plotted against wire diameter, extrapolation of the curve to zero wire diameter will indicate the drag caused by the forward movement of the transition only. The drag of the model with the transition at the proper location can be used to extrapolate to the higher Reynolds numbers.

A second method is to introduce turbulence into the airstream by screens just ahead of the model. It is difficult to figure the exact screen size and distance, and perhaps the trip-wire method is superior.

Jacobs in Ref. 7:1 suggests that extrapolations of drag coefficients be based on the formula

$$C_{D2} = C_{D1} \left(\frac{RN_2}{RN_1}\right)^{0.11} \qquad (7:2)$$

when C_{D1} values are from tests at a Reynolds number above 8,000,000. Equation 7:3 will also work for Reynolds numbers from 2,500,000 on up.

Figure 7:3 shows the drag coefficients corresponding to different amounts of laminar and turbulent boundary layers at various Reynolds numbers. Zero form drag is assumed. In this chart are shown the theoretical minimum wing drag of 100 per cent laminar flow and the decrease in drag coefficient due to extension of the laminar layer. For example, extension of the laminar layer from 20 to 60 per cent at $RN = 2,000,000$ reduces the drag coefficient from 0.0073 to 0.0048.

In extrapolating drag coefficients, it is necessary to make due allowance if the Reynolds number of the tunnel data is the

"effective" Reynolds number. This procedure is necessary because the part of the drag associated with skin friction decreases
with increasing Reynolds number. Thus for a given effective
Reynolds number the friction coefficients are larger than at a
numerically equal test Reynolds number. The difference between measured drag and the actual drag at the equivalent free
air Reynolds number may be read from the turbulent drag curve
of Fig. 7:1. An example is given.

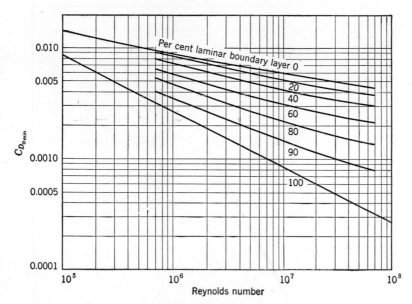

FIG. 7:3. $C_{D0\,min.}$ vs. log RN for various percentages of laminar flow. Zero
form drag assumed.

Example 7:1

The drag of a wing is measured at a test Reynolds number of 3,000,000
and a turbulence factor of 2.0. The measured drag coefficient is 0.0082.
Find the equivalent free air drag coefficient.

1. As $RN_e = TF \times RN$

$$RN_e = 2.0 \times 3,000,000 = 6,000,000$$

2. From the turbulent drag curve of Fig. 7:1, $C_D = 0.0073$ at $RN =$
3,000,000 and 0.0066 at $RN = 6,000,000$.

$$\Delta C_D = 0.0073 - 0.0066 = 0.0007$$

3. The measured drag is therefore too high by 0.0007, and $C_D = 0.0082$
$- 0.0007 \approx 0.0075$.

Special attention should be paid to the extrapolation of C_D at $C_{L \text{ max.}}$. In many cases the tunnel engineer neglects the drag increase that accompanies the increase of $C_{L \text{ max.}}$ with Reynolds number, and predicted glide angles near $C_{L \text{ max.}}$ are then considerably above the attained values.

7:2. Scale Effects on the Lift Curve. The effect of Reynolds number on the lift is also profound. In *TR* 586 (Ref. 7:1)

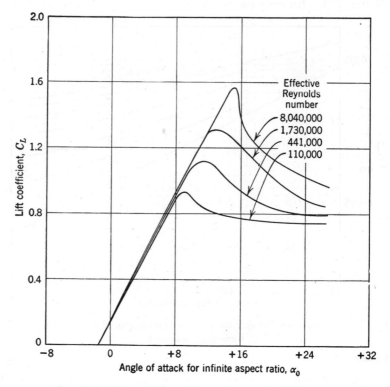

FIG. 7:4. Effect of Reynolds number on the lift curve.

Jacobs indicates that variations in lift curve slope caused by increasing Reynolds number are very small, but in general the lift curve will be straightened up; the slope will increase slightly;[*] and the stall will become more abrupt. (See Fig. 7:4.) Lift curves already straight at the lower Reynolds numbers will be extended at higher ones. It follows that $C_{L \text{ max.}}$ and the angle

[*] At very low values of the Reynolds number, about 150,000, the lift curve again steepens, and $dC_L/d\alpha$ may then exceed 2π/radian.

at which it occurs are increased. The amount of the increase of both angle and $C_{L\,max.}$ are of paramount value to the tunnel engineer.

The method outlined in Ref. 7:1 enables the $C_{L\,max.}$ at Reynolds numbers below 8,300,000 to be determined for a large group of airfoils and enables the engineer to estimate possible Reynolds number effects on new airfoils.

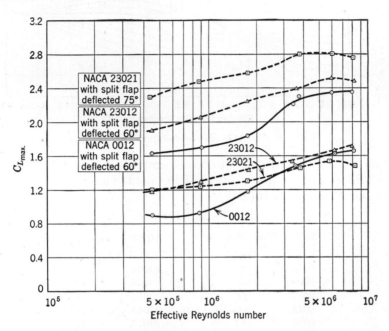

FIG. 7:5. Effect of Reynolds number on $C_{L\,max.}$, flaps down.

The method is to read the $C_{L\,max.}$ at $RN_e = 8,300,000$ and the stall type from Table 7:1. Then the increment (usually negative) is selected from Fig. 7:6 and added to the high Reynolds number $C_{L\,max.}$ to get $C_{L\,max.}$ at the desired Reynolds number. Unfortunately this seemingly simple method is of lessened value in most practical cases for two reasons: first it concerns *section* $C_{l\,max.}$ values when wing $C_{L\,max.}$ values are usually needed; and, second, in view of recent airfoil changes the tunnel engineer will probably not find the desired airfoil in Table 7:1. Though a method considering local downwash and local Reynolds numbers exists (Ref. 6:7) that enables the wing $C_{L\,max.}$ as well as the loca-

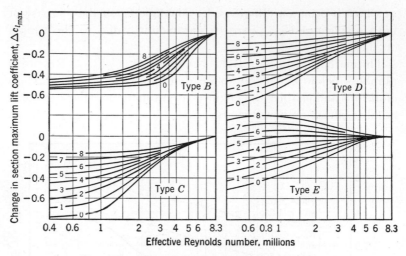

Fig. 7:6. Effect of Reynolds number on $C_{L\,max}$.

tion of the first stalled area to be determined, it is useless without full information as to the effect of Reynolds number on the particular airfoil in question.

TABLE 7:1

Airfoil NACA	Scale effects on $C_{L\,max}$	Airfoil NACA	Scale effects on $C_{L\,max}$
0006	A	23006	A
0009	B_0	23009	C_2
0012	C_0	23012	D_2
0015	D_0	23015	D_2
0018	E_0	23018	E_2
0021	E_1	23021	E_2
0025	E_2		
0030	$..$	43012	D_4
		43015	D_4
2212	C_3	43018	E_4
2409	B_2	63012	D_6
2412	C_2	63018	E_7
2415	D_2		
2418	E_2		
4406	A		
4409	B_4		
4412	C_4		
4415	D_4		
4418	E_4		
4421	E_5		

The way around the problem is largely empirical. Many tunnel engineers have had sufficient experience correlating tunnel data with flight tests so that they feel qualified to estimate $\Delta C_{L\,max.}$ due to Reynolds number. In most cases their estima-

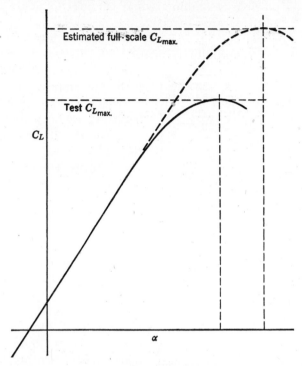

Fig. 7:7.

tions run around $\Delta C_{L\,max.} = 0.15$ for the range from a tunnel test at $RN_e = 1,500,000$ to full scale $RN = 6,000,000$. They then proceed as follows:

1. The straight part of the lift curve from tunnel data is extended with the same slope.

2. Through the value of $C_{L\,max.}$ (full scale) as estimated, a horizontal line is drawn.

3. The curved portion of the test lift curve is then raised until it has the proper value of $C_{L\,max.}$ and shifted laterally until it joins the straight part of the constructed full-scale lift curve.

The net result is a full-scale lift curve having the proper value of zero lift, slope, and $C_{L\,max.}$, but probably having an angle of maximum lift that is too great and a stall that is too gentle. These two deficiencies are not serious, however, and the engineer has at least something with which he can work.

Since the speed of the airplane is reduced for landing, it is sometimes possible to obtain tests at landing Reynolds number in a tunnel of moderate capacity.

As will be seen in Fig. 7:5, the increment of lift due to a deflected flap is essentially constant with changes in Reynolds numbers. This is both fortunate and important, for not infrequently flap changes are necessary on a plane already constructed. In such a case the full-scale $C_{L\,max.}$ is known, and the increments due to various flap arrangements are accurately determined in the tunnel.

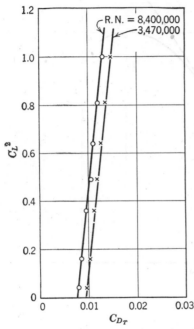

FIG. 7:8. Plot of $C_L{}^2$ vs. C_{DT} for an NACA 23012 at two Reynolds numbers.

Maximum lift coefficients measured in different wind tunnels agree much better when based on "effective" Reynolds numbers (see Sect. 3:6) than when based on the test Reynolds numbers. Increased Reynolds numbers obtained by added turbulence are satisfactory for maximum lift measurements.

7:3. Scale Effects on Total Airplane Drag. After the proper locations of the transition points are assured by adequate test Reynolds number or other artifices, there still remains the problem of accounting for the items left off and in general of devising a way to extrapolate the results out to full scale. This problem is twofold: first the full-scale minimum drag coefficient must be obtained; second, the rate of change of drag with C_L must be determined. The latter is essentially the determination of the span efficiency factor, e. One approach is as follows:

It has been observed (Fig. 7:8) that, when $C_L{}^2$ for a given

airplane is plotted against the total drag coefficient C_{DT}, the graph
is nearly a straight line.   Further, since we may write

$$e = \frac{1}{\sqrt{\dfrac{dC_D}{dC_L{}^2}}\, \pi AR} \qquad\qquad (7:3)$$

it becomes apparent that the slope of the line $dC_D/dC_L{}^2$ may be
used to find e.   (See also Sect. 5:2.)   Fortunately the slope of
this line is practically independent of Reynolds number, and a

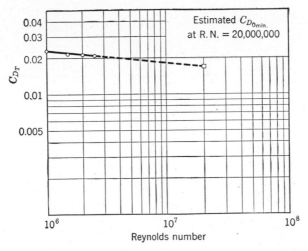

FIG. 7:9.   Plot of C_{DT} vs. log RN.

wind-tunnel test may hence be used to determine full-scale e.
A plot of the 23012 airfoil at two Reynolds numbers is given in
Fig. 7:8.

The determination of the amount the $C_L{}^2$ vs. C_{DT} curve is
moved over (i.e., the scale effect on $C_{D0\,min.\,(ship)}$) with increasing
Reynolds number is not so simple; in fact, no direct rule is known.
If similar tests have been completed in the past and flight tests
made, perhaps the comparison may yield the ΔC_D necessary.
For an entirely new ship, the minimum drag may be measured
at several velocities, and a plot of $C_{D0\,min.}$ vs. log RN may be
made.   The straight line that usually results from such a plot
may be extrapolated to find the approximate full-scale $C_{D0\,min.}$
(Fig. 7:9).

A third method of extrapolating total ship drag to full-scale Reynolds number is as follows:

1. Plot C_D vs. C_L, tunnel data.

2. Subtract $C_{Di} = C_L^2/\pi AR$ from the C_D plot to obtain $C_{D0\,(tunnel)}$.

3. Estimate $C_{L\,max.}$ (full scale) from Figs. 7:4, 7:5, Ref. 7:1, or other sources, and extend C_{D0} until it is horizontal at $C_{L\,max.}$. The increased curvature of the C_{D0} curve should be moved to an increased C_L in a manner similar to that described in Sect. 7:2.

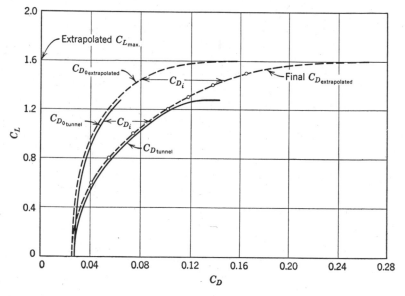

FIG. 7:10.   Extrapolating airplane drag curve to full-scale Reynolds number.

4. Decrease $C_{D0\,min.\,(tunnel)}$ by the C_D change in wing drag from tunnel Reynolds number to full scale. See Fig. 7:1. (This is the controversial step. Some engineers make no change to tunnel $C_{D0\,min.}$ as manufacturing irregularities on the actual ship may increase the drag as much as increased Reynolds number decreases it.)

5. Add C_{Di} back in to get the final extrapolated drag curve. In this step use values of C_L up to $C_{L\,max.}$ (full scale).

The three steps outlined above for getting full-scale values from tunnel data are successful only when applied by experienced aerodynamicists. Fortunately, the change due to Reynolds number is usually small and invariably less than the drag added by the miscellaneous items—pitot tubes, venturis, wing walkways, skin joints, leakage, landing gear, etc., not tested in the usual tunnel program. The effect of these items may be estimated from data gathered from full-scale tests, either flight or in a full-scale tunnel. Such data are covered in many of the NACA reports.

7:4. Miscellaneous Scale Effects. Naturally, since the control and stability surfaces are lifting surfaces, it may be expected that they will be subjected to scale effects not unlike those experienced by wings. Usually such effects are neglected; static longitudinal and lateral stability are considered to be equal for model and full-scale ship, except that those factors affected by the stalling of a surface may be expected to have the stall shown by the model delayed slightly in the full-scale ship. This effect is particularly noticeable on ailerons, where the aileron deflection for maximum C_l and the value of maximum C_l are both increased by increased Reynolds number, not, unfortunately, by any established factor.

The effective range of an aerodynamic balance may also be greater on the full-scale ship than on the model.

The one family of measurements that appears to be unaffected by scale is the pressure-distribution group. Studies made at low Reynolds number appear practically identical with those of high Reynolds number. (See also Sect. 9:1.) Pressure distributions are, of course, affected by Mach number. (See Sect. 7:5.)

7:5. Mach Number Effects. In recent years a second flow parameter has come into prominence, succeeding Reynolds number as an indicator of similar flow patterns. This is Mach number, the ratio of the speed V of air under given conditions to the speed of sound under the same conditions V_c. Expressed symbolically, Mach number $MN = V/V_c$.

For speeds up to around 300 mph, the condition of similar flow patterns may be met by equal Reynolds numbers. As the speed increases above this region, Mach number effects become increasingly larger, until, as the speed of sound is approached, Reynolds number effects become secondary as criteria of flow similitude. The type of shock wave is, however, still influenced by the Reynolds number at which it occurs.

Unfortunately, whereas an increasing Reynolds number is usually associated with a decreasing drag coefficient, high Mach number is accompanied by a greatly increased drag coefficient and by a numerically larger moment coefficient.

Specifically, the Mach number effects should be broken down into three regimes: (1) subsonic flow (no local velocities exceed the speed of sound); (2) transonic flow ("through" the speed of sound—say from $MN = 0.9$ to $MN = 1.1$; and (3) supersonic (freestream speed is above the speed of sound).

In the subsonic range the lift and lift curve slope increases approximately as $1/\sqrt{1 - M^2}$ for a constant angle of attack and the drag coefficient and moment coefficient increase to a lesser

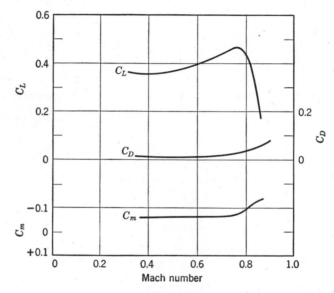

Fig. 7:11. C_L, C_D, and C_m vs. Mach number at constant angle of attack.

degree. The drag increase, it is interesting to note, consists largely of increased form drag, the skin friction increasing but slightly.

After the body reaches the critical force speed,* the changes in the coefficients become more pronounced. The drag and moment coefficients continue their increase of numerical value and at an increased rate. The lift coefficient, and hence the slope of the lift curve, breaks sharply and shows decreasing values (Fig. 7:11).

After the freestream velocity of the body has exceeded the speed of sound, there is a tendency for the drag coefficient to

* The "critical speed" is reached when the velocity at some point on a body reaches the local speed of sound. The "critical force speed" is the speed at which the forces change rapidly owing to shock-wave effects.

return to the low-speed value. Some projectiles apparently complete this cycle, having the same drag coefficient at a Mach number of 2.0 as at 0.3, but of course much more drag. Wind-tunnel tests of airfoils at a Mach number of 2.0 (Ref. 7:7) indicate that their high-speed coefficients are not as low as their low-speed coefficients by a factor of about 4.0. Information in both the transonic and supersonic regimes is so meager and question-

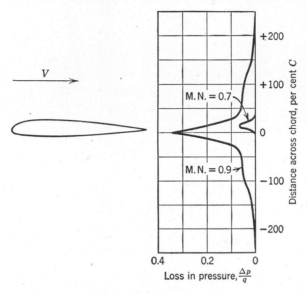

Fig. 7:12.

able that no definite conclusions can yet be drawn about the effects of high-speed flight.

There are two reasons why wind-tunnel testing above the critical speed is difficult. The first and most important is the large blocking (see Sect. 6:19) caused by the profound flow change associated with the shock wave. Perhaps this is most clearly seen in Fig. 7:12, where the wakes for both low and high velocity are compared. It is seen that the rapid pressure rise through the shock wave causes severe separation, spreading the flow so that the wake close to the trailing edge, normally having a width of 0.2 chord, may become 5.00 chords wide. In the tunnel the presence of this large area of low-velocity flow dictates that a velocity much higher than normal must exist outside the wake for a constant amount of air to pass through the test section. This accelerated air, previously near the speed of sound, complicates the flow still further.

A second difficulty encountered in wind-tunnel testing near the speed of sound may be found from examining photographs of the shock wave. The wave, visible in photographs made with the Schlieren process, proceeds from the sharp leading edge of

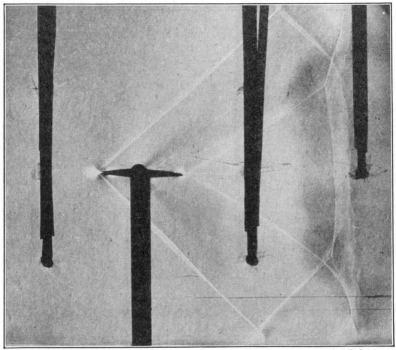

Courtesy Cornell Aeronautical Laboratory.

Fig. 7:13. Schlieren photograph of 10 per cent thick double-wedge airfoil at $MN = 1.7$. Shock waves and their echo are clearly discernible. (The black vertical members are pressure leads and model mounts, and are not in the tunnel.)

an airfoil operating above the speed of sound, extending outward in much the same manner as the bow wave of a boat. The angle between the path of the airfoil and the wave θ_M is approximately the "Mach angle," which is defined as

$$\theta_M = \sin^{-1} \frac{1}{MN} \qquad (7:4)$$

where MN = Mach number of the airfoil.

When the speed of the airstream just slightly exceeds the velocity of sound, the Mach angle is, say, 85 degrees and the shock wave proceeds nearly vertically upwards from the airfoil. It then strikes the roof of the tunnel and echoes back to interfere with the normal free air flow. At twice the speed of sound, $\theta_M = 30°$, and the echo occurs downstream where the rebound is less important.

In actual flight, the wave is undesirable. It absorbs large amounts of energy while it is heating the air passing over the body, and the separation causes large form drag. It is advantageous, therefore, so to shape the body that the critical speed occurs at as late a Mach number as possible. This is accomplished by designing the body to have very small negative pressures so that the amount that the freestream velocity is increased in passing over the body is small.

The critical-force speed of a body may be approximately determined from low Mach number pressure surveys by a method outlined by Greene (Ref. 7:9). The procedure (plotted in Fig. 7:14) will yield the approximate critical force Mach number when the minimum (or "peak") value of $\Delta p/q$ is known from low-speed data or calculated from incompressible potential flow theory (Ref. 7:3).

Example 7:2

Low-speed tests indicate that an airfoil has a peak pressure of $-0.6q$. What is the approximate critical-force Mach number?

In Fig. 7:14, follow out along the $\Delta p/q = -0.6$ curve until it strikes the critical curve at A. Read the theoretical critical-force Mach number = 0.72 directly below A.

It has been found that sharp entries increase the critical-force speed, as does locating the maximum body thickness rearward. Unfortunately a sharp leading edge cannot support a smooth flow through a large angle of attack range, and airfoils designed for very high speeds usually show low values of $C_{L\,max.}$.

Attention is drawn to the presenting of the critical speed as a function of V_c. As V_c varies with temperature, being equal to $49.1\sqrt{°\text{Rankine}}$, and hence decreases with altitude (Fig. 7:15), the critical speed of an airplane is lower in miles per hour at altitude than at sea level.

The theory first advanced by Glauert indicated that at constant angle of attack the lift, and hence the slope of the lift

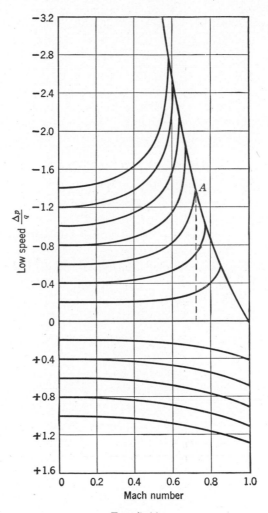

FIG. 7:14.

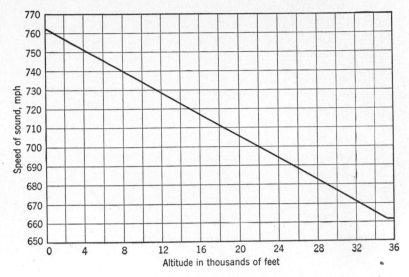

FIG. 7:15.   Effect of altitude on the velocity of sound, standard atmosphere.

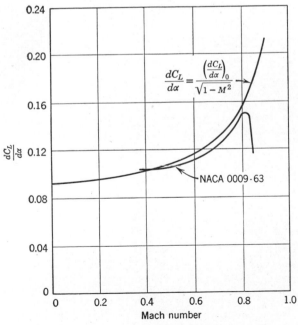

FIG. 7:16.   Slope of lift curve vs. MN, Glauert's theory and practice.

curve of an airfoil, would increase numerically with increasing Mach number by the ratio $1/\sqrt{1 - M^2}$. Early wind-tunnel tests seem to corroborate the theory, at least partially (Ref. 7:5). But the conditions for the airplane are not the same as for an airfoil. Here many critical speeds are present, and the Mach number effects occur in progression, not simultaneously. Usually the first shock waves occur at the wing-fuselage juncture where the speed increase over the wing adds to that over the fuselage. Next the cowling and windshield are affected. Last of all is the

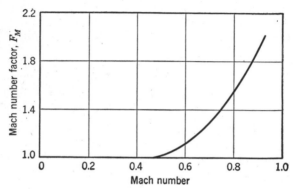

FIG. 7:17. Typical plot of drag increase for complete airplane vs. Mach number.

wing shock wave. The rate of increase of drag coefficient with Mach number is therefore less than for an airfoil alone. One way of estimating this increase is to base it on flight tests of a similar airplane. Sometimes a general curve is employed, using flight Mach numbers or some similar parameter. Such a curve is shown in Fig. 7:17. The value of the airplane $C_{D0 \text{ min.}}$ at a given Mach number M is found from

$$C_{D0 \text{ min. } M} = C_{D0 \text{ min. } 0} \times F_M \qquad (7:5)$$

where $C_{D0 \text{ min. } M}$ = minimum drag coefficient at M.
$\quad C_{D0 \text{ min. } 0}$ = minimum drag coefficient at low speed.
$\quad F_M$ = Mach number factor from Fig. 7:17.

Since increased angle of attack rapidly increases the minimum pressure on the upper side of the wings and fuselage, critical speeds drop rapidly with increasing α (or C_L). Minimum pressures as read on a wind-tunnel model at various angles of attack could be used to find the critical speed at which Mach number effects begin, and then a curve similar to Fig. 7:17 but "starting" at an earlier Mach number could be used to estimate the increase in drag coefficient for angles other than zero.

It is not unusual to locate the starting point of the general curve by pressure surveys of the wing-fuselage juncture.

A second method, in use by many engineers in this field, considers the Mach number factor F_M a function of M/M_{cr}. The critical Mach number employed, M_{cr}, is that of the thickest wing section and may be determined from low-speed tests and Fig. 7:14. The curve itself is determined from flight tests.

At the present time it is not known whether the effective induced drag coefficient, C_{Die}, should also be increased by F_M. Though compressibility will change the span load distribution by affecting the thicker wing root sections first, the resulting amount of change of the induced drag coefficient is probably not as great as the parasite drag change. Until better information is available, it is suggested that F_M be applied to the parasite drag coefficient only.

No set form is available for presenting the results of tests at high Mach numbers. Sometimes plots of C_D, C_L, and C_m against Mach number are made for a constant angle of attack. This shows the change in coefficients with Mach number all right, but not in terms directly usable for performance calculations. Holding C_L constant is some improvement, but a more direct method yet is presented below.

In the usual terminology

$$L = \frac{\rho}{2} S V^2 C_L \qquad (7:6)$$

For a given airplane at a constant altitude where the velocity of sound is V_c,

$$L = \frac{\rho}{2} S \frac{V^2}{V_c^2} C_L V_c^2 = (\text{const.}) \, M^2 C_L \qquad (7:7)$$

If we plot C_D, C_m, and stick force against $M^2 C_L$, we have the conditions of flight most directly compared, for at a given altitude the airplane flies at a constant value of $M^2 C_L$.

In conclusion, the author believes that the general effects of flying at speeds approaching the speed of sound are as follows:

1. The drag coefficients will be greater than those measured at low speeds, but the increase may be less than indicated by published wind-tunnel tests.

2. Since the thicker sections near the root of the wing show Mach number effects earliest, the lift to support a given load must come from the thinner outer panel, increasing the bending moment in the wing.

3. The moment coefficients may have greatly increased values as compared with those determined from low-speed tests. This

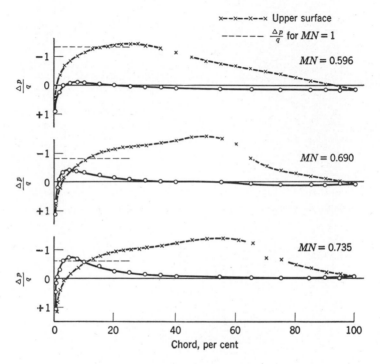

Fig. 7:18. Effect of Mach number on pressure distribution, NACA 4415 at $-0°15'$.

in conjunction with decreased lift above the critical-force speed could pitch the airplane seriously and is more important than items 1 and 2 since lift and drag changes only affect the performance.

4. High-speed flutter caused by compression waves and more rapid excitation will increase in importance.

5. Compressibility effects on aerodynamic balances may be severe enough to warrant complete reconsideration of the problem.

6. The heat rise caused by bringing the air in a cowling to airplane speed will increase cooling difficulties, but probably this will not be critical. It amounts to about 50° F at 500 mph.

7. Wind-tunnel tests to determine the above will probably require smaller models for a given jet size than are customarily used in low-speed testing, since blocking effects appear to be excessive in the high Mach number range.

8. The strength increments necessitated by compressibility effects lead to considerable increase of structural weight and a consequent diminution in performance.

That the effect of Mach number on airfoil pressure distribution is severe may be inferred from the change in pitching moment coefficient. The shock-wave progression on one airfoil is shown in Fig. 7:18.

PROBLEMS

7:1. Calculate the drag coefficients for 100 per cent laminar and 100 per cent turbulent boundary-layer flow. $V = 300$ mph, $MAC = 7$ ft. Use standard sea-level air. Check your answer with Fig. 7:3.

7:2. The minimum pressure on a certain wing is $\Delta p/q = -1.4$. Find (a) the critical Mach number, and (b) the velocity necessary to obtain this critical Mach number at 30,000 ft, standard atmosphere.

7:3. Calculate the speed of sound at 20,000 ft and check with Fig. 7:15.

7:4. Calculate $dC_L/d\alpha$ for $M = 0.5$ if $dC_L/d\alpha$ for $M = 0.0$ is 0.073.

7:5. If a certain clean airplane has a $C_{D0\,min.} = 0.0250$ at 100 mph, estimate $C_{D0\,min.}$ for 500 mph at sea level, standard conditions.

REFERENCES

7:1. E. N. Jacobs, The Variation of Airfoil Section Characteristics with Reynolds Number, *TR* 586, 1937.

7:2. T. von Kármán, Compressibility Effects in Aerodynamics, *JAS*, July, 1941.

7:3. T. Theodorsen, General Potential Theory of Arbitrary Airfoils, *TR* 452, 1932.

7:4. E. Heinkel, The Raising of Aircraft Speeds in Recent Years, Lilienthal-Gesellschaft für Luftfahrtforschung, October, 1938.

7:5. H. Glauert, The Effect of Compressibility on the Lift of an Airfoil, *R&M* 1135, 1927.

7:6. Geo. W. Brady, Flight Testing with a Propeller Thrustmeter, *SAE Journal*, July, 1944.

7:7. Antonio Ferri, Experimental Results with Airfoils Tested in the High-Speed Tunnel at Guidonia, *TM* 946, 1940.

7:8. John Stack, Compressible Flows in Aeronautics, *JAS*, April, 1945.

7:9. L. M. Greene, The Attenuation Method for Compressible Flow Systems, *JAS*, July, 1945.

CHAPTER VIII

AUXILIARY TESTING EQUIPMENT

Besides the fundamental balance, pitot-static tubes, yawheads, and wake survey rakes, a few inexpensive auxiliary items offer interesting opportunity for investigation and are downright mandatory for some special tests. In this group are such items as a boundary-layer mouse, Kiel tubes, smoke flow apparatus, etc.

8:1. Boundary-Layer Mouse. The boundary-layer mouse (Fig. 8:1) is a bank of flat total-head tubes arranged to read the total head in several places very close to the surface of the wing (Ref. 8:1). It is used to locate the point of transition from laminar to turbulent boundary layer and to investigate boundary-layer thickness. The operation of the mouse is as follows:

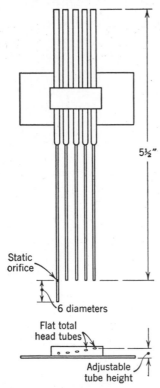

Static orifice

5½"

6 diameters

Flat total head tubes

Adjustable tube height

FIG. 8.1. A boundary-layer mouse.

The type of boundary-layer flow existing at some point on an airfoil may be determined from the velocity gradient in the boundary layer. Gradients for laminar and turbulent boundary layers appear in Fig. 8:2. The mouse is first attached to the wing (Scotch cellophane tape will do) near the leading edge with the total-head tubes adjusted to be in the boundary layer. Readings of the four total heads and one static head are taken, and, since the static pressure is essentially constant across the boundary layer, the four velocities may be calculated. The mouse is then moved to points farther back on the wing,

288

and the process is repeated, yielding a plot similar to Fig. 8:3. A cross plot of Fig. 8:3 yields Fig. 8:4, the velocity in the boundary layer at a constant height above the surface. The interpretation of Fig. 8:4 is that as the flow progresses along the wing the boundary layer thickens, and points at constant height become progressively deeper in the boundary layer and hence have slower velocities. Finally the transition region is reached; the thick-

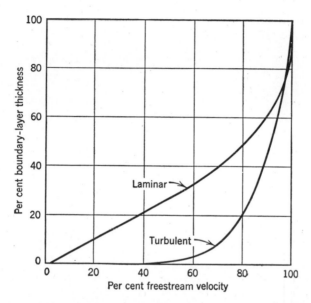

Fig. 8:2. Velocity distribution in laminar and turbulent boundary layers.

ened boundary layer is scrubbed off by the turbulent air; and the point returns to a higher velocity. Figure 8:4 indicates that, in the example graphed above, transition took place about the 18 per cent chord point. It will be noticed that the change from laminar to turbulent flow occurs in a region rather than at a point. The length of this region increases with Reynolds number.

Many methods are in use to determine the location of the transition region. They include:

1. Plotting the velocity gradient in the boundary layer and determining whether the flow is laminar or turbulent by the slope of the gradient.

2. Crossplotting 1, determining the beginning of transition as the point where the velocity is smallest.

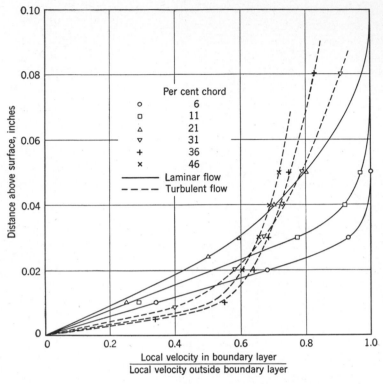

FIG. 8:3.

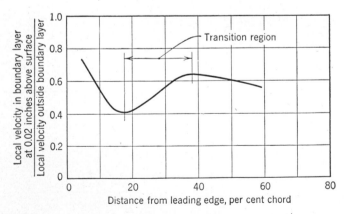

FIG. 8:4. The velocity in the boundary layer at a constant small height above the surface.

3. Reading the static pressure at a small height above the surface, determining the transition by a slight dip in the plot of static pressure vs. per cent chord.

4. Reading the dynamic pressure at a small height above the surface and noting the minimum value of q from a plot of q vs. per cent chord.

5. Reading either q, static pressure, or total head and noting the transition point by slight oscillations in the fluid column.

6. Reading the velocity at a small height above the surface with a hot-wire anemometer, and noting the transition as a region of unsteadiness in the meter.

7. Reading the velocity at a small height above the surface with a hot-wire anemometer, and noting start of transition as the point of minimum velocity.

8. Carefully emitting smoke from flush orifices and noting transition by the dispersal of the smoke stream.

9. Painting the model with special chemicals that evaporate slowly. The evaporation will proceed most rapidly where the flow is turbulent.

Of the above, 1 and 2 seem simplest and most direct. The "special chemicals" mentioned in 9 consist of an emulsion containing china clay and nitrobenzene. The procedure is to spray the wing with the emulsion, leaving a white finish. Just before a test the nitrobenzene is sprayed on. As its index of refraction is about the same as the china clay particles, the white completely disappears. When the wind stream is applied the nitrobenzene evaporates most quickly in the turbulent boundary layer, and in a few minutes the turbulent region has become white again, the laminar layer remaining unaffected. Photographs of this process are quite striking.

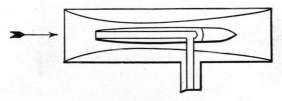

FIG. 8:5. Kiel tube.

8:2. Kiel Tubes. Kiel tubes (Fig. 8:5) are total-head tubes so arranged that their accuracy is unimpaired through wide variations in yaw angles (Fig. 8:6). Inside cowlings and in

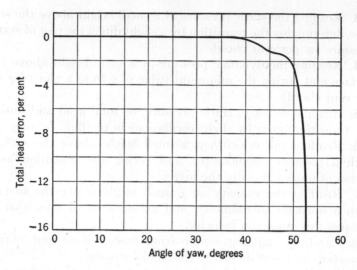

FIG. 8:6.   Effect of yaw on Kiel tube.

other places where the flow direction is uncertain, they are useful in measuring the total head (Ref. 8:2).

8:3. Apparatus for Flow Visualization.   It would be difficult to exaggerate the information that can be obtained from actually seeing the flow pattern about complex models.   Sometimes an entirely new slant can be obtained, as well as a graphic verification of the spreading and contracting of the streamlines.   Flow patterns may be made visible by smoke or the Fales method, while separation can be identified with simple thread tufts.

Several chemicals, for example titanium tetrachloride and tin tetrachloride, will produce smoke when brought into contact with damp air.   Both compounds are corrosive.   Smoke "bombs" and candles may be obtained from the armed forces, but they are difficult to control.   All in all, the cleaned smoke from rotted wood seems to be as good as any.

Since most tunnels are of the return type in which returned smoke might easily hide nearly everything, and since smoke tests are at best messy except in specially designed smoke tunnels, it is suggested that the wind-tunnel operator utilize tufts or streamers for visualization.   These, usually wool or thread not over 2 in. long, may be fastened to the model by Scotch cellophane tape.   When the tape is removed, the traces left may be washed off with benzene, which does not affect the usual finishes. Possibly the most rapid method of installing tufts is to attach them about every 4 in. to the tape before application. Whole strips can then be put on at once. For wing tests, streamers at the 15, 30, 45, 60, and 75 per cent chord points are adequate, and from them the whole stall pattern may be progressively traced. A stall "picture" is illustrated in Fig. 8:7. This type of set-up may not be photographed with the usual high shutter speeds as the movement of the tufts due to unsteady flow would not be apparent. However, at $\frac{1}{50}$ second

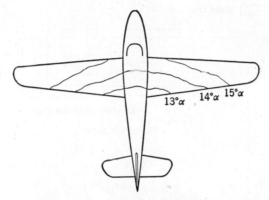

FIG. 8:7. Typical stall pattern. Note stall beginning at wing root so that ailerons remain effective.

the moving tufts show up blurred, and the stall progress may be noted. Additional visual observations are usually in order to establish the advent of unsteady flow, intermittent stall, and full stall.

A streamer may also be of use mounted at the end of a fishpole so that vortices and roughness may be traced about the model without the proximity of the investigator disturbing the flow. If this necessitates the operator's entering the tunnel, goggles are needed. Although his appearance is a bit silly, a particle of dust in his eye at 60 to 100 mph is no laughing matter.

The Fales method consists of mounting a half model (split through the plane of symmetry) on a glass plate, and lightly coating both plate and model with a mixture of lampblack and kerosene. The air flow spreads the mixture along the streamlines so that after the tunnel has been stopped the flow pattern remains. Good pictures can then be made of the flow pattern, and if the lampblack is spread sufficiently thin only a minimum will be blown into the tunnel.

Another method, useful in the higher-speed range where good flow is indicated by the lack of large density changes in the air, is called the "striae" system and makes use of an apparatus

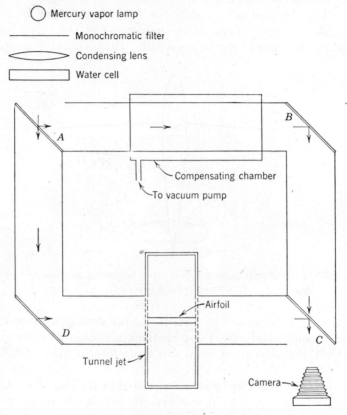

Mercury vapor lamp

Monochromatic filter

Condensing lens

Water cell

FIG. 8:8. Diagrammatic set-up for striae system.

called the "interferometer." This was developed by the Germans during World War II. The arrangement is as follows:

Monochromatic light (see Fig. 8:8) from a mercury-vapor lamp is separated at A by a half-silvered mirror. Part of the light continues around a free air space, and part passes across a two-dimensional model in a test section. The two light beams are brought together again by the half-silvered mirror at C. The minute differences in the two paths produce striae at the viewing lens or camera, and any changes in density due to the air-density changes over the model appear as deformations of the even striae field.

8:4. Vernier Manometer. The ordinary meter stick for measuring a column of liquid is not sufficient if fluid heights are to be determined accurately. Instead a precision vernier manometer must be used (Fig. 8:9). The salient features of such an

Fig. 8:9. Vernier manometer.

arrangement include: (1) a rotatable indicator piece so that arbitrary slopes can be used on the fluid meniscus to increase accuracy; (2) a vernier scale for precise reading; (3) a suitable damping arrangement; (4) a variable-height indicator or a variable-height reservoir so that the system is null and no error is incurred by having a variation in reservoir level as the fluid column changes.

If fluid heights to be measured are large, it would be better to move the reservoir and keep the indicator at eye level, rather than vice versa as shown in Fig. 8:9.

8:5. Multiple Manometers. Frequently it is necessary to read a large number of static pressures simultaneously. An instrument useful for this type of work is a bank of pressure tubes called a multiple manometer (Fig. 8:10). Features useful in a multiple manometer include an adjustable-height reservoir, individual damping of each tube, and adjustable tube angle. A glass tubing known as "barometer" tubing has a thick wall and is quite accurately made. For photography, however, thin-wall tubing is more satisfactory. Since the simultaneous reading of

FIG. 8:10. A multiple manometer.

50 to 80 liquid columns is usually required, photographic methods or direct printing on sensitized paper should be used. The following difficulties must be surmounted: (1) Liquid columns should be damped so that surging is at a minimum. The instantaneous eye of a camera cannot take average pressures. (2) The lag between testing and inspection of results can be serious if the usual period for developing and printing is observed.

The connections of the multiple manometer should be checked frequently by letting a low pressure at the orifice raise a fluid column and hold it when the orifice is sealed. The simple "response" check is not sufficient, for leaking tubes respond readily to a sudden increase of pressure. All tubes should be blown free of condensate at frequent periods.

Not infrequently a manometer tube will fail to level properly owing to either dirt in the glass tube or a bubble in the line. Care is necessary if accurate readings are desired.

Sometimes the pressures to be measured require that fluids heavier than alcohol be utilized, and several of these are listed in Table 8:1. Only pure liquids should be employed, for the heavy portions will settle out of a mixture.

TABLE 8:1

Liquid	Specific Gravity (approx.)	Remarks
Alcohol (see Sect. 3 : 2)	0.80	All around the most satisfactory.
Water	1.00 *	Makes a poor meniscus due to excessive surface tension †
Methylene chloride	1.30	Attacks rubber.
Bromobenzene	1.50	Quite volatile.
Ethyl bromide	1.50	Too volatile to use.
Carbon tetrachloride	1.59	Attacks rubber, but is cheap and otherwise good.
Acetylene tetrachloride	1.59	Attacks rubber.
Ethylene dibromide	2.13	Quite volatile; low surface tension and meniscus poor.
Acetylene tetrabromide	2.97	Attacks rubber.
Mercury	13.78	Oil the meniscus for best results.

* 0.998 at 70° F.

† The surface tension may be made acceptable through the addition of a wetting agent such as used in photographic processes.

The liquids that attack rubber may sometimes be used with synthetic rubber tubing or most of the plastic tubing now available.

For photographic work it is usually necessary to color the fluid to make the detail in the films easier to read. Ordinary ink will work for water and alcohol, as will any of a great number of textile dyes, but inasmuch as many dyes will fade if iron is present it is usually advisable to make all metal parts of the manometer of brass. Black is a very suitable color, and alcohol may be so dyed with a commercial dye called Nigrosine 12525; Buffalo Chrome Black, 2 BN; or Direct Black, E concentration.

8:6. Electric Measuring Devices. There are several methods for measuring forces or pressures electrically, most of them depending on amplifying the effect that tiny deflections have on the capacitance, inductance, or resistance of the unit. For example, the resistance of a carbon pack varies as the pressure on it, and the current it passes for a fixed voltage may be used as an index of the load. The amount of current needed to keep the core of a solenoid in a fixed location is an index of the load on it. The change in capacitance of a plate condenser with small deflections of the plates may again indicate a load. The resistance of a wire changes with the tension in the wire, and the current

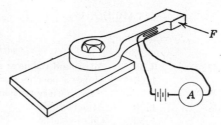

FIG. 8:11.

passed for a fixed voltage may indicate the tension. And so ad infinitum—a hundred different set-ups may be possible. It should be borne in mind that through amplification the most minute changes may be noted and that remarkable accuracy is possible. In most of the set-ups, care must be taken to allow for the effects of temperature both on the unit and on any reference marks.

The measurements of control surface hinges moments offer a good opportunity for the use of an electrical measuring device. The design criteria call for a small unit, unaffected by tempera-

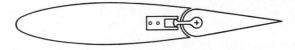

FIG. 8:12.

ture, capable of being read remotely, and allowing only small deflections. These conditions are admirably met by the electric wire strain gauge.

An electric wire strain gauge is outlined in Fig. 8:11. It consists of an arm upon which tiny wire coils have been cemented. A load at F, by deflecting the beam but a minute amount, will stretch the wires glued to the tension surface of the beam. This changes the resistance of the wires on that side and hence varies the current that will flow through them for a fixed voltage. The

Courtesy Lockheed Aircraft Corp.

FIG. 8:13. Set-up for evaluating ground effect.

gauge may be calibrated by applying known moments and reading the amount of current that flows for each. In operation, then, the sensitive ammeter indicates the actual hinge moment. In actual practice the simple system outlined above must have added complications to allow for temperature changes.

8:7. Ground Plane. When an airplane is in the landing attitude and close to the ground the effect of the ground on the horizontal tail surfaces is very pronounced. Sometimes 10 more degrees of elevator deflection are required to stall the airplane when it is close to the ground than when it is at altitude. As landing is frequently the critical condition for the determination of elevator size an accurate test must be performed in the wind tunnel for the information of the design group. Such a test may be performed in conjunction with a flat panel that spans the tunnel beneath the model. (See Fig. 8:13.) This panel, called a ground plane, is superior to mounting the model near the tunnel floor as the thick boundary layer found there would impair the results. The dimensions of the ground plane are important too. One well-known aircraft manufacturer found that, besides extending to the walls, the ground plane must extend a full tail length ahead of the fuselage nose and an equal amount behind the tail before accurate simulation of the ground was accomplished. See Sect. 6:16 for boundary corrections for this type of test.

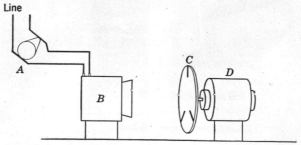

Fig. 8:14. A Strobotachometer.

8:8. Accurate RPM Measurement. A device that will measure certain values of the rpm well within 1 rpm is shown in Fig. 8:14. The operation is described as follows:

The shaft whose rpm is to be set, A, has a breaker so arranged that once each revolution an impulse is sent to a Strobotach, B. Hence one flash of light is emitted from the Strobotach each revolution and, falling upon the disk C which is whirled at a constant known rpm by the synchronous motor D, "stops" the disk once each revolution of the shaft A. If, say, one radial line is painted on the disk, and the synchronous motor turns 1800 rpm, then when the shaft A turns at 1800 rpm a single "stopped" mark will appear on the disk. If the shaft A turns 3600 rpm it will be seen that two stopped marks will appear. Using various numbers of evenly spaced lines a wide, almost limitless, number of rpms are measurable to the accuracy of the power-line frequency that runs the synchronous motor. In general it is possible to adjust the tests so that one of the measurable rpm's satisfies the criteria.

8:9. Schlieren Process. The Schlieren process is an optical device for making visible the shock waves that appear in the flow about a model in the sonic-velocity region. The basic arrangement is shown in Fig. 8:15. The operation is as follows:

Light from a point source A is made into a parallel beam by a lens B and directed across the model M in the high-speed tunnel F. The rays of light that pass through the region of constant density (no shock waves) are gathered by lens C and again brought to a point at D. Here a knife edge is brought up until it blocks all those unbent light rays and prevents them from impinging in the screen E. Light rays that pass through the region of shock waves are bent by the changed index of refrac-

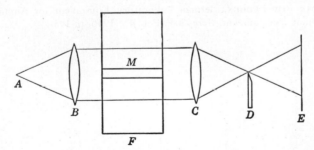

FIG. 8:15. Diagrammatic Schlieren set-up.

tion of air and, entering lens C at an angle, are not brought to a point at D. They therefore escape around the knife edge and appear on the screen E. It is seen that this method separates the shock-wave light so that it becomes visible.

Figures 4:11 and 7:13 are photographs made by the Schlieren process.

A simpler set-up that yields less definition is called the "shadowgraph" method. It consists merely of an even light source at B in Fig. 8:15 and a translucent screen at C. The waves become visible as light shadows on the screen.

8:10. Auxiliary Test Sections. The usual rectangular or round three-dimensional test section may be easily converted to a two-dimension test section by the addition of two vertical walls spaced at any desired gap, with provision for mounting a short-span constant-chord model between them. This arrangement has three advantages over spanning the entire test section: (1) the model has less area and hence the forces are smaller although the Reynolds number is large; (2) if a contraction is arranged between the vertical walls, higher speed than in the normal jet may be obtained; and (3) the smaller-span model is easier to construct.

An arrangement that facilitates the two-dimensional insert employs the usual balance model mounting struts to support the section model.

REFERENCES

8:1. ABE SILVERSTEIN, Determination of Boundary-Layer Transition on Three Symmetrical Airfoils in the NACA Full-Scale Wind Tunnel, *TR* 637, 1939.

8:2. G. KIEL, A Total-Head Meter with Small Sensitivity to Yaw, *TM* 775, 1935.

8:3. SIR ROY FEDDEN, German Laboratory Equipment for Aircraft and Power Plant Development, *Aeroplane*, Feb. 15, 1946, p. 195.

CHAPTER IX

SMALL WIND TUNNELS

In order to avoid the impression that useful wind tunnels must have a large jet and a speed of 100 mph or more, it seems pertinent to discuss some uses of smaller tunnels. A 30-in. tunnel was used by Van Schliestett in the program presented in *TN* 506 (Ref. 6:11), and a still smaller tunnel was used by Merrian and Spaulding (Ref. 3:1) in their outstanding calibrations of pitot-static tubes. Other examples could be given of successful programs carried out with the most inexpensive equipment.

The fundamental advantage of a small wind tunnel is traceable to the economics of tunnel operation. Small tunnels cost less to build and less to run. Though economy in operation is frequently neglected in tunnel proposals, it should not be, especially when it is realized that the electricity cost alone of some tunnels exceeds $100 an hour!

A further advantage of a small tunnel is the small size of the models and the consequent savings in construction time. Small size may be a disadvantage, it is true; but those who have shaped a solid mahogany block 6 by 4 feet know well what is meant.

The most successful tests made in a small tunnel are, obviously (1) those unaffected by Reynolds number and (2) those where any change due to Reynolds number is inconsequential.

9:1. Tests Unaffected by Reynolds Number. The tests most completely free from Reynolds number effects are those embracing pressure readings. Such experiments as static-pressure surveys and the aforementioned pitot-static calibration are in this group. The value of pressure distributions around airfoils is well known and has been given renewed attention recently by a greatly increased interest in boundary-layer flow and in airfoils in general. Individual companies have been tending to design their own airfoils. The small tunnel can play an important part in this work. The many criteria (see Sect. 4:15) which are determinable from pressure surveys are within reach of nearly all wind tunnels.

Many experiments concerning wind-tunnel boundary corrections are suitable for the small tunnel. These, too, are unaffected by Reynolds number.

A further use of a small tunnel is in the study of flow patterns. Such studies are accomplished by sketching the behavior of tufts which are emplaced all over the model. These drawings require both a skilled artist and a lot of tunnel time. So little is known of proper shaping for the best flow that it is not at all unusual for this type of test to be performed.

The progress of the stall over a wing is also essentially unchanged by Reynolds number, although the entire stall is usually delayed on the full-scale airplane.

Two tests for military airplanes that could be performed in a small tunnel include jettison tests of the drop-type external fuel tanks and tests of the flow from gasoline dump valves. Both these actions frequently develop unforeseen complications.

It should be noted that the expression "unaffected by changes in Reynolds number" must not be taken too broadly. By it is customarily meant that *reasonable* changes in Reynolds number produce little effect, and in turn this implies that the range under consideration will be free from movement of the transition point, i.e., above $RN_e = 2,500,000$, or transition points artificially fixed (see Sect. 7:1). The absence of change in e, and $\alpha_{Z.L.}$ is limited by these stipulations. Pressure distributions at low angle of attack and the slope of the lift curve seem almost unaffected on down to $RN = 200,000$. There are few accurate data below a Reynolds number of 200,000 on which to base further discussion.

9:2. When Reynolds Number May Be Ignored. Tests wherein any variations of results due to Reynolds number are inconsequential embrace both qualitative tests and tests wherein the taking of data is secondary, i.e., using tunnel testing for instruction purposes.

Qualitative tests are those that are expected to lead either to more testing or to abandonment of the project. They include the testing of radical ideas with a searching attitude for something promising. A recent project of that type encompassed the testing of airfoils that drooped the leading edge instead of, or in conjunction with, a conventional trailing edge flap. The search was instigated by a hope for a decrease of moment and perhaps an increase of lift. Since the low Reynolds number tests failed to show any evidence of either (although the angle of maximum lift was greatly increased), the project was abandoned.

Other tests of a similar nature can easily be conceived.

9:3. The Small Wind Tunnel for Instruction. Almost no type of testing is performed in a large tunnel that cannot be duplicated in a small tunnel, the possible exception being tests of powered models. Hence a small tunnel is invaluable for instruction.

Courtesy Georgia Institute of Technology.

FIG. 9:1. A small wind tunnel.

Many schools have a small wind tunnel, not unlike that shown in Fig. 9:1, for the use of undergraduates. The jet size is about 24 in. by 36 in., and the overall dimensions are such that a space 14 ft by 30 ft is sufficient for the tunnel and motor. Twenty to twenty-five horsepower will provide 100 mph in the test section.

Walls for the test section are designed so that they may be wholly or partially removed, thus enabling tests to be performed with open or closed jet and studies to be made of asymmetrical boundaries.

Many of these smaller tunnels do not use a six-component balance. The necessity for completing a test in the usual laboratory period of three to four hours precludes as complete a test as might be desired.

A list of experiments suitable for instruction is presented below. Each requires about three hours. Doubtless, as trends change, additional tests may be added, and many of those suggested below will become obsolescent.

Experiment 1.   Jet Calibration

Tunnel condition: Open jet, balance out.

Apparatus: Pitot-static tube, yawhead, turbulence sphere, 2 micromanometers, meter stick.

Tests: 1. Read dynamic pressure at 2-in. stations across jet. Plot per cent variation in dynamic pressure from centerline value against station.

2. Read angle of flow at 2-in. stations across jet. Plot flow inclination in degrees against station.

3. Determine the turbulence.

4. Read static pressure at tunnel centerline from plane of jet to exit cone at 3-in. intervals. Plot static pressure against station.

5. Read dynamic pressure at tunnel centerline for various pressures in the settling chamber. Plot dynamic pressure against settling chamber pressure.

Experiment 2.   Balance Alignment and Aspect Ratio

Tunnel condition: Open jet, balance in.

Apparatus: Two wings of similar profile and chord but different aspect ratio, 4 and 6.

Tests: 1. Install wing of $AR = 6$. Read L, D, M from below zero lift to stall.

2. Invert model and repeat.

3. Same for wing of $AR = 4$.

4. Plot all data, and make alignment and boundary corrections. (Final data include tare drag and interference, but with models of about 3-in. chord the evaluation of these effects is extremely difficult.) Note on plots $\alpha_{Z.L.}$, $\dfrac{dC_L}{d\alpha}$, $C_{L\ max.}$, $C_{d0\ min.}$, C_{m0}, ac.

Experiment 3.   Tailsetting and Downwash

Tunnel condition: Open jet, balance in.

Apparatus: Model with horizontal tail having variable incidence.

Tests: 1. Read L, D, M from zero lift to stall with tail off.

2. Repeat with tail on, elevator zero, and tail incidence $-8°$ to $8°$.

3. Plot α vs. C_m, and downwash ϵ vs. α. Determine α_{tail} and tail incidence for $C_L = 0.2$.

Experiment 4. Static Longitudinal Stability

Tunnel condition: Open jet, balance in.
Apparatus: Model with removable tail and movable elevators.
Tests: 1. Run model from zero lift to stall reading L, D, M. Tail off.
2. Repeat with tail on and elevators 0, $-5°$, $-10°$, $-15°$.

3. Plot C_m vs. C_L for each elevator setting and C_m vs. δ_e. State $\dfrac{dC_m}{dC_L}$.

Also plot C_L vs. α.

Experiment 5. Profile Drag by Momentum Theory

Tunnel condition: Closed tunnel, balance out.
Apparatus: 12-in. chord airfoil, wake survey rake, meter stick, multiple manometer.
Tests: 1. Read wake $0.7c$ behind airfoil trailing edge with wake survey rake from $\alpha = -3°$ to $6°$. Plot C_{d0} vs. α.
2. Read wake at $\alpha = 0$ at 40, 50, 60, 70, 80, 90 mph (indicated). Plot C_{d0} vs. Reynolds number.

Experiment 6. Pressure Distribution

Tunnel condition: Closed jet, balance out.
Apparatus: Pressure wing; multiple manometer.
Tests: 1. With tunnel set at 60 mph read the pressure distribution for eight angles of attack including zero lift, maximum lift, and after the stall. Calculate and plot the normal and chordwise pressure distributions to get C_N, C_C, and C.P., and plot these quantities against α.

Experiment 7. Dynamic Stability

Tunnel condition: Open jet, balance out.
Apparatus: Flying wing model, dynamic stability rig.
Tests: At 40, 60, 80 mph disturb model and time oscillations. Plot period vs. velocity.

Experiment 8. The Boundary Layer

Tunnel condition: Open jet, balance out.
Apparatus: 15-in. chord NACA 0015 wing, mounting rig, boundary-layer mouse, manometer.
Tests: Place mouse at 5, 10, 15, 20, 25, 30, and 35 per cent chord, and read dynamic pressures at 0.03, 0.06, 0.09, 0.12 in. from surface. Determine transition region by plotting velocity profiles and velocity at constant height.

ANSWERS TO PROBLEMS

3:1. 5.2% water, sp. gr. = 0.796 at 26° C.

3:2. ——

3:3. T.F. = 1.64.

3:4. ER = 2.68.

5:1. ——

5:2. e = 0.962.

5:3. $\dfrac{dC_D}{dC_L}$ = 0.0893 and 0.0876.

5:4. 0.218, C.P. = 0.468.

5:5. ——

5:6. 0.998.

6:1. 0.191 lb.

6:2. 0.141 lb.

6:3. u_1/V = 0.121.

6:4. $\Delta\alpha_i$ = 0.91°.

6:5. ——

6:6. ——

6:7. (a) −0.134, (b) +0.134, (c) 0.085, (d) 0.160, (e) 0.110.

6:8. V' = 102.4.

7:1. C_{DL} = 0.0006; C_{DT} = 0.0054.

7:2. (a) M.N. = 0.58, (b) 395 mph.

7:3. 705 mph.

7:4. $\dfrac{dC_L}{d\alpha}$ = 0.0843.

7:5. C_{D0} = 0.0303.

APPENDIX I

Wind-Tunnel-Model Construction

The type and the construction of the wind-tunnel model are dictated by the tunnel in which it is to be tested and the type of test to be made. After the obvious and paramount necessity of extreme accuracy, accessibility and maintenance are next in importance. Working conditions in a wind tunnel are at best very trying. The temperature may vary from 30° F in winter to 140° F in summer. The model is usually so placed that accessibility is at a premium, and repair facilities may or may not be available. All these factors demand that changes be as simple as possible, and that the model with all its parts and additions be thoroughly tested outside the tunnel before tests are commenced.

In general, models made of laminated mahogany will be adequately strong without steel beams for tests up to 100 mph. Above that, and until about 300 mph, wood models with steel load members are satisfactory; for the higher speeds metal is in order. These speed criteria are, of course, very rough and general. A very thin model might easily require solid steel construction although testing is to be at only 100 mph. The criteria for model strength is deflection rather than yield load limits, as great rigidity is desirable. In the high-speed range margins of safety of the order of 4.0 are usually required. It is advisable to provide metal beams for any control surfaces in order to maintain the best accuracy of the hinge alignment.

A wing fitting of the type shown in Fig. A1 is in general use. It will be seen that it provides an attachment for a dummy bayonet. Two sealing blocks are needed for both upper and lower surfaces, one with a slot to allow a strut to pass, and one solid to be used when the dummy system is not employed. (It will be recalled that during the process of testing the model must be mounted both normal and inverted, with and without the image

309

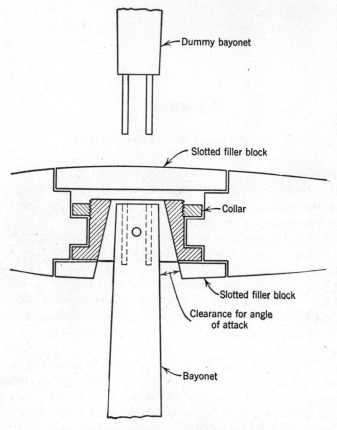

FIG. A1. Typical model attachment fitting.

system.) The second set of blocks may be omitted and the slot
sealed with tape if so desired.

MATERIAL

The most satisfactory material for wind-tunnel models to be
used up to about 300 mph is well-seasoned Honduras mahogany.
This wood is easy to work, glues well, takes all types of finish,
and is little subject to warping. A second choice is walnut, also
a nice wood to work but likely to have curly grain and hence
being more difficult to work to close tolerances. Some of the
softer woods, plastic, plaster, and metals can be used; each has
its characteristic advantages and disadvantages for construction
and maintenance.

Form Block

The mahogany form block should be composed of laminations from ⅜ to ¾ in. wide. They should be cut from larger pieces and have alternate strips turned end for end so that any warping tendency will be resisted. The block should be glued according to standard practices; i.e., glue should be fresh, pressure adequate, and drying time sufficient (1 to 5 days). When practical, two or three weeks' seasoning is desirable.

Necessary pressure tubes and steel beams may either be incorporated in the block or added later, depending on the design.

Forming the Model

Usually models have many component parts, each to be made separately. This works out well with the construction procedure because it is advisable to make each part from 1/16 to ⅛ in. oversize and allow some additional seasoning over and above that needed for the block, to allow any strains in the block a chance to be relieved by warping.

The last fraction of an inch is then worked down to female templates by files, scrapers, and sandpaper. The day should be so planned that time remains to spray at least one coat of clear lacquer after the piece is done to seal it and prevent warping due to changes in its moisture content.

Finishes and Accuracy

Model makers differ in their opinions of suitable finishes. The choice is usually between three types, all quick drying: shellac, clear lacquer, or pigmented lacquer. Shellac and the clear lacquers seem to yield a slightly thinner coat (0.002 to 0.005 in.) than the pigmented lacquer (0.003 to 0.008 in.). On the other hand many model makers believe that the smoothest finish is obtained only with the pigmented lacquer. Regardless of the choice, an adjustment in the templates should be made to allow room for the finish. Those finishes put on and sanded back to zero thickness are not believed to offer sufficient protection and moisture seal.

The usual procedure to follow in applying a finish is to apply and sand four to six coats, using progressively finer waterproof sandpaper. When inspection indicates the surface to be filled, a rubbing compound may be used to obtain a high gloss. The model should be waxed before shipping and again after it is mounted in the tunnel.

A model for a 7 by 10 tunnel should have the wing contour accurate to 0.005 in. to the true contour, and fuselage to within 0.01 in. No perceptible ridges or joints should be permitted.

Air passages, radiator openings, and cooling entrances may be simulated by an indenture of the entry without any completed flow passages. Such passages if completed would have Reynolds numbers too low for satisfactory testing. A parallel situation exists for all small excrescences: aerials, bomb racks, pitot-static tubes, and the like. They too would show such scale effect that their true effect could not be measured, and hence they are left off.

Pressure Models

Pressure models for tests of the type described in Sect. 4:15 require additional care in design and construction. Usually the pressure taps on the wing are located at 0, 1.25, 2.5, 5.0, 10.0, 15.0, 20.0, 30.0, 40, 50, 60, 70, 80, 90, 95, and 100 per cent of the chord on both upper and lower surface at several spanwise stations. This obviously necessitates a large number of tubes, which should be brought out from the model under circumstances least influencing the flow. First, however, let us consider the design of the pressure orifices themselves.

If static pressure orifices are kept small (say about $\frac{1}{32}$ in. in diam.), negligible difference is found between drilling them perpendicular to the surface or perpendicular to the chord. But it is certain that they must be absolutely flush. A copper or brass tube has a tendency to form a slight ridge as the softer wood is filed down about it. Some designers use metal strips at the section where the orifices are to be, thus avoiding the difficulties of filing dissimilar materials. An artifice practiced by the Canadian National Research Council seems a satisfactory arrangement. This embraces a solid transparent plastic plug leading down to the buried brass tubes. After the airfoil is shaped, holes are drilled down to the tubes through the plastic. As the plastic offers filing characteristics similar to those of wood, remarkable smoothness is attained.

The leads from the pressure taps are most easily made of plastic tubing, which has little tendency to kink or leak and has good bending qualities. A sort of multiple tube is available that furnishes 10 leads about $\frac{1}{32}$ in. in diameter in a thin flat strip $\frac{1}{16}$ in. thick by 1 in. wide. It is hard to envision a more compact arrangement.

The connection of the model tubes to the multiple manometers is most easily made through commercially available cluster plugs. These connect 50 tubes in a leakproof trouble-free manner and save a great deal of tunnel time. It is suggested that multiple manometers be designed with 52 tubes to allow a static tube at each end and yet make full use of the standard cluster connectors.

When speed rather than accuracy is the major factor, pressure models can be made from the solid type by belting the model parallel to the airstream with strips of the multiple plastic tubing mentioned in the paragraph above. Holes drilled in the tubing at the selected stations enable pressures to be read at one chordwise station per tube. Actually, of course, the presence of the flat tubing alters the true contours and hence also alters the pressure distribution about the model. The error so introduced is surprisingly small in most cases.

APPENDIX II

Numerical Constants and Conversion of Units

1. Speed of Sound, V_c.

$V_c = 49.1\sqrt{°R} = 65.9\sqrt{°K}$, ft/sec.

$°R = °\text{Fahrenheit} + 459.6$.

$°K = °\text{Centigrade} + 273.0$.

2. Standard Sea-Level Conditions.

Pressure $p_0 = 14.7$ lb/sq in. $= 29.92$ in. Hg.

Density $\rho_0 = 0.002378$ slug/cu ft.

Viscosity $\mu_0 = 3.73 \times 10^{-7}$.

Speed of sound $V_{c0} = 763$ mph.

Temperature $t_0 = 59°$ F.

3. Standard Atmosphere.

Temperature decreases $1°$ F for each 280 ft of altitude until 35,332 ft. Above 35,332 ft temperature is constant at $-67°$ F.

Pressure decreases according to

$$p = (1.910 - 0.01315Z)^{5.256}$$

up to 35,332 ft, and according to

$$p = 6.94e^{(1.69 - 0.0478Z)}$$

above 35,332 ft. In both formulas above, Z is in thousands of feet, and p is in inches of mercury. Density decreases according to

$$\rho = \rho_0 \frac{p}{p_0} \frac{T_0}{T}$$

Viscosity decreases according to

$$\mu = (358.3 + 0.987 \times °C)10^{-9}$$

or

$$\mu = (340.8 + 0.548 \times °F)10^{-9}$$

4. Conversion Factors

A. LENGTH

Multiply	by	to obtain
Inches	2.54	centimeters
Feet	30.48	centimeters
	0.3048	meters
Miles	5280	feet
	1.609	kilometers
	0.8684	nautical miles
	314	

Multiply	*by*	*to obtain*
Centimeters	0.3937	inches
Meters	39.37	inches
	3.281	feet
	1.094	yards
Kilometers	3281	feet
	0.6214	miles
	1094	yards

B. AREA

Square inches	6.452	square centimeters
Square feet	929.0	square centimeters
	144	square inches
Square centimeters	0.1550	square inches
Square meters	10.76	square feet

C. VOLUME

Cubic feet	1728	cubic inches
	0.02832	cubic meters
	7.4805	U. S. gallons
U. S. gallons, dry	1.164	U. S. gallons, liquid
	0.83267	imperial gallons
	3.785	liters
Imperial gallons	0.03531	cubic feet
	4.546	liters
	277.4	cubic inches
U. S. gallons, liquid	0.1337	cubic feet
	231	cubic inches
	4	U. S. quarts
Cubic meters	35.31	cubic feet
	1.308	cubic yards
	264.2	U. S. gallons

D. VELOCITY

Feet/minute	0.01667	feet/second
	0.01136	miles/hour
Feet/second	1.097	kilometers/hour
	0.5921	knots
	0.6818	miles/hour
Miles/hour	0.447	meters/second
	1.467	feet/second
	1.609	kilometers/hour
	0.8684	knots
Kilometers/hour	0.9113	feet/second
	0.5396	knots
	0.6214	miles/hour
	0.2778	meters/second
Meters/second	3.281	feet/second
	3.6	kilometers/hour
	2.237	miles/hour

E. Weight

Multiply	by	to obtain
Ounces (avoirdupois)	0.0625	pounds (avoirdupois)
Pounds (avoirdupois)	16.0	ounces (avoirdupois)
Tons (short)	2000	pounds (avoirdupois)
	907.18	kilograms
	0.90718	tons (metric)
Tons (long)	2240	pounds (avoirdupois)
	1016	kilograms
Tons (metric)	1000	kilograms
	2205	pounds
	1.1025	tons (short)
Kilograms	21,205	pounds

F. Pressure

Pounds/square inch	0.06804	atmospheres
	2.036	inches of mercury
	703.1	kilograms/square meter
Pounds/square foot	0.19242	inches of water
	4.883	kilograms/square meter
Atmospheres	76.0	centimeters of mercury
	29.92	inches of mercury
	1.033	kilograms/square centimeters
	14.7	pounds/square inch
	2116	pounds/square foot
Inches of water	5.198	pounds/square foot
	25.38	kilograms/square meter
	0.07349	inches of mercury
Kilograms/square meter	0.2048	pounds/square foot

G. Temperature

To change Fahrenheit to Centigrade
   1. Add 40.
   2. Multiply by $\frac{5}{9}$
   3. Subtract 40.
To change Centigrade to Fahrenheit
   1. Add 40.
   2. Multiply by $\frac{9}{5}$.
   3. Subtract 40.
To change Fahrenheit to Rankine, add 459.6.
To change Centigrade to Kelvin, add 273.0.

INDEX